Shape, Space and Measures

Gillian Rich

Published by Letts Educational
The Chiswick Centre
414 Chiswick High Road
London W4 5TF
tel: 020 8996 3333
fax: 020 8742 8390
email: mail@lettsed.co.uk
website: www.letts-education.com

Letts Educational is part of the Granada Learning Group. Granada Learning is a division of Granada plc.

First published 2003

ISBN 1 84085 8850

British Library Cataloguing in Publication Data

A catalogue record for this book is available from the British Library.

Commissioned by Helen Clark

Project management by Vicky Butt

Cover design by bigtop, Bicester, UK

Editorial, layout and illustration by Hart McLeod, Cambridge

Production by PDQ

Printed and bound by Canale, Italy

Contents

Year 7

Year 8

Objectives are numbered consecutively within each topic as laid out in the Mathematics Framework, pages 6–11. Objectives listed in bold type are Key Objectives.
S = Shape, Space and Measures   C = Calculations

YEAR 9

Objectives are numbered consecutively within each topic as laid out in the Mathematics Framework, pages 6–11. Objectives listed in bold type are Key Objectives. Objectives in italic are listed in the Framework as containing material suitable for more able students.
S = Shape, Space and Measures   C = Calculations

How to use this book

The Letts *Exercise Bank* series has been written specifically to match the Framework for Teaching Mathematics. Each book contains exercises focused on a particular Framework topic, and can be used alongside any course or Scheme of Work.

The book is clearly divided into work for Years 7, 8 and 9. Each unit contains Essential Exercises, Consolidation Exercises and Challenging Exercises.

Throughout this book you will see the following symbols:

✓ This indicates a 'self test' question. Pupils can check their understanding of each unit by using the answers provided at the back of the book (page 128).

This indicates that a calculator is required.

Problem-solving questions are indicated by this symbol.

Questions featuring this symbol are intended as homework.

ANGLES AND SHAPES

Essential Exercises

1 Name the following shapes.

a

b
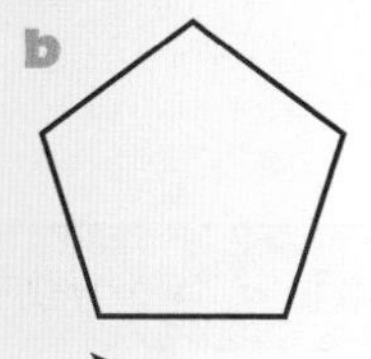
c
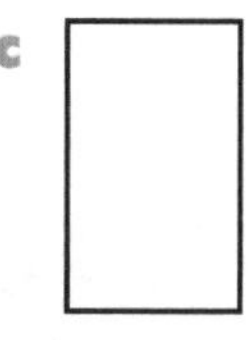

d
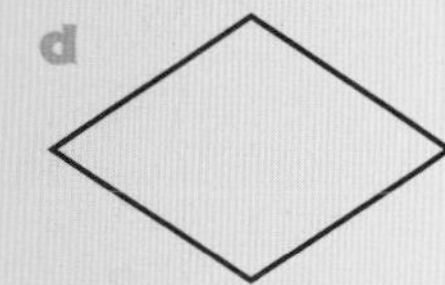
e

f
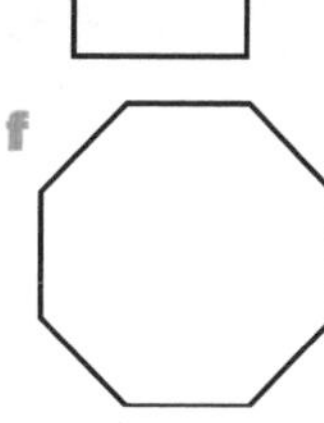

2 Match each diagram a–f to the correct definition **i–vi**.

a
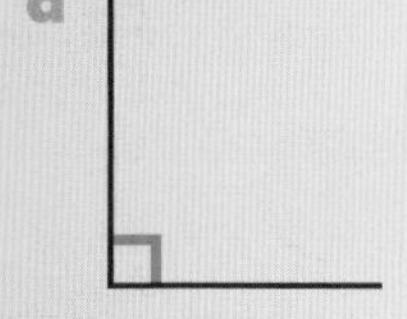
b
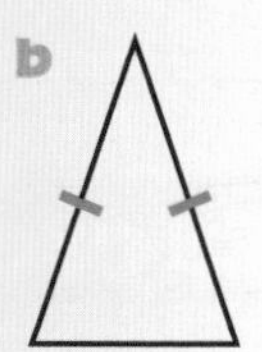
c
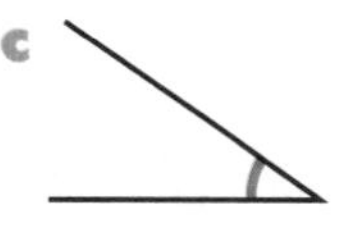

d
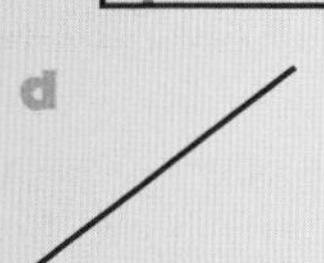
e
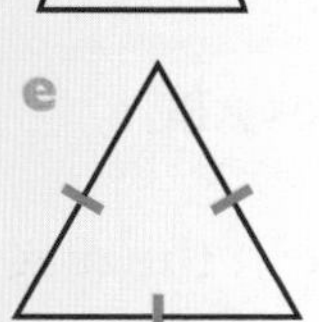
f

i ✓ line segment **ii** acute angle **iii** perpendicular lines
iv equilateral triangle **v** right angle **vi** isosceles triangle

3 Write parallel, perpendicular or neither for each of the following diagrams.

a ✓

b
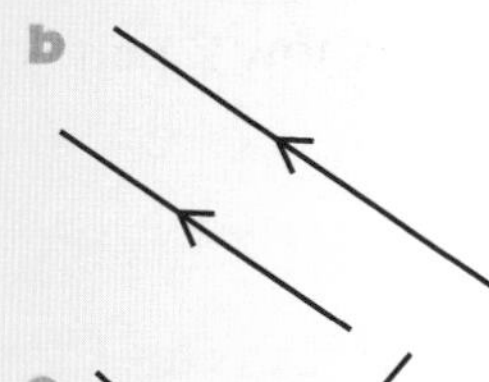
c

d
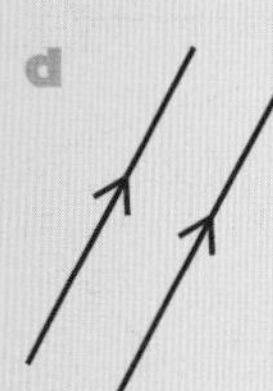
e
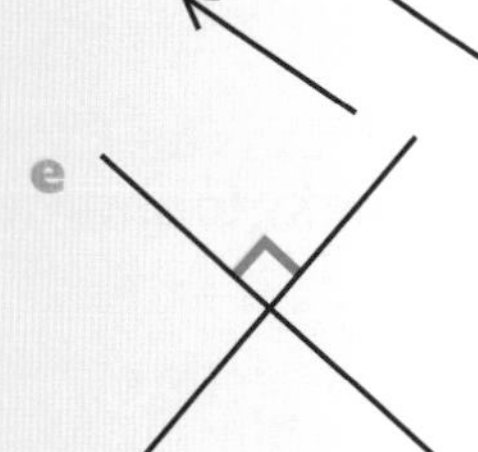
f
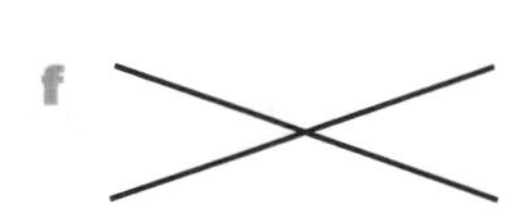

Consolidation Exercises

4 Draw the following shapes.

a parallelogram **b** right-angled triangle **c** hexagon
d kite **e** trapezium **f** square

5 Complete the following table.

	Name	Number of sides	Vertices
a	triangle		
b ✓	quadrilateral		
c	pentagon		
d	hexagon		
e	heptagon		
f	octagon		

Challenging Exercises

6 Draw any triangle and mark the vertices ABC.

7 **a** Draw any rectangle DEFG and mark in the diagonals.
b On your diagram use marks to show a pair of parallel lines.

8 Copy this isosceles triangle. On your diagram use marks to show a pair of equal sides and a pair of equal angles.

9 Copy this diagram and use marks to show 2 pairs of parallel lines.

10 Copy this equilateral triangle. Use marks to show equal angles and equal sides.

ANGLES AND LINES

Essential Exercises

1 Copy these diagrams and mark 2 equal angles.

a 

b 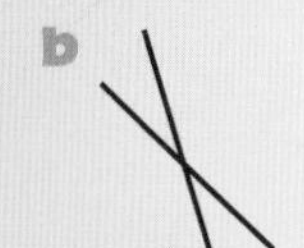

c 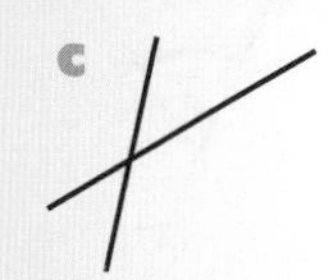

d 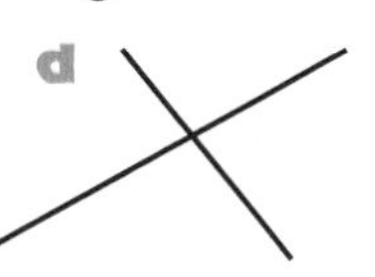

e **f** 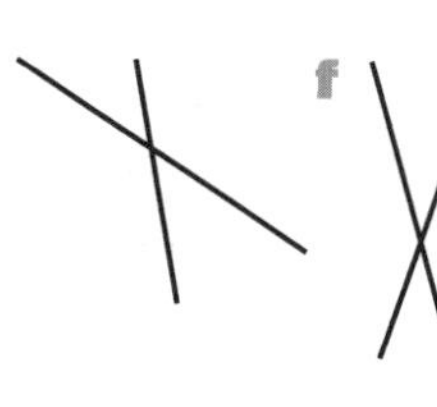

2 Find the size of the angle marked x.

a 

b 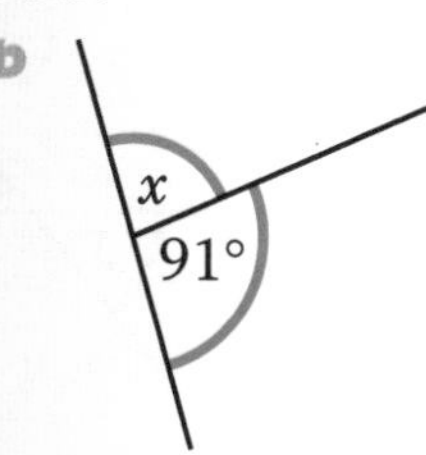

c 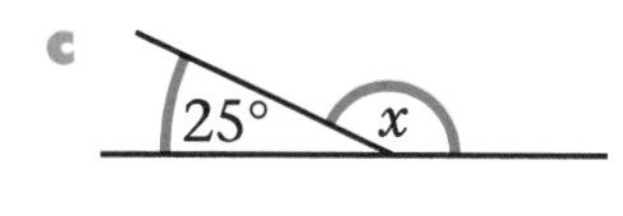

d 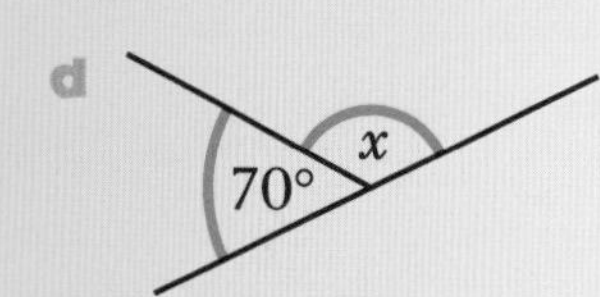

e 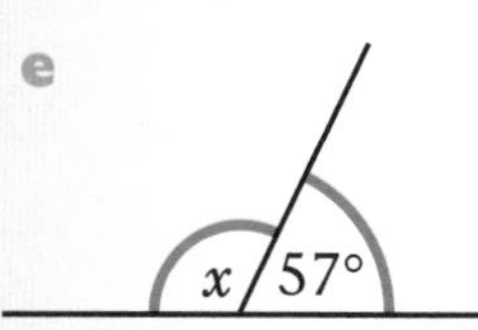

f 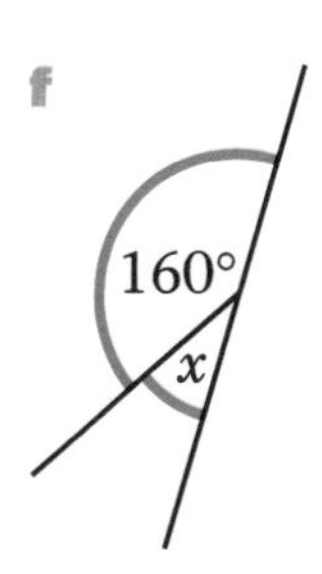

3 Find the size of the angle marked y.

a 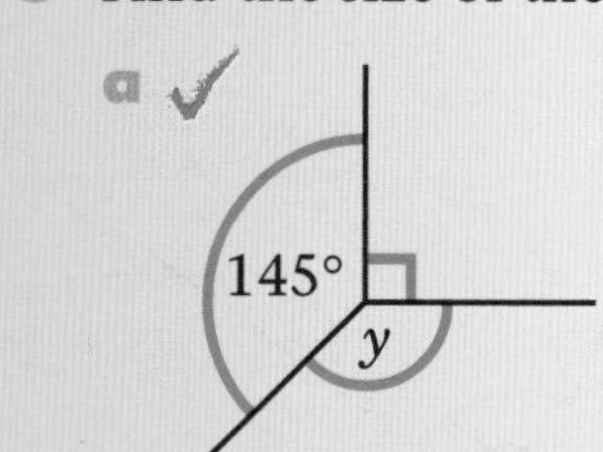

b 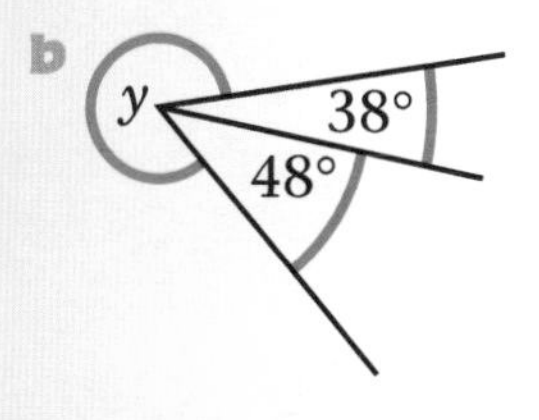

c 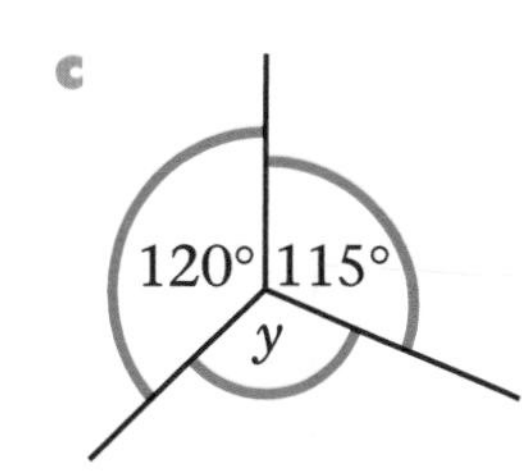

d 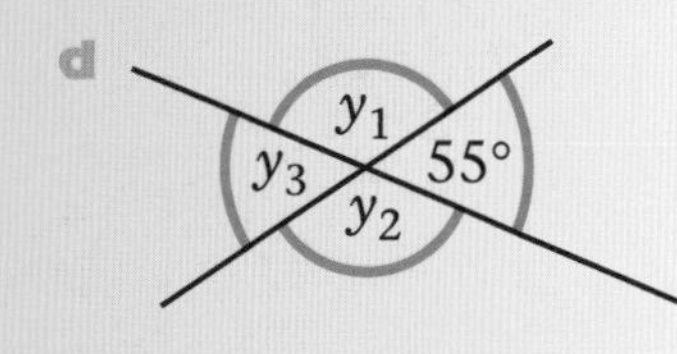

e 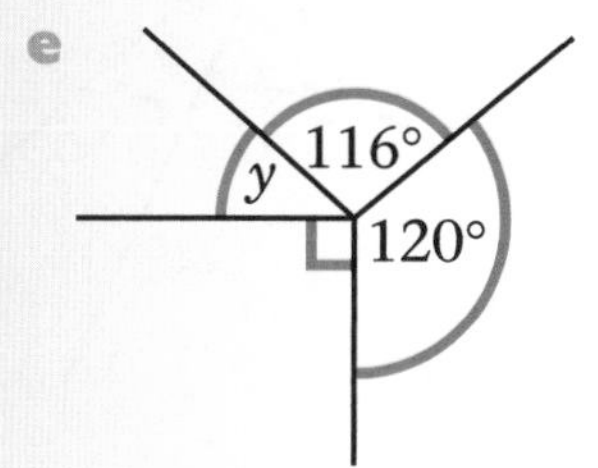

f 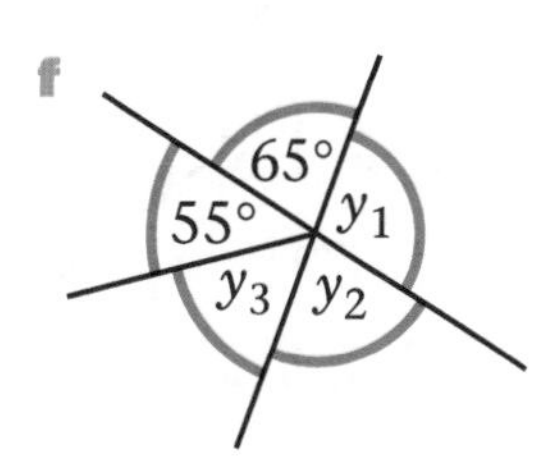

Consolidation Exercises

4 Copy these diagrams and mark the angle equal to y.

a

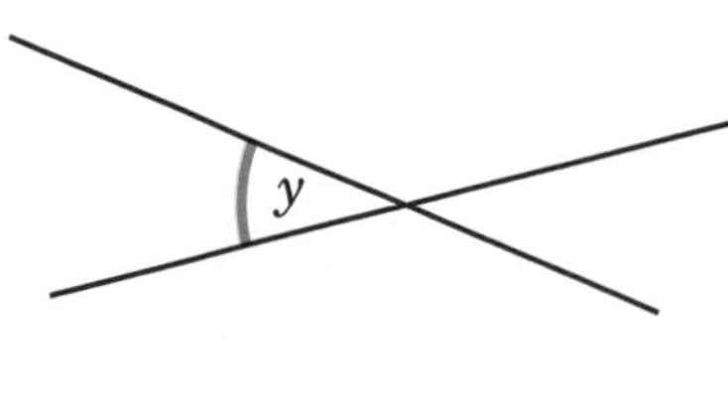

b

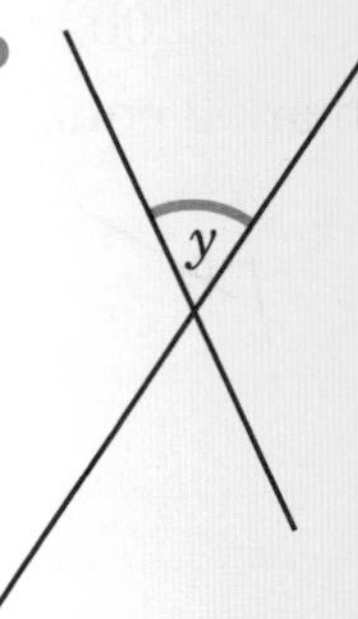

c

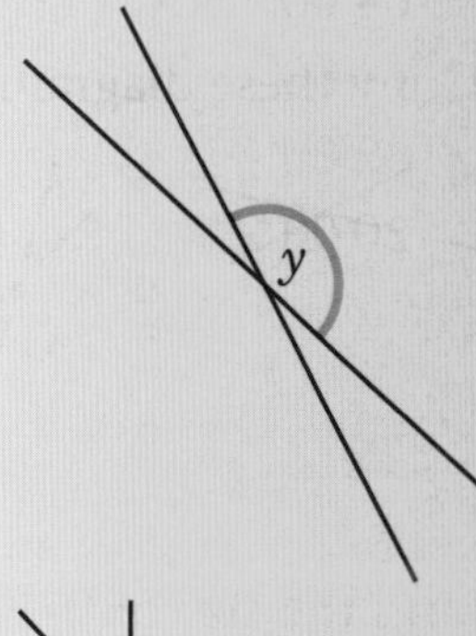

d

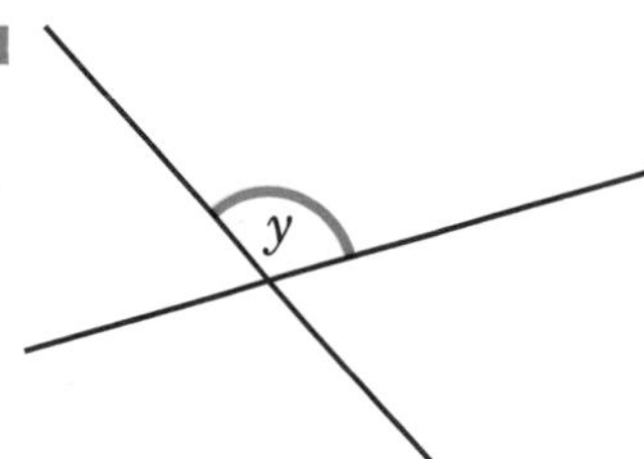

e

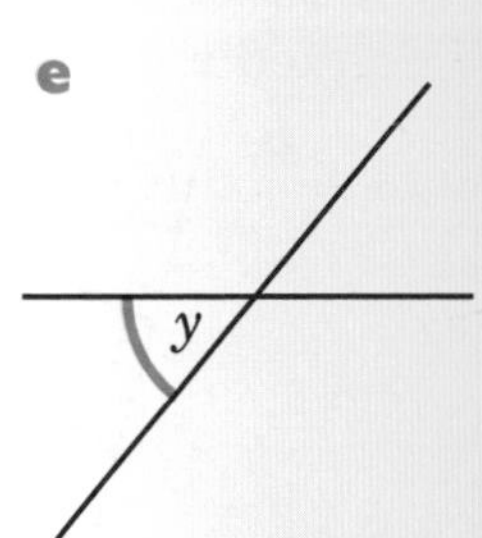

f

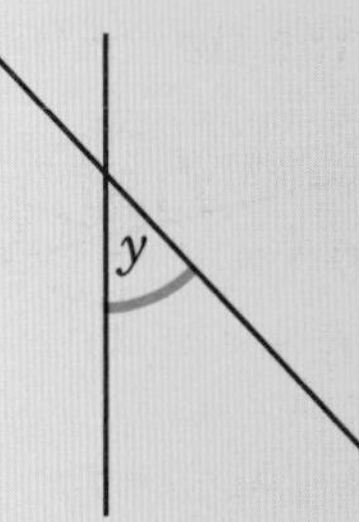

5 Find the size of the angle y.

a

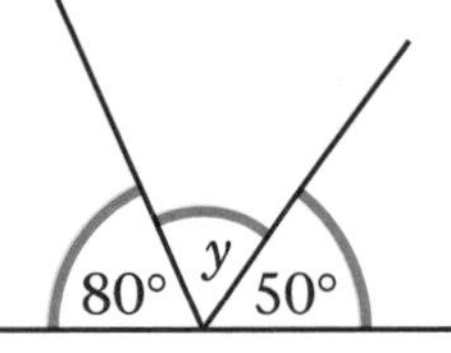

b

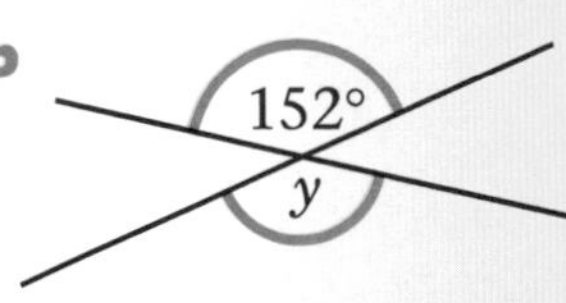

c

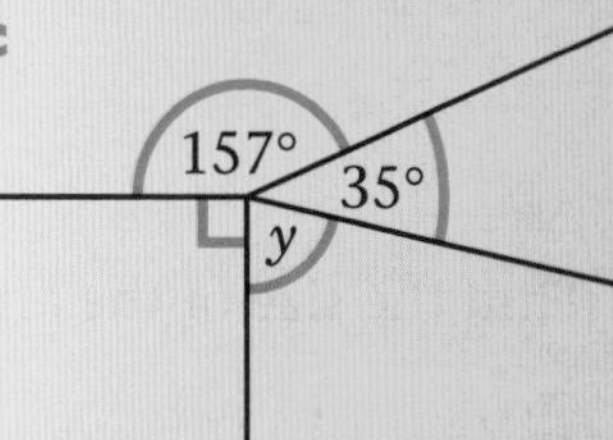

d

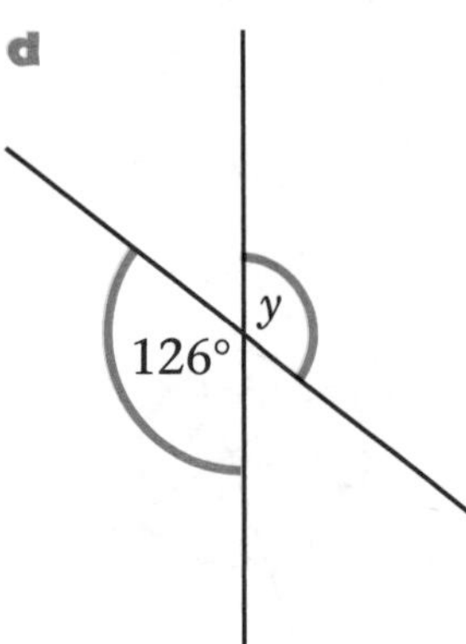

e

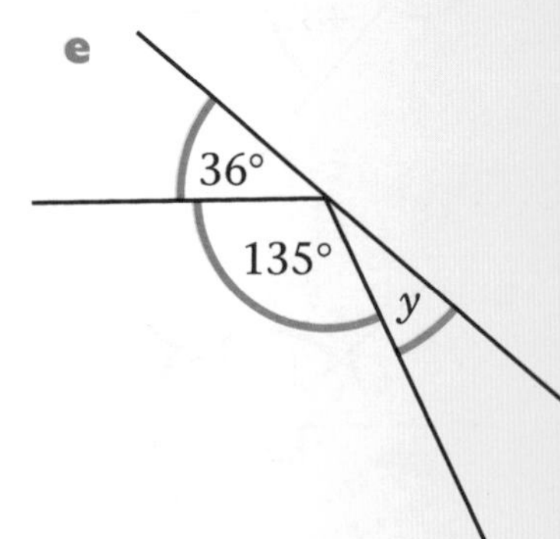

f

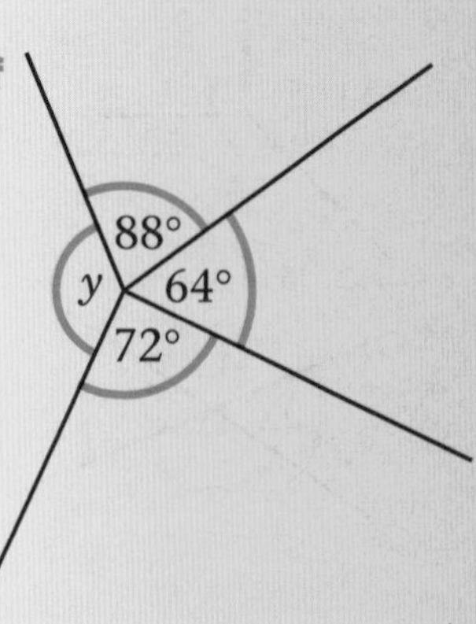

6 What is the size of the smaller angle between the hands of a clock at the following times?

a 15 00 **b** 13 00
c 04 00 **d** ✓ 17 00
e 11 00 **f** 16 00
g 02 00 **h** 18 00
i 20 00 **j** 21 00

Challenging Exercises

7 Draw 2 intersecting lines. Measure all 4 angles formed. What do you notice? Repeat this twice. Can you work out a rule about angles formed by intersecting lines?

8 Mark a point on your page. Draw 3 straight lines from the point. Measure the 3 angles formed. What is the sum of the 3 angles?
Now mark a point and draw 4 straight lines from it. Measure the 4 angles formed. What is the sum of the 4 angles?
What do you think will be the sum of the angles formed when you have 5 lines at a point?
Check your theory by drawing the lines.

9 Draw any triangle. Measure each angle.
Now add the angles. What is the total?
Repeat this twice. Can you come to any conclusion about the angle sum of a triangle?

10 Draw 2 parallel lines on your page. Now draw 2 more parallel lines crossing the first pair. Mark the lines to show they are parallel.
What shape have you formed? Measure the interior angles of your shape. What do you notice?

TRIANGLES AND QUADRILATERALS

Essential Exercises

1 Remove triangle ABC from the following 6 diagrams. What shape is left?

a

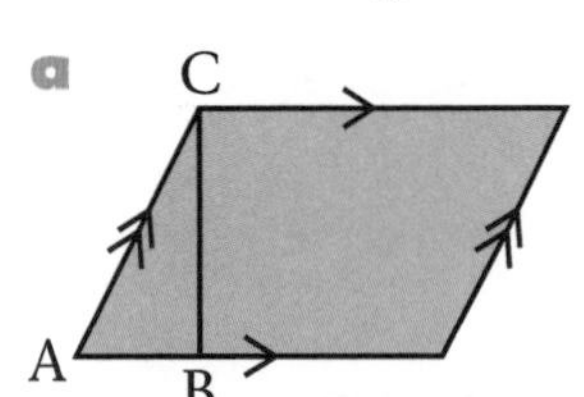

b

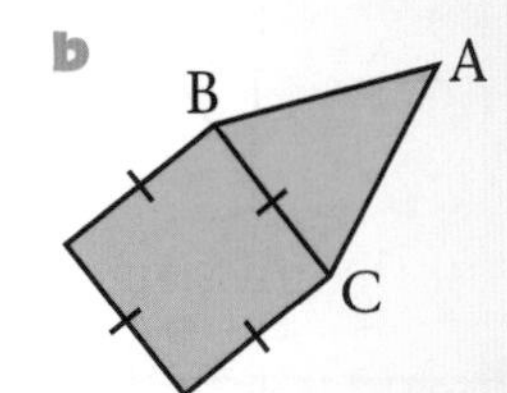

c

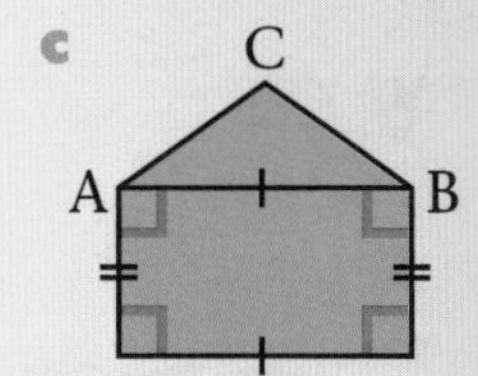

d

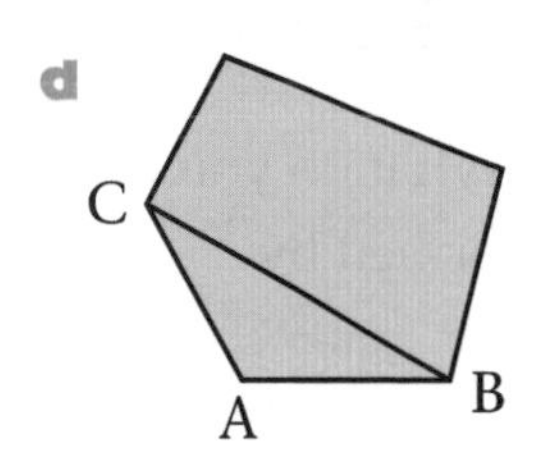

e

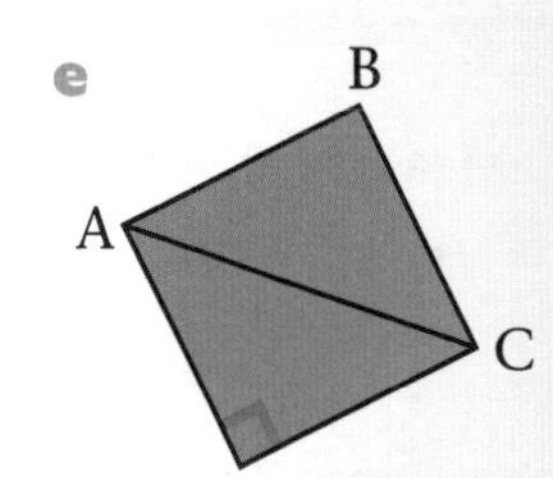

f

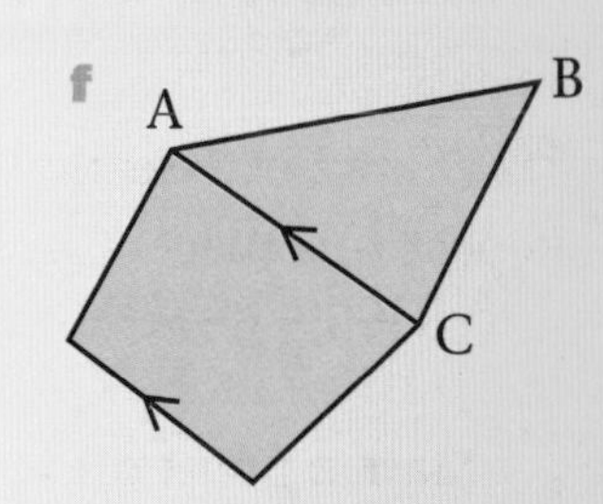

2 Write down the missing name for each of the following triangles.

a ✓ A ______________ triangle has 3 different angles and 3 different sides.

b A ______________ triangle has 3 equal angles and 3 equal sides.

c A ______________ triangle has 2 equal angles and 2 equal sides.

d A ______________ triangle has a right angle.

e A ______________ triangle has 3 acute angles.

f A ______________ triangle has an obtuse angle.

3 Write down the missing name for each of the following quadrilaterals.

a A ______________ has 4 right angles and 4 equal sides.

b A ______________ has 4 right angles and 2 pairs of equal sides.

c A ______________ has 2 pairs of equal, parallel sides.

d A ______________ has 4 equal sides, opposite sides are parallel.

e A ______________ has 1 pair of parallel sides.

f A ______________ has 2 pairs of adjacent, equal sides.

Consolidation Exercises

4 Look at the angles and sides of these triangles, then give them a name.

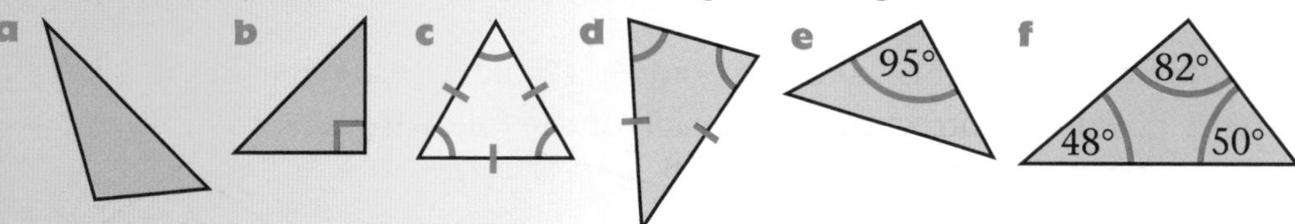

5 Copy these sentences and fill in the missing words.

- **a** A square has diagonals that _________ each other at _________ angles and has __ lines of symmetry.
- **b** The diagonals of a rectangle are _________. It has __ lines of symmetry.
- **c** The diagonals of a rhombus _________ each other at _________ angles. It has __ lines of symmetry.
- **d** A parallelogram has __ lines of symmetry.
- **e** The diagonals of a kite intersect at _________ angles. It has _________ of symmetry.
- **f** An isosceles triangle has _________ of symmetry.
- **g** An equilateral triangle has __ lines of symmetry.

Challenging Exercises

6 How many triangles of equal size do you need to make the following regular shapes?

a ✓ pentagon	**b** square	**c** octagon
d hexagon	**e** decagon	**f** rhombus

7 Imagine a square piece of paper. Fold it in half and half again. What size is the side of the new square?

8 Imagine a rectangular piece of paper. Fold it in half and half again. What sizes are the sides of the new rectangle?

9 Draw a square. Join the mid-points of its sides. What shape is formed? Draw a rectangle. Draw its diagonals. What sort of triangles are formed?

10 Draw a square. Draw its diagonals. Remove one of the triangles. What shape is left?

11 What different shapes can you get by folding a square piece of paper?

7 Solid shapes

Essential Exercises

1 Cubes or cuboids?
Write down the correct name for each of the following shapes.

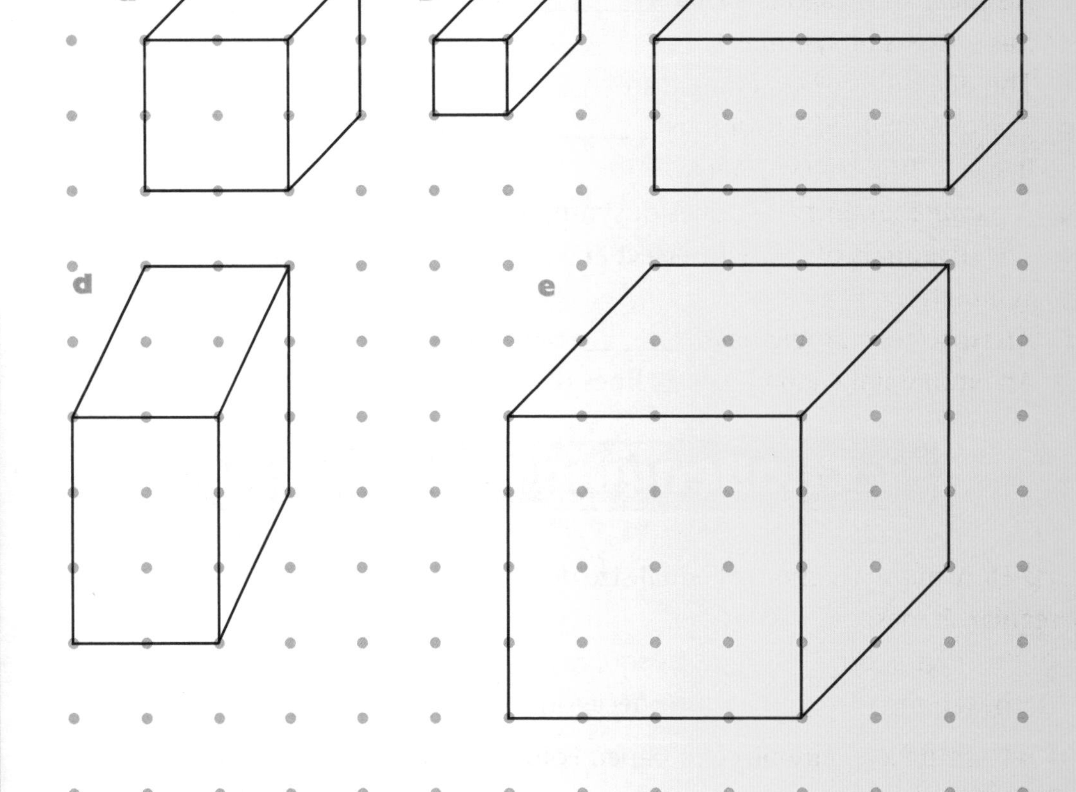

2 Describe the 2D shapes you would use to make these 3D shapes.

- **a** cube
- **b** cuboid
- **c** square-based pyramid
- **d** tetrahedron
- **e** triangular prism

Consolidation Exercises

3 Copy the table below and fill in the gaps.

	Name	Faces	Vertices	Edges
a	cube			
b ✓	cuboid			
c	tetrahedron			
d	square-based pyramid			
e	triangular prism			

4 Draw the following solid shapes.

- **a** sphere
- **b** cylinder
- **c** hemisphere
- **d** tetrahedron
- **e** triangular prism
- **f** cube

Challenging Exercises

5 Draw 3 different prisms and 3 different pyramids. Label each drawing.

6 You have 4 equal cubes. How many different solid shapes can you make with them? Draw them on isometric paper.

7 You have 4 equal cuboids. How many different solid shapes can you make with them? Draw them on isometric paper.

8 Draw a triangular prism. What type of triangle have you used? Draw 3 more triangular prisms using different triangles.

7 Transformations

Essential Exercises

1 Copy the following shapes and reflect them in the dotted mirror line.

a

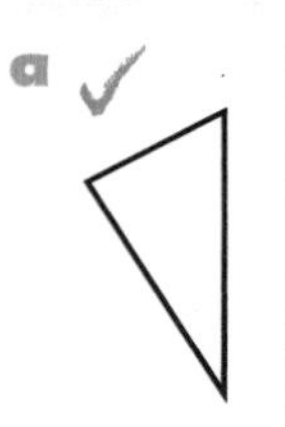

b

c

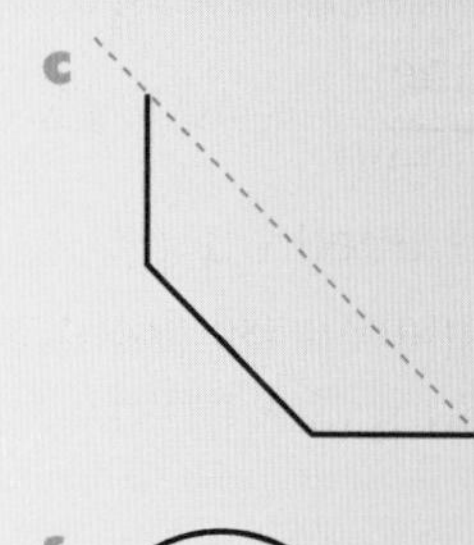

d

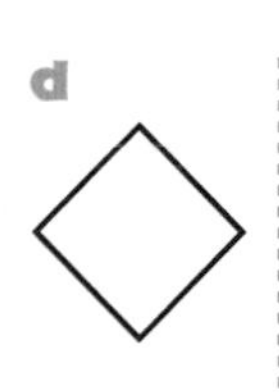

e

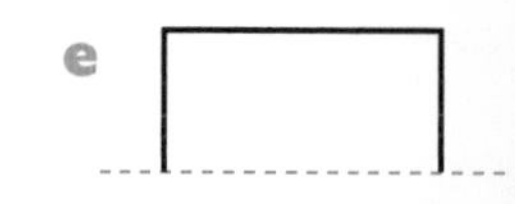

f

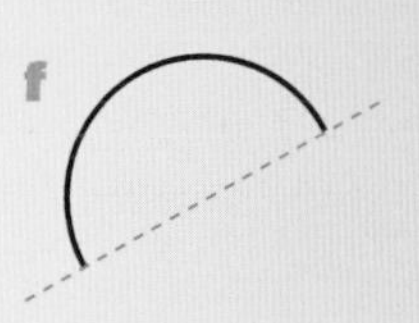

2 Look at the diagram on the right.

Rotate figure A through 90° clockwise about the origin.

Rotate figure B through 90° anticlockwise about the origin.

Rotate figure C through 90° clockwise about (1, 1).

Rotate figure D through 90° anticlockwise about (1, 1).

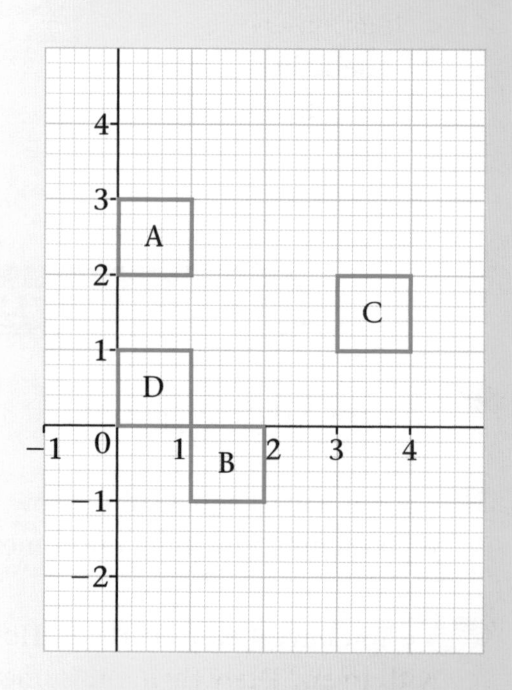

3 Using the same diagram, write down the vector needed to map the following.

a A onto B **b** C onto B **c** D onto B

d B onto A **e** D onto C **f** A onto C

4 State whether the following letters have reflection or rotation symmetry, both or neither.

a M **b** A **c** T **d** H **e** S

Consolidation Exercises

5 **a** How many lines of symmetry do the following shapes have?
b What order of rotation symmetry does each shape have?

i 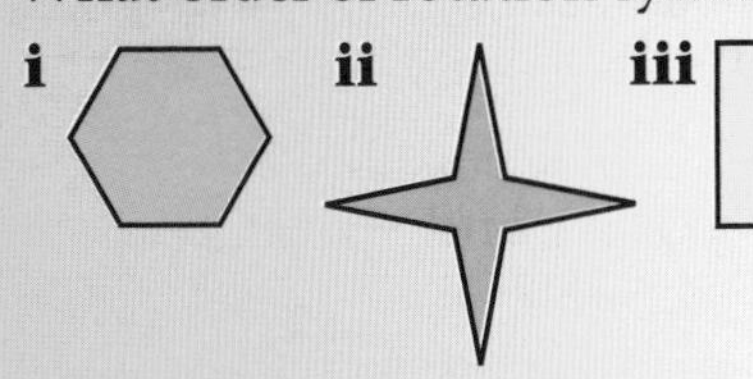 ii 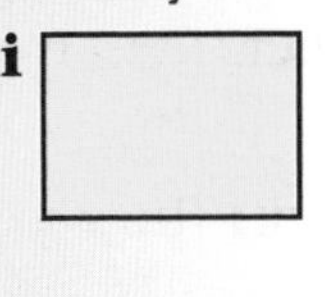 iii 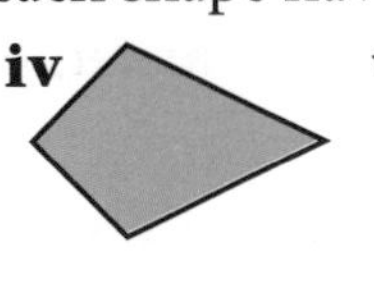 iv  v 

vi

6 Repeat question 1 but this time reflect the shapes in 3 parallel dotted mirror lines. The first has been done for you.

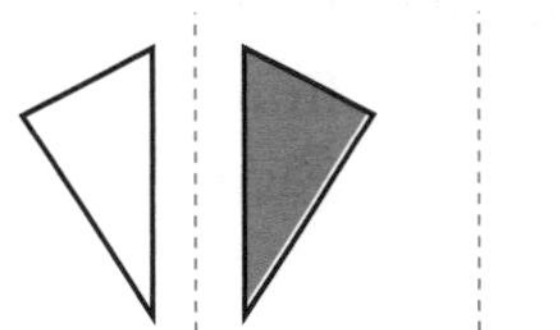 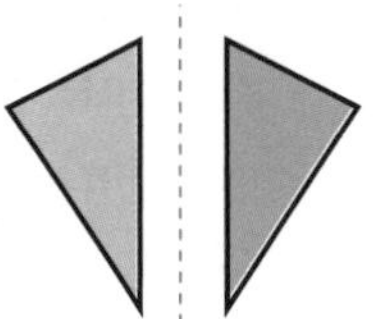

Challenging Exercises

7 Write your first name in capital letters.
Now reflect each letter in a horizontal mirror line.
Next, reflect each letter in a vertical mirror line.
Now reflect each letter in a sloping line.
What do you notice about the reflections? Write down your comments.

8 Cut a rectangle from a piece of paper. Write down its length and breadth.
Fold it along a line of symmetry.
Fold it again along a line of symmetry.
Write down the new measurements. Compare them with the original.
What do you notice?

9 Draw a shape on a piece of squared paper.
Use repeated reflections to design a sheet of wrapping paper.

10 Use squared paper for the following.

a Draw a rectangle.
Now draw a similar rectangle, but double the size of the original.

b Draw the letter T.
Now draw a similar letter T, but three times the size of the original.

c Draw a number 7.
Now draw a similar number 7, but half the size of the original.
How did you work out the new lengths?

Coordinates

Essential Exercises

1 **a** Draw crossed axes on squared paper.
b Label the origin 0.
c Label the x-axis $+x$ and $-x$ and label the y-axis $+y$ and $-y$.
d Mark the x-axis from -5 to $+5$.
e Mark the y-axis from -5 to $+5$.
f Mark a point in each quadrant and give the coordinates of each point.

2 Points A–K are shown on the diagram.
Write down the coordinates of each point.

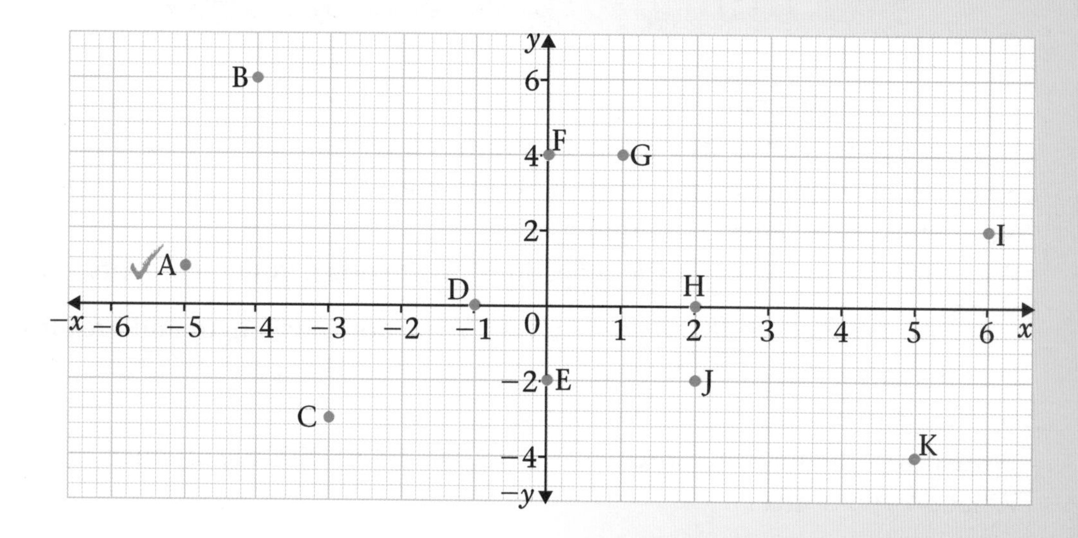

3 In the diagram above, what shapes are formed by the following sets of points?
a ABD
b ABDC
c FGIH
d EFJ

Consolidation Exercises

4 **a** ✓ Draw axes with both x-axis and y-axis marked from 0 to 8.
b Plot the following points:
A(2, 2), B(3, 1), C(6, 1), D(8, 2), E(4, 2), F(4, 6), G(4, 8).
c Join A → B → C → D → A
d Join A → F → E
e Join D → G → E
f What shape have you drawn?

5 **a** Draw axes with both x-axis and y-axis marked from 0 to 14.
b Plot the following points:
A(7, 1), B(8, 3), C(14, 3), D(8, 10), E(7, 14), F(6, 10), G(0, 3), H(6, 3).
c Join A → B → C → D → E → F → G → H → A
d Join H → F
e Join B → D
f What shape have you drawn?

6 **a** Draw axes with x-axis marked from 0 to 12 and y-axis marked from 0 to 7.
b Plot the following points:
A(5, 1), B(10, 1), C(12, 5), D(11, 4), E(5, 5), F(3, 7), G(1, 6), H(3, 5), I(3, 6).
c Join A → B → C → D → E → F → G → H → A
d What shape have you drawn?

Challenging Exercises

7 The points (−1, 3) and (3, 3) are 2 vertices of a rectangle.
Suggest coordinates for the other 2 vertices.
Calculate the area and perimeter of the rectangle.

8 Plot the points (−1, 3), (1, 5), (3, 3).
What fourth point will make the following shapes?
a parallelogram
b kite
c arrowhead
Could you make any other shapes?

MEASUREMENT

Essential Exercises

1 Look carefully at the angles drawn below.

i Estimate the size of each angle. Write down your answer.

ii Now use your protractor to measure each angle. Write down your answer.

a

b

c

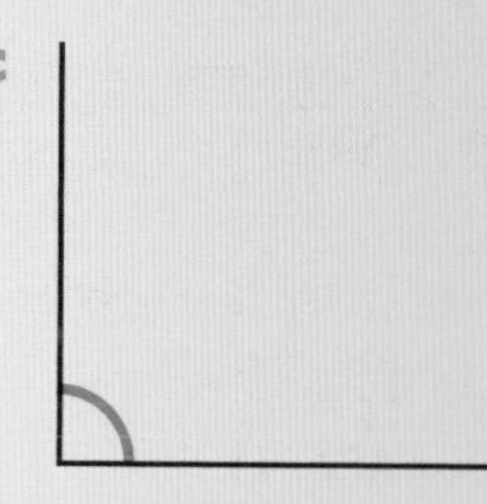

d

e

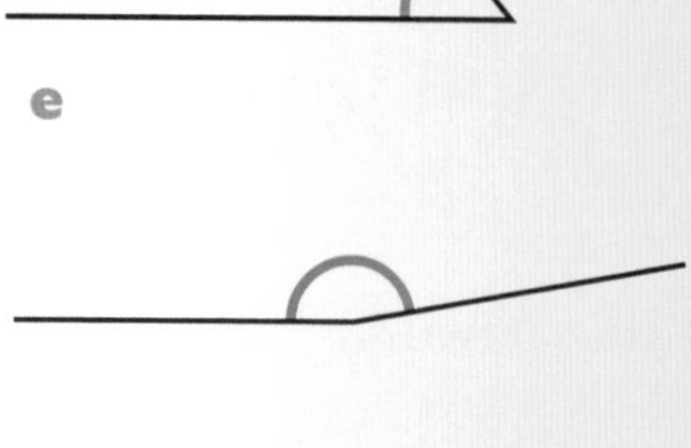

f

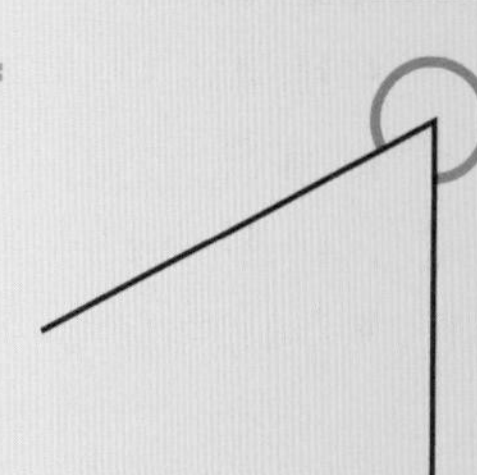

2 Draw the following angles.

a 45° **b** 112° **c** 83°

d 135° **e** 27° **f** 170°

Consolidation Exercises

3 Measure the following angles in this diagram.

a $A\hat{B}C$

b $D\hat{B}A$

c $F\hat{B}E$

d $F\hat{B}D$

e ✓ $D\hat{B}C$

f $A\hat{B}F$

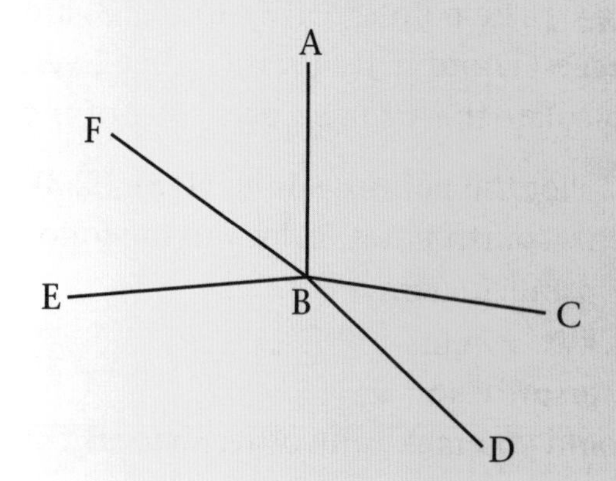

4 Measure these angles and then draw them yourself.

a

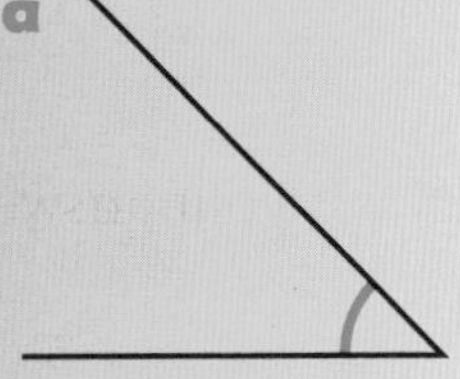

b

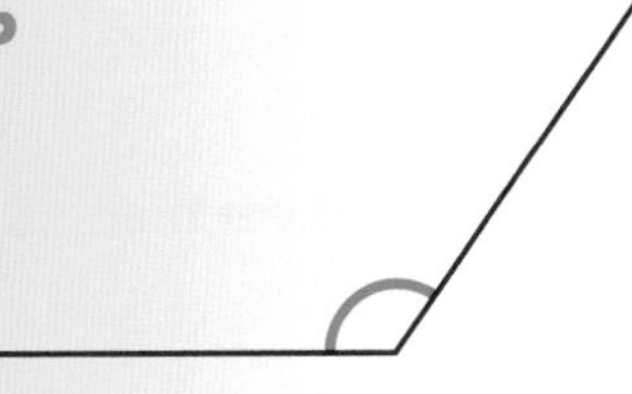

c

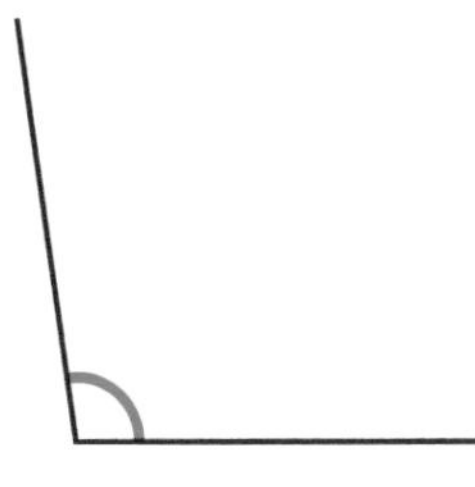

d

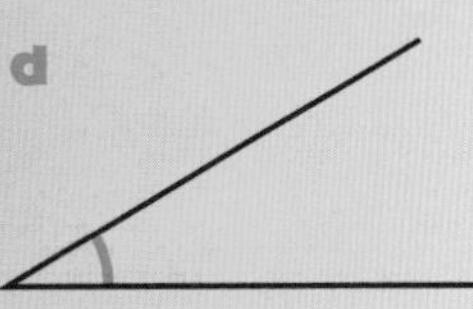

e

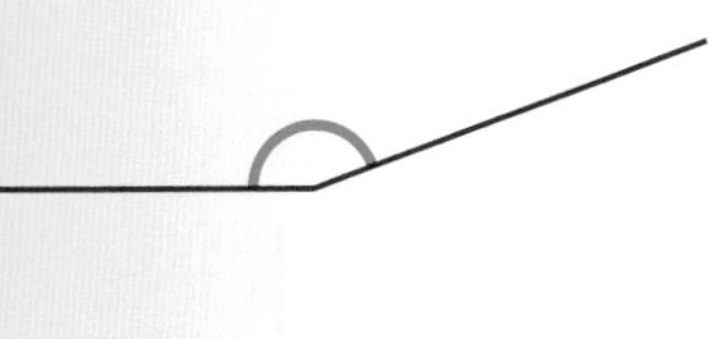

f

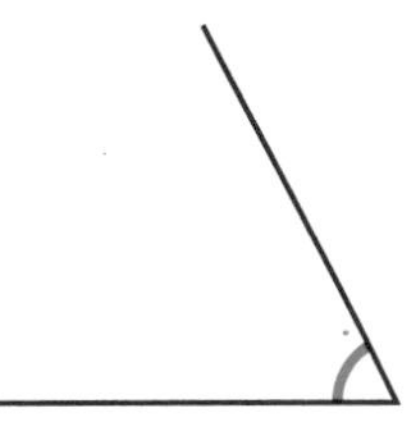

Challenging Exercises

5 Measure the sides and interior angles of these shapes.

a

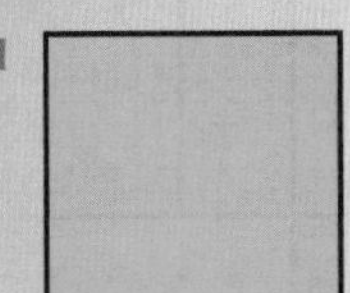

b

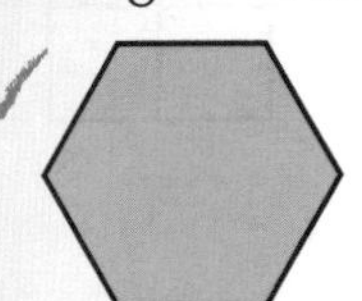

c

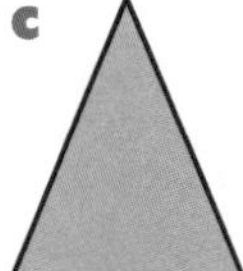

d

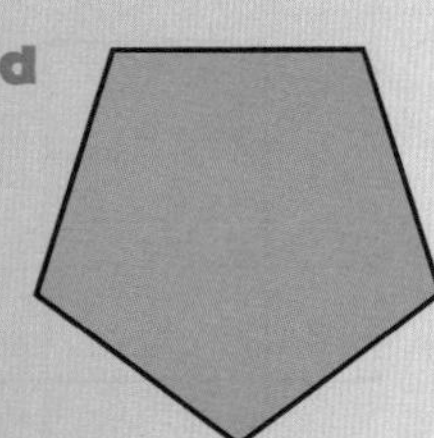

e

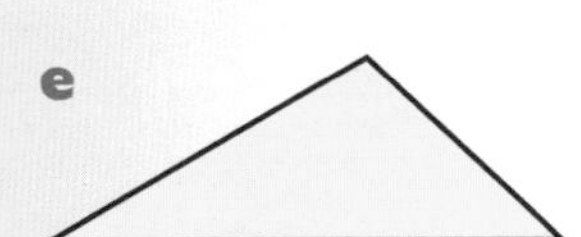

f

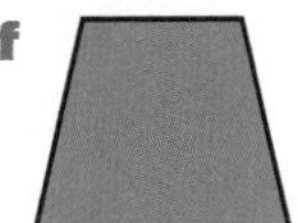

6 Construct triangle ABC given the following measurements.

a AB = 6 cm, $\hat{A} = 35°$, $\hat{B} = 50°$

b AB = 4.5 cm, AC = 6 cm, $\hat{A} = 75°$

c AB = 5.5 cm, $\hat{A} = 48°$, $\hat{B} = 53°$

d AB = 5 cm, AC = 7 cm, $\hat{A} = 105°$

e AB = 7 cm, $\hat{A} = 63°$, $\hat{B} = 55°$

f AB = 7 cm, AB = 8 cm, $\hat{A} = 82°$

Measure $\hat{C}$ in each triangle.

Can you make a rhombus from any of the triangles **a–f**?

Essential Exercises

1 Look at these nets of cubes.
Copy them onto squared paper.
When each is folded, which edge will meet marked edge E?
Mark it with an arrow on your diagram.

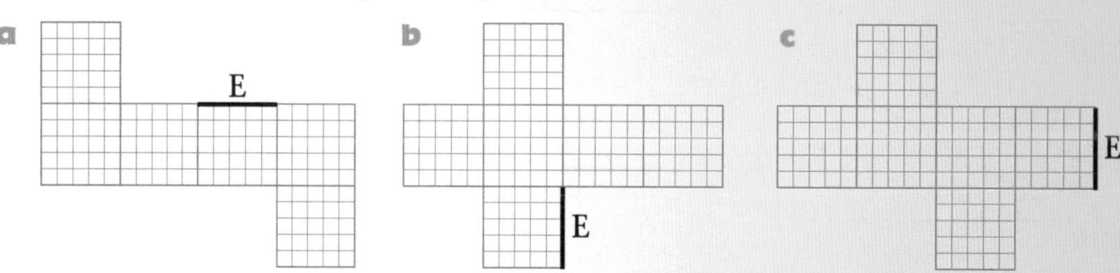

2 Is it possible to make a cuboid from the following nets? Write 'true' or 'false'.

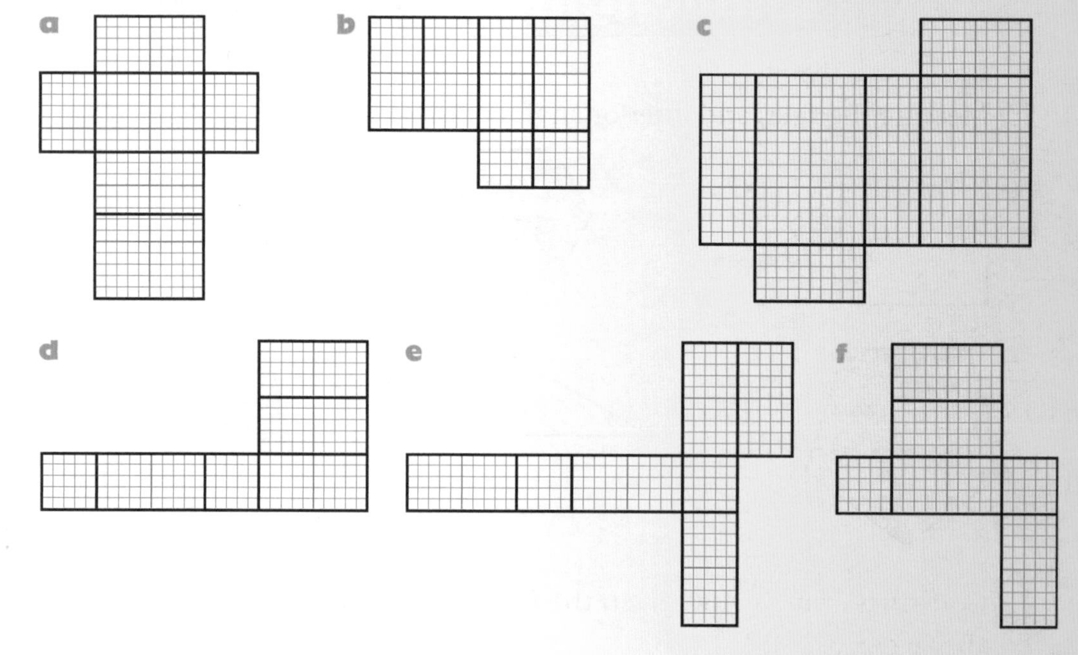

3 Draw nets for the following shapes.

a cube
b cuboid
c cone
d triangular prism
e tetrahedron
f square-based pyramid

Consolidation Exercises

4 What shapes can you make from the following nets?

a ✓

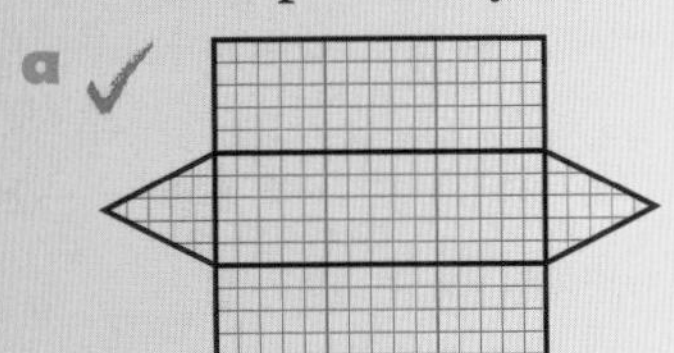

b

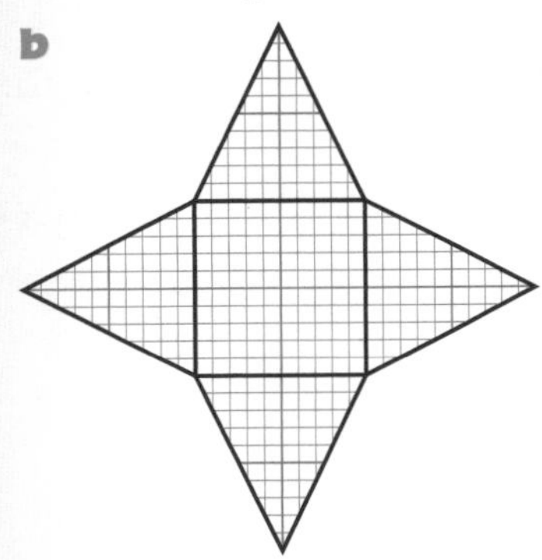

c

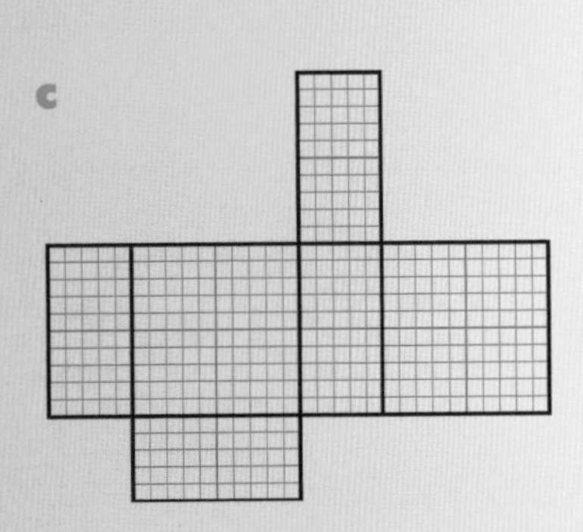

d

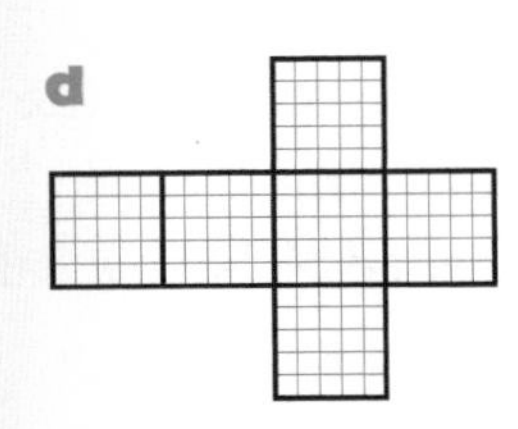

5 Draw accurate nets for the following shapes.

a cube, edge 3 cm

b cuboid, edges 3 cm, 4 cm, 5 cm

c tetrahedron, edge 3 cm

Challenging Exercises

6 ✓ Imagine 2 identical tetrahedrons.
If their bases are stuck together, how many faces, edges and vertices will the new shape have?

7 Using squared paper, draw the nets and form the solids in question **4**.

8 How many different nets can you draw to make a cube?

Units

Essential Exercises

1 Name 2 things that could be measured in:

- **a** metres
- **b** litres
- **c** grams
- **d** millimetres
- **e** square metres
- **f** kilometres.

2 Which unit would you use to measure the following?

- **a** the length of a piece of string
- **b** the weight of sugar needed to bake a cake
- **c** the capacity of a petrol tank
- **d** the time taken to travel to school
- **e** the area of a football field
- **f** the capacity of a coffee mug
- **g** the length of a bus
- **h** the weight of a pencil
- **i** the capacity of a milk carton
- **j** the time taken to fly around the world
- **k** the area of your bedroom
- **l** the distance a discus can be thrown

3 1 gallon $\approx$ 4.5 litres

- **a** A petrol tank has a capacity of 11 gallons. Approximately how many litres does it hold?
- **b** A water-butt holds 210 litres of rain water. Approximately how many gallons does it hold?

Consolidation Exercises

4 Read the following scales.

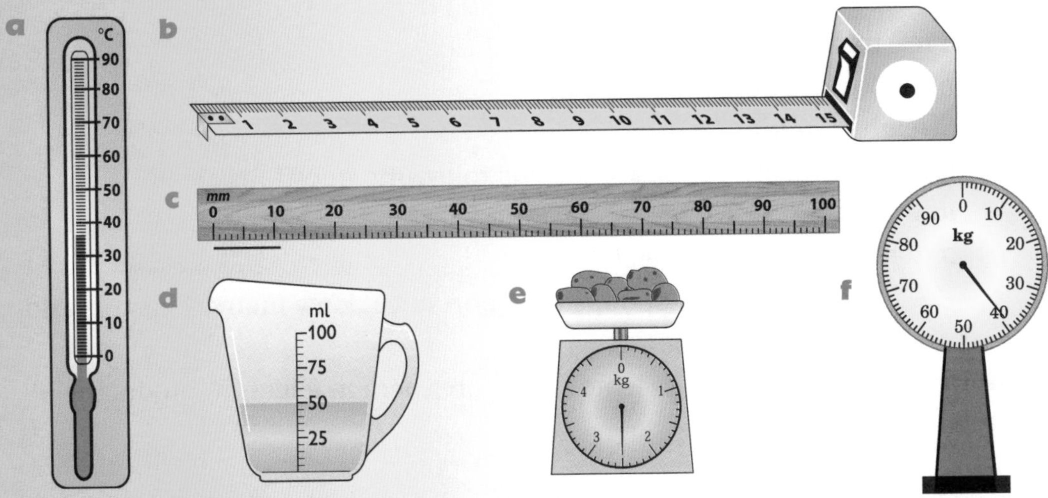

5 Write down the correct answer for each of the following.

a	a decade is	10 years	15 years
b	water freezes at	−32°C	0°C
c	✓ ski-ing weather is	−32°C	10°C
d	March has	30 days	31 days
e	15 minutes is	$\frac{1}{2}$ hour	$\frac{1}{4}$ hour
f	water boils at	100°C	200°C

Challenging Exercises

6 Estimate the following, giving appropriate units.

a the weight of a CD
b the height of a bus stop
c the capacity of a tablespoon
d the width of a door
e the length of a tennis court
f the capacity of a teacup
g the thickness of your maths textbook

7 Write the following measures in the units shown in brackets.

a ✓ 8.5 kg (g)
b 2.2 cm (m)
c 33 mm (cm)
d 3.234 *t* (kg)
e 2 h 43 min (min)
f 5530 ml (*l*)
g 2 days 8 h (h)
h 4260 g (kg)

USING UNITS

Essential Exercises

1 A teaspoon measures about 5 ml.
A tablespoon measures about 15 ml.
1 ml weighs 1 gram.
Using these measurements, answer the following questions.

- **a** How many ml in 1 tablespoon?
- **b** How much does 5 ml weigh?
- **c** ✓A recipe uses 2 tablespoons of lemon juice. How many ml is this and how much does it weigh?
- **d** How many teaspoons of lemon juice are there in a lemon, producing 4 tablespoons?

2 This is a timetable of some trains travelling from London Victoria.

London, East Croydon, Gatwick Airport, Lewes, Seaford and Eastbourne.

Monday to Friday *(continued)*

		SN	SN 1	SN 1 Y	SN	SN 1	SN 1 Y	SN	SN 1	SN	SN 1 Y	SN	SN 1
London Victoria	dep	...	...	1447	...	...	1517	...	...	...	1547	...	...
Clapham Junction	dep	...	...	1453u	...	...	1523u	...	...	...	1553u	...	...
London Bridge	dep	...	...	*1440f*	...	...	*1510f*	...	...	...	*1540f*	...	...
East Croydon	dep	...	...	1503	...	...	1533	...	...	...	1603	...	...
Gatwick Airport	dep	...	...	1521	...	...	1551	...	...	...	1621	...	...
Three Bridges	dep	...	...	*1514f*	...	...	*1544f*	...	...	...	*1614f*	...	...
Haywards Heath	dep	...	...	1535	...	...	1607	...	...	...	1635	...	...
Wivelsfield	dep	...	...	...	...	...	1611	...	...	...	...	...	...
Plumpton	dep	...	...	1544	...	...	...	...	...	...	1644	...	...
Cooksbridge	dep	...	...	...	...	...	...	...	...	...	1648	...	...
Lewes	dep	1527	1539	1553	1557	1609	1623	1627	1639	1657	1654	1657	1709
Southease	dep	1533	...	...	1603	...	...	1633	...	↳	...	...	...
Newhaven Town	dep	1537	...	...	1607	...	...	1637	...	...	...	1705	...
Newhaven Harbour	dep	1539	...	...	1609	...	...	1639	...	...	...	1707	...
Bishopstone	dep	1541	...	...	1611	...	...	1641	...	...	...	1710	...
Seaford	arr	1544	...	...	1614	...	...	1644	...	...	...	1713	...
Glynde	dep	...	...	...	...	1614	...	...	...	...	...	...	1714
Berwick	dep	...	...	...	...	1620	...	...	...	...	1703	...	1720
Polegate	dep	...	1552	1605	...	1626	1635	...	1652	...	1708	...	1726
Hampden Park (Sussex)	dep	...	...	...	...	1631	...	...	1656	...	...	...	1730
Eastbourne	arr	...	1558	1612	...	1635	1642	...	1700	...	1715	...	1734

London, East Croydon, Gatwick Airport, Lewes, Seaford and Eastbourne.

Monday to Friday *(continued)*

		SN 1 Y	SN	SN 1	SN	SN 1	SN	SN 1	SN 1 Y	SN	SN 1	SN	
London Victoria	dep	1616	...	...	...	1646	...	...	1716	...	*1736f*	...	
Clapham Junction	dep	1622u	...	...	...	1652u	...	...	1722u	...	*1743f*	...	
London Bridge	dep	*1610f*	...	...	...	*1645f*	...	...	*1713e*	...	1745	...	
East Croydon	dep	1633	...	...	...	1703	...	...	1733	...	1800	...	
Gatwick Airport	dep	1651	...	...	...	1721	...	...	*1740f*	...	*1758f*	...	
Three Bridges	dep	*1644f*	...	...	...	*1719f*	...	...	1753	...	...	...	
Haywards Heath	dep	1707	...	...	...	1733	...	...	1803	...	1826	...	
Wivelsfield	dep	1711	...	...	...	1738	...	...	1807	...	1831	...	
Plumpton	dep	...	...	...	...	1744	...	...	...	...	1837	...	
Cooksbridge	dep	...	...	...	...	1748	...	...	...	...	1841	...	
Lewes	dep	1723	1727	1739	1757	1754	1757	1809	1822	1824	1832	1847	1904
Southease	dep	...	1733	...	↳	...	...	...	...	...	...	...	↳
Newhaven Town	dep	...	1737	...	...	...	1805	...	1830	...	1841	...	...
Newhaven Harbour	dep	...	1739	...	...	...	1806	...	1832	...	1843	...	...
Bishopstone	dep	...	1741	...	...	...	1809	...	1835	...	1847	...	...
Seaford	arr	...	1744	...	...	...	1812	...	1839	...	1850	...	...
Glynde	dep	...	...	1744	...	...	...	1814	...	...	...	1852	...
Berwick	dep	...	...	1750	...	...	...	1820	...	1833	...	1858	...
Polegate	dep	1735	...	1756	...	1807	...	1826	...	1839	...	1904	...
Hampden Park (Sussex)	dep	...	...	1800	...	1812	...	1830	...	1844	...	1908	...
Eastbourne	arr	1744	...	1804	...	1815	...	1834	...	1851	...	1914	...

- **a** How long does it take to travel from London Victoria to Lewes?
- **b** How could you travel from London Victoria to Newhaven Harbour? How long would it take?
- **c** Which is the fastest train from East Croydon to Haywards Heath?
- **d** Paul needs to check in at 16 30 before catching a flight from Gatwick Airport. On which train should he travel from London Victoria?
- **e** Julie's flight arrives at Gatwick Airport at 15 00. It will take her an hour to disembark and clear customs. Which is the first train, travelling to Eastbourne, that she could catch?

Consolidation Exercises

3 The petrol tank of a car holds 52 litres of petrol when full. The car uses petrol at a rate of 1 litre per 15 km. Copy and complete the following table.

	Distance (km)	Fuel used (litres)	Fuel left (litres)	Fraction of tank left
a ✓	45 km			
b		26 litres		
c		39 litres		
d	240 km			
e		13 litres		
f	150 km			

Challenging Exercises

4 The table shows the favourite subjects of pupils in Year 8.

Subject	Girls	Boys
Art & Design	9	8
English	12	8
French	12	9
History	10	9
Maths	14	15
Sciences	9	9

a How many pupils are there in Year 8?

b Which subject is most popular with girls?

c Which subject is least popular with boys?

d What percentage of boys chose the most popular subject?

e What percentage of girls chose the least popular subject?

f The same number of boys and girls chose Sciences. Does this mean that this subject is equally popular among boys and girls? Give reasons.

5 a A litre of petrol costs 72.5p. Jack fills the petrol tank of his car with 26 litres of petrol.

i Work out the cost of the petrol showing all your working.

ii Using approximate values, check if your answer is correct.

b The cost of a litre of petrol is increased by 3p.
What is the cost of filling the petrol tank now?

7 Types of Angles

Essential Exercises

1 Copy and complete the following statements.

a ✓ An acute angle is less than ________.

b A right angle is ________.

c An obtuse angle is greater than ________, but less than ________.

d A reflex angle is any angle greater than ________.

e A complete revolution is ________.

f Half a turn is ________.

2 Write the type of angle for each of the following.

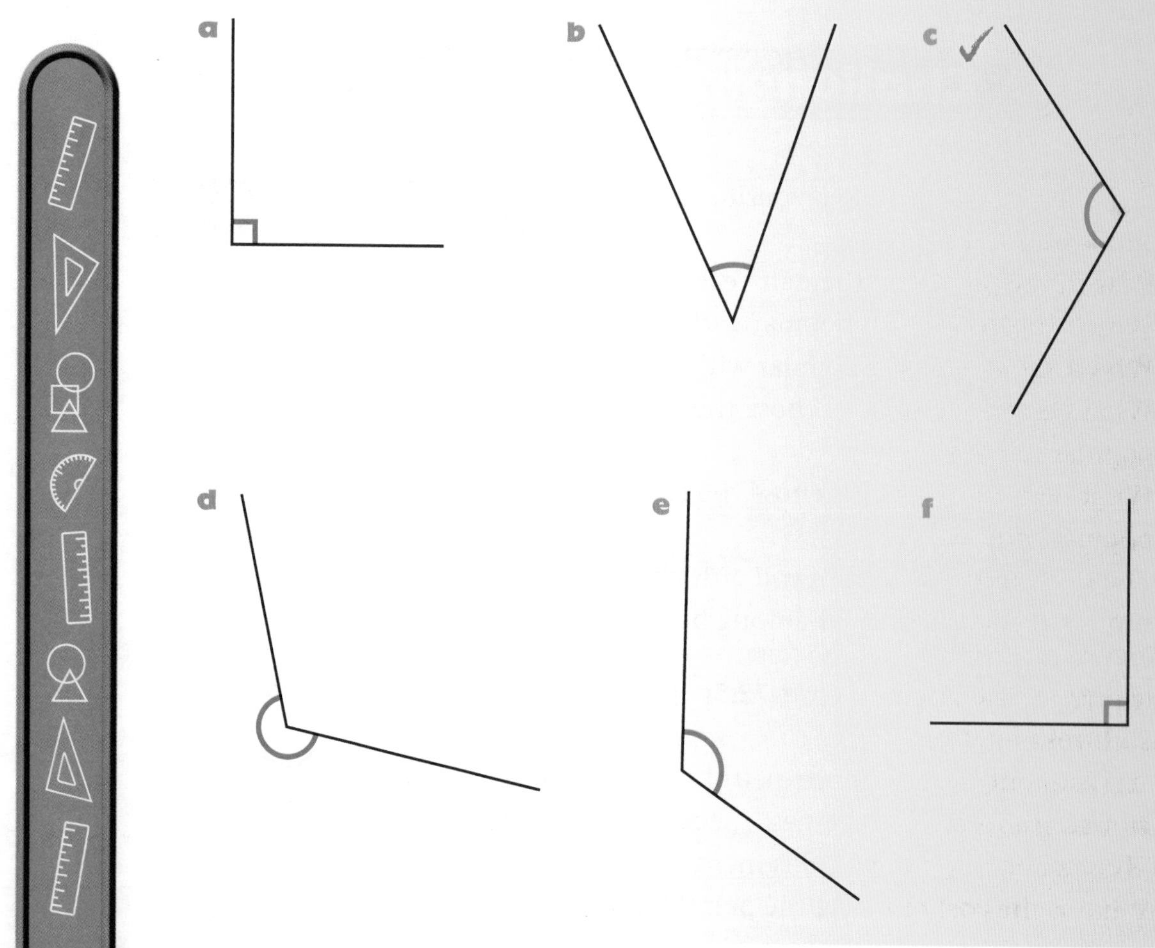

Consolidation Exercises

3 ✓ **a** **b**  **c** **d** 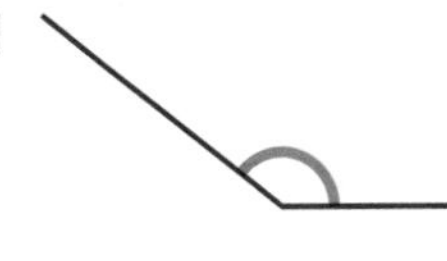

Match each angle **a**–**d** with the correct name **i** to **iv**.

i acute **ii** obtuse **iii** reflex **iv** right angle

e Which is the largest angle?

f Which is the smallest angle?

Look at the diagrams on the right.

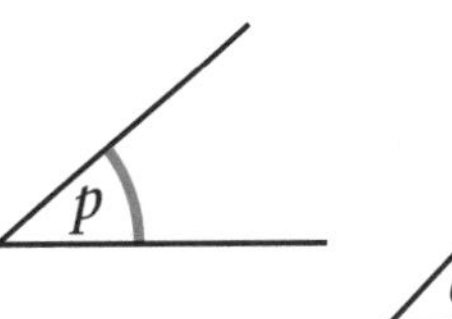

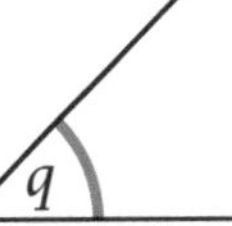

g Is $p > q$? Yes or no? Explain your answer.

4 Look carefully at each of the angles drawn below. Estimate the size of each angle, then measure them with your protractor. Write down your estimate, measurement and name the type of angle for each.

a 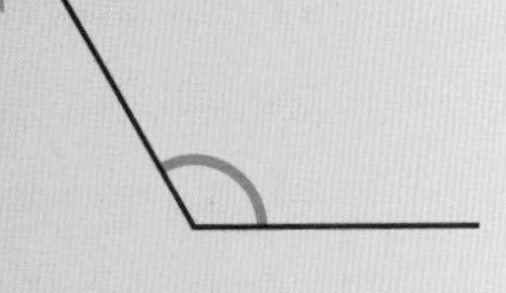
b 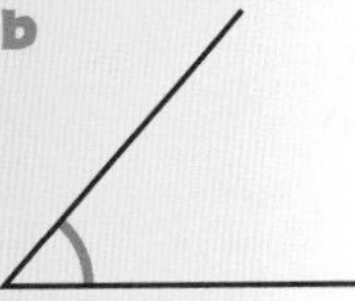
c 
d 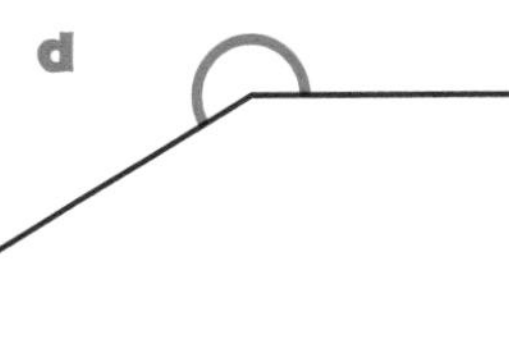

e 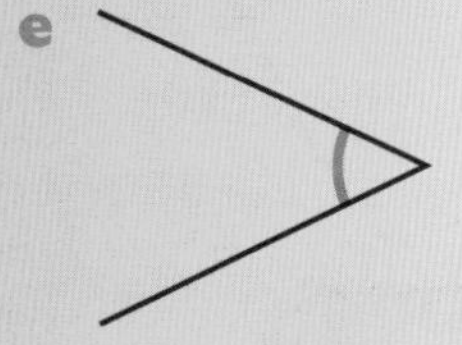
f 
g 
h 

Challenging Exercises

5 Draw a line for each of the lengths given below. Label each line AB. Starting at the point shown in brackets (A or B) draw the stated type of angle, e.g. acute. Measure your angle and write the measurement on your drawing.

a 5 cm acute (A)
b 7.5 cm right angle (A)
c 84 mm reflex (B)
d 37 mm obtuse (A)
e 6.8 cm acute (A)
f 4.9 cm obtuse (B)
g 62 mm right angle (B)
h 9 cm acute (A)

Area and perimeter

Essential Exercises

1 Using a pinboard or squared paper, draw as many shapes as you can that have an area of 4 square units.
Find the perimeter of each shape.

2 Draw a rectangle ABCD.
Draw one diagonal AC.
Find the area of triangle ABC using the sides of the rectangle.

3 Copy and complete the following table.

	Shape	Base	Height	Area	Perimeter
a	square	3 cm			
b	rectangle	6 cm	5 cm		
c ✓	rectangle		10 cm	120 cm^2	
d	rectangle	7 cm		28 cm^2	
e	square		5 cm		
f	square			36 cm^2	

Consolidation Exercises

4 Draw 4 equal right-angled triangles on squared or dotted paper and cut them out. Make the shapes given below. Copy them and write down the name, area and perimeter of each shape.

a rectangle **b** rhombus **c** trapezium

5 A rectangle has a fixed area of 24 cm^2. Draw as many rectangles as you can with this area. Find the rectangle with the smallest perimeter.

6 A rectangle has a fixed perimeter of 28 cm. Draw as many rectangles as you can with this perimeter. Find the rectangle with the largest area.

Challenging Exercises

7 A picture has a frame shown shaded in this diagram. What is the area and perimeter of the photograph?

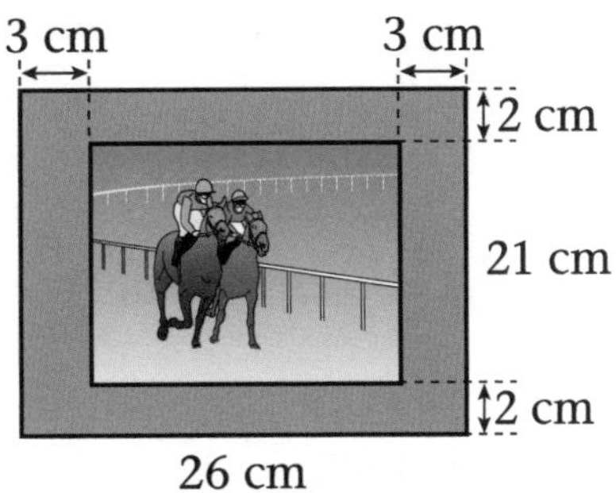

8 Find the area of the lawn in this garden.

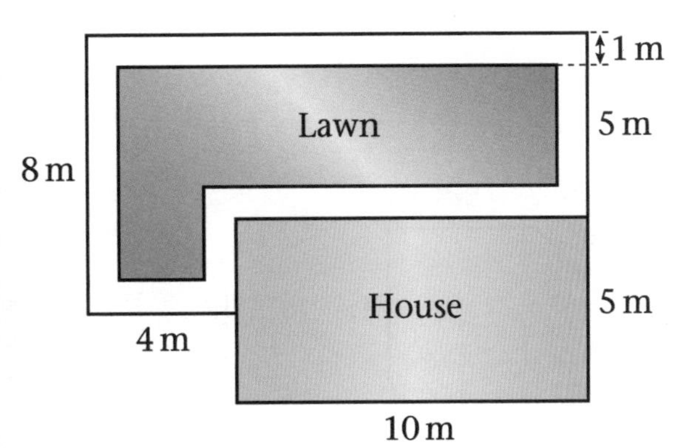

9 These shapes have been formed from rectangles. Find the area and perimeter of each shape.

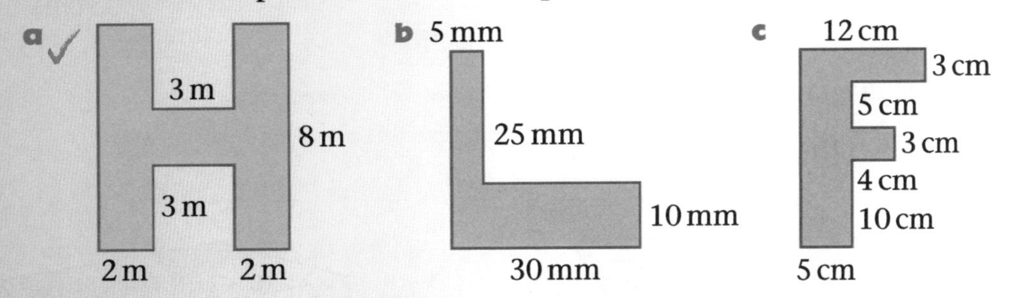

10 These shapes have been formed from rectangles. Find the shaded area of each shape.

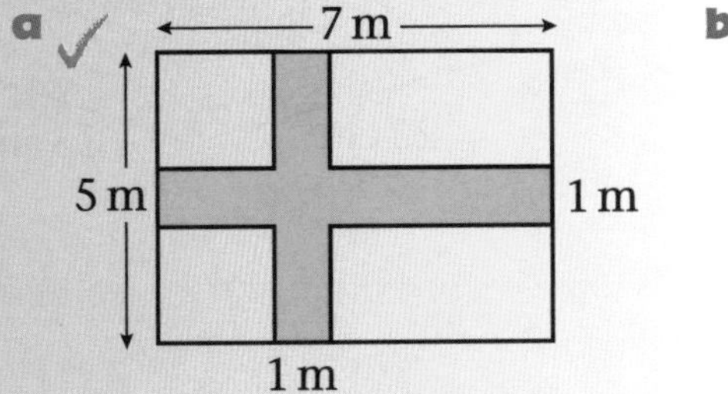

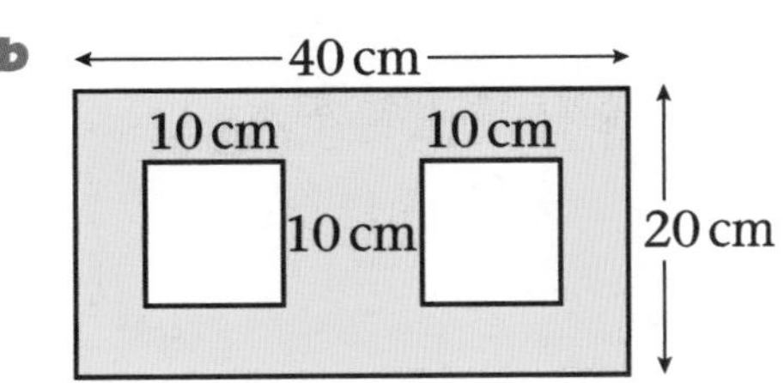

Surface Area

Essential Exercises

1 Calculate the surface area of each of the following solids.

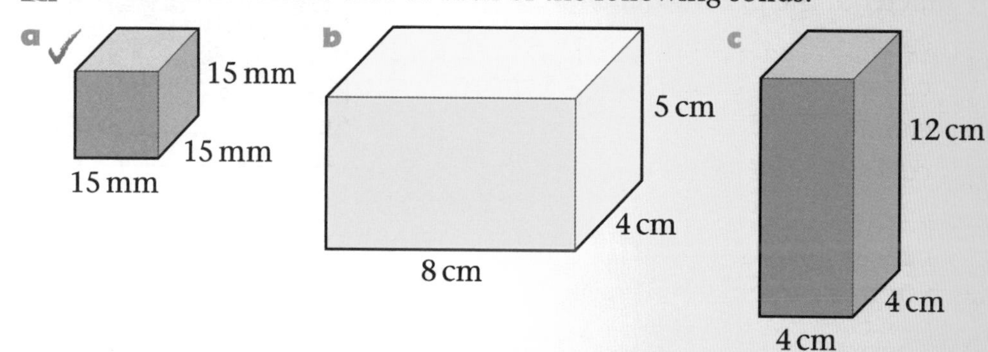

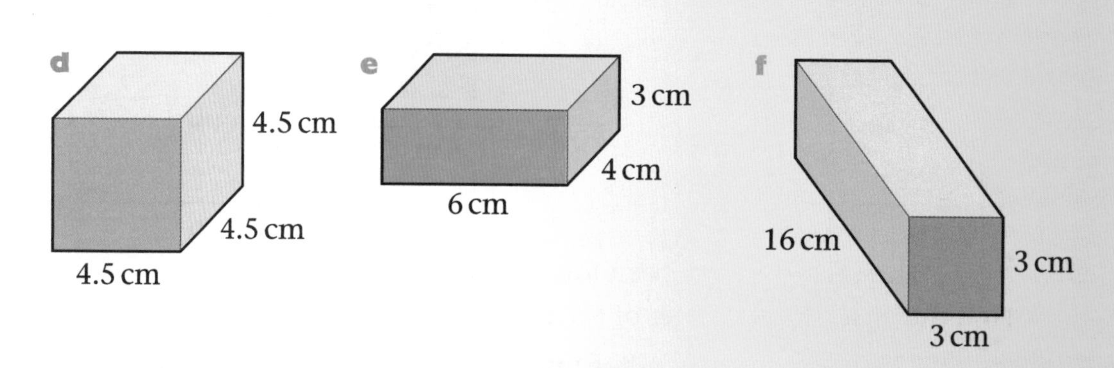

2 The diagram shows 2 cereal boxes.

Which has the greater surface area?

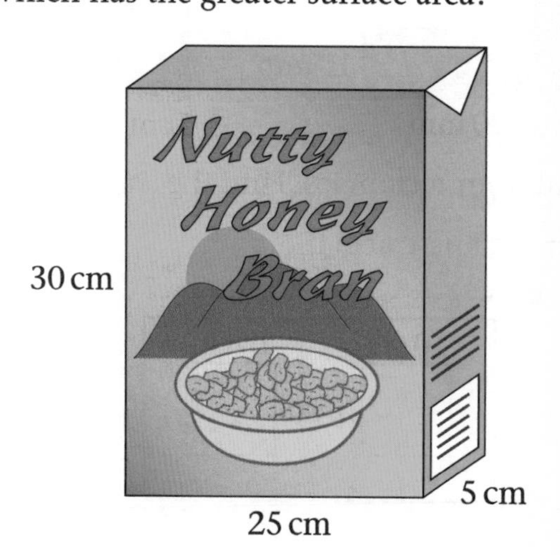

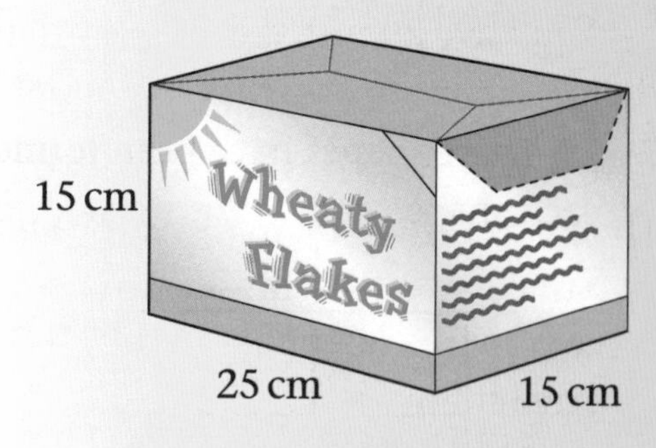

Consolidation Exercises

3 Copy and complete the following table.

	Shape	Length	Breadth	Height	Surface area
a	cube	3 cm			
b ✓	cuboid	4 cm	5 cm	6 cm	
c	cuboid	5 cm	10 cm	7.5 cm	
d	cube			7 cm	
e	cuboid	3.5 cm	8 cm	4 cm	
f	cuboid	45 mm	50 mm	50 mm	

4 What is the surface area of each of the following shapes?

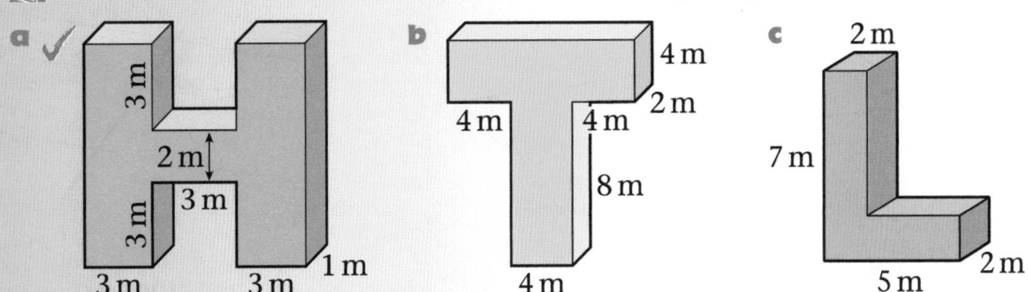

Challenging Exercises

5 You have 20 unit cubes. How many different cuboids can you make from them? What can you find out about their surface areas?

6 Write down your estimate of the surface area of the objects listed below. Then check your answer by measurement and calculation.

a a calculator
b your maths textbook
c a matchbox
d a CD case
e a cassette case
f a cereal packet

Finding Angles

Essential Exercises

1 Copy the diagrams below. Indicate the angle that is alternate to a.

a

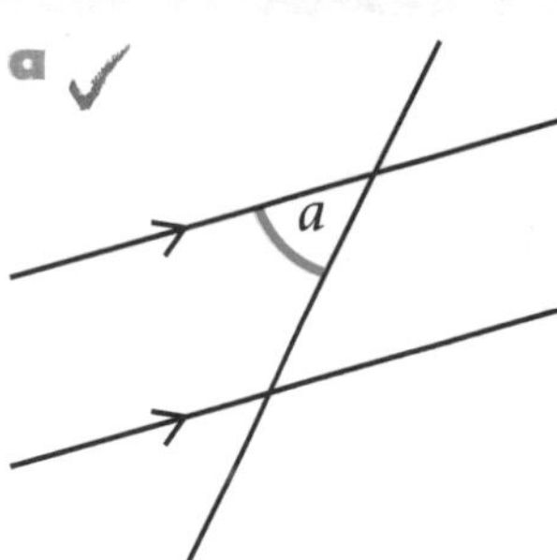

b

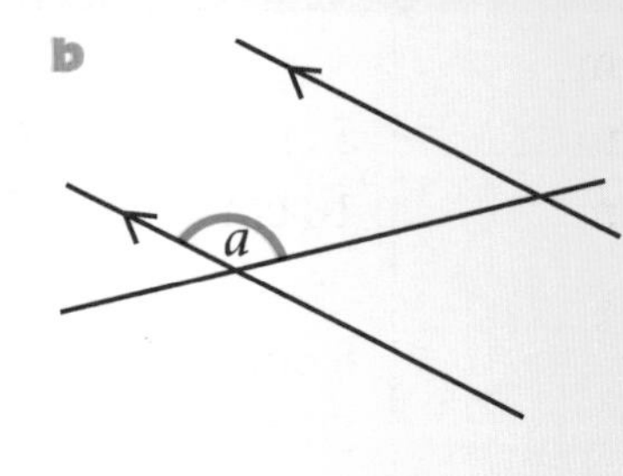

c

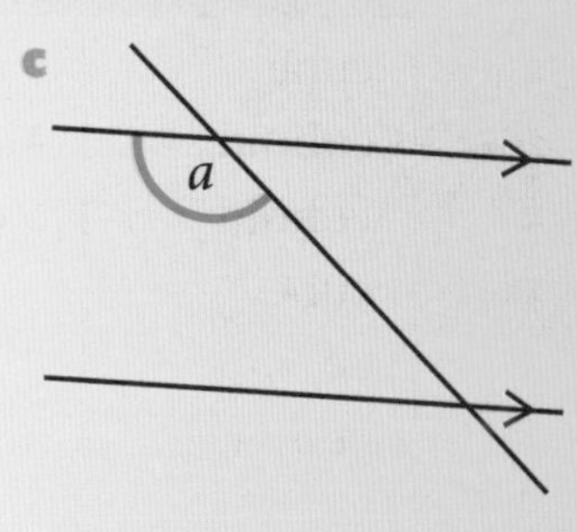

d

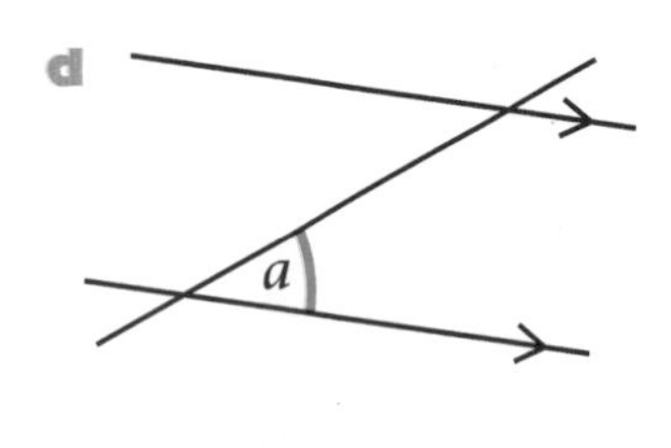

e

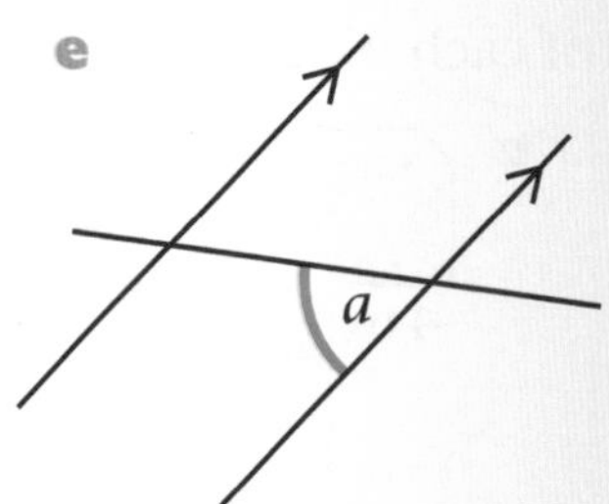

f

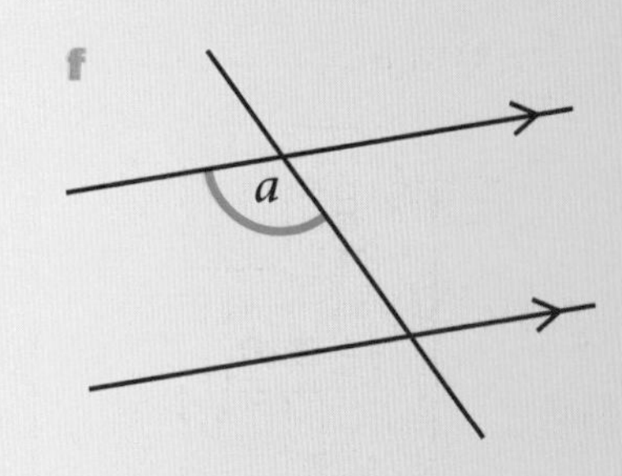

2 Copy the diagrams below. Indicate the angle that is corresponding to c.

a

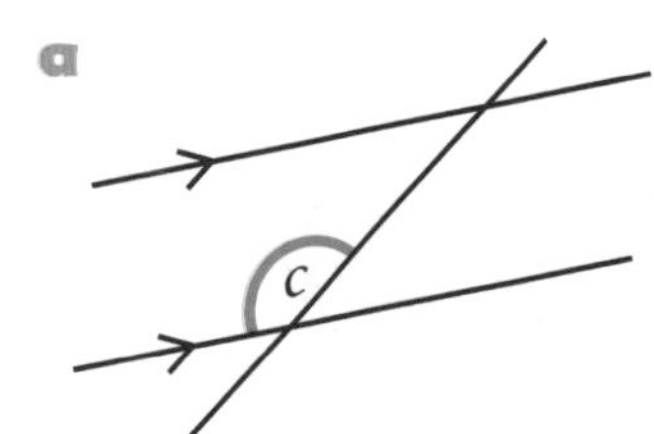

b

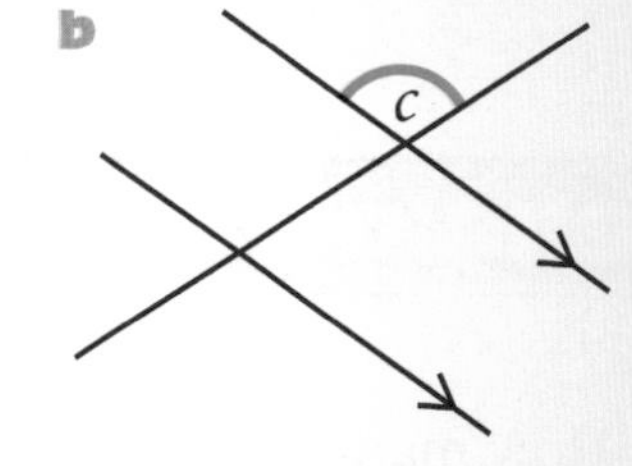

c

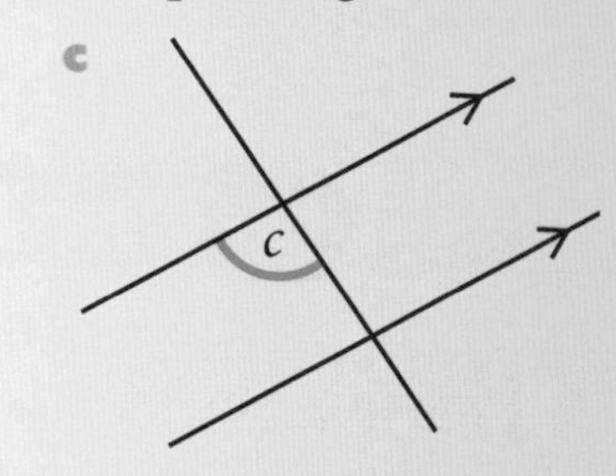

d

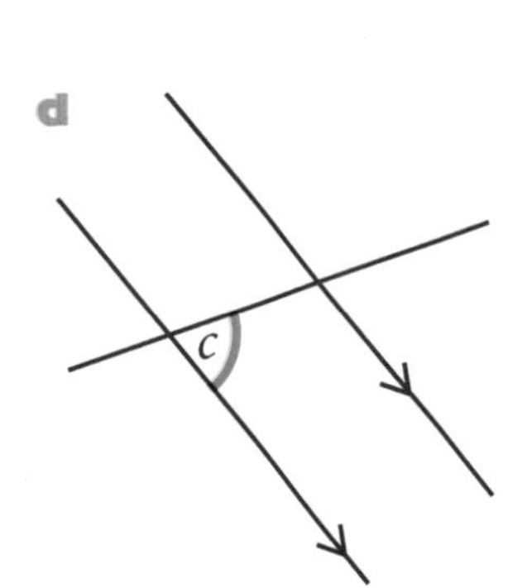

e

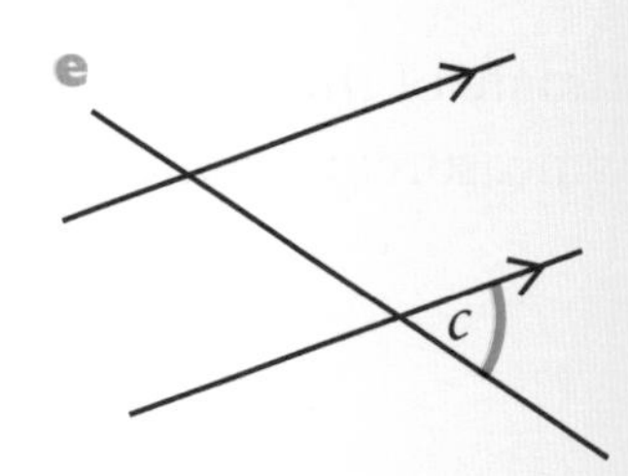

f

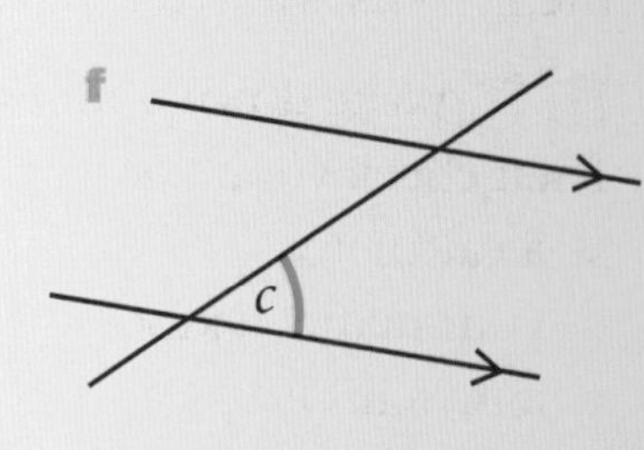

3 Write down the missing angles from the following statements.

a Complementary angles add up to ________.

b Supplementary angles add up to ________.

c **i** ✓ $25° + ? = 90°$

ii $? + 63° = 90°$

iii $45° + ? = 90°$

iv $17° + ? = 90°$

v $? + 32° = 90°$

vi $56° + ? = 90°$

d **i** $125° + ? = 180°$

ii $? + 63° = 180°$

iii $57° + ? = 180°$

iv $107° + ? = 180°$

v $? + 73° = 180°$

vi $96° + ? = 180°$

4 Calculate the missing angles in these triangles and quadrilaterals.

a ✓

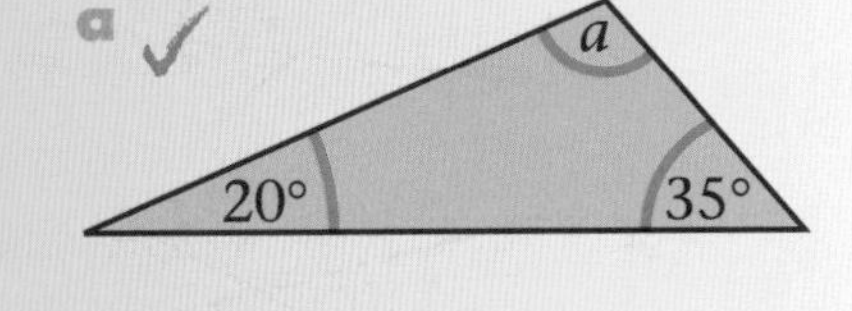

b

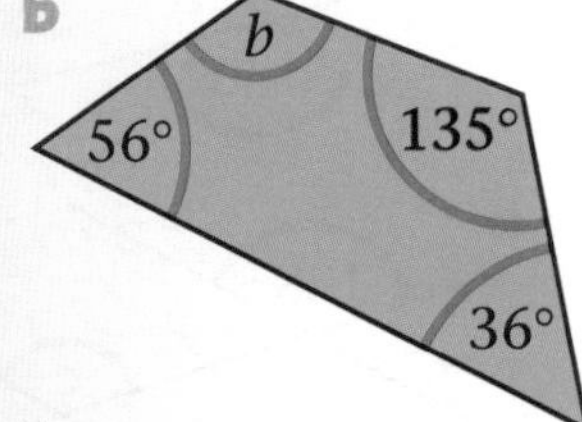

c

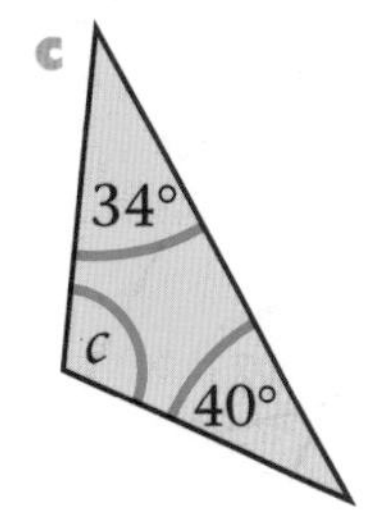

d

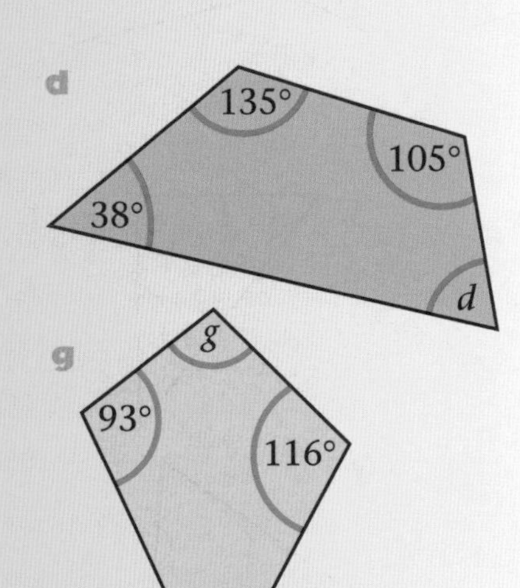

e

f

g

h

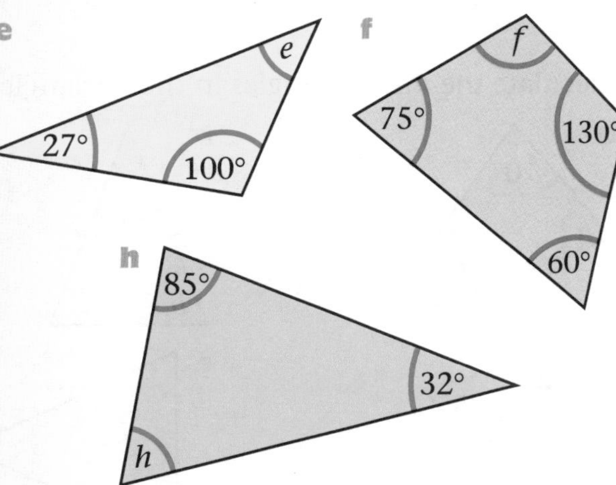

Consolidation Exercises

5 Find the angles marked *a* in the following diagrams.

a

b

c

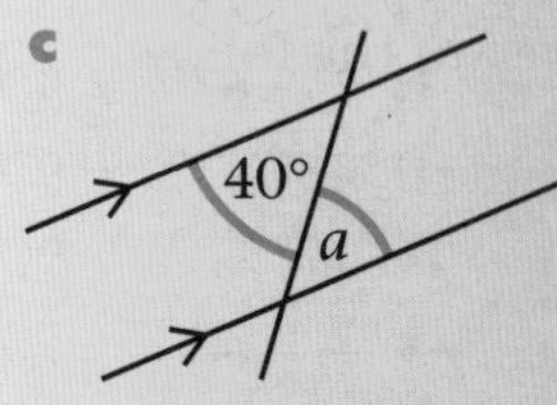

d

e

f

6 Find the angles marked *c* in the following diagrams.

a

b

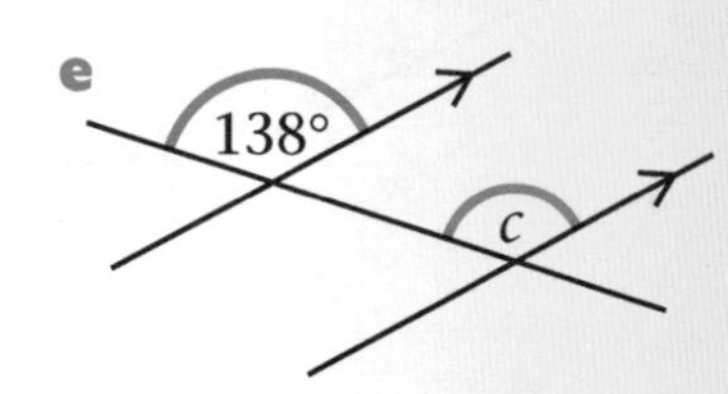

c

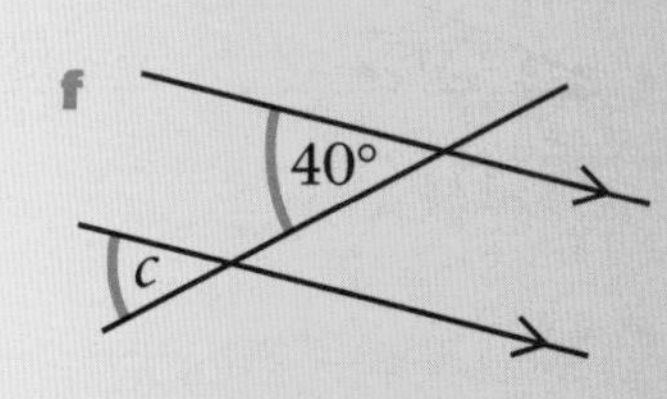

d

e

f

7 Calculate the missing angles in these triangles.

a

b

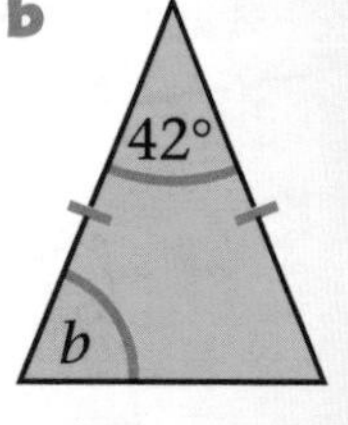

c

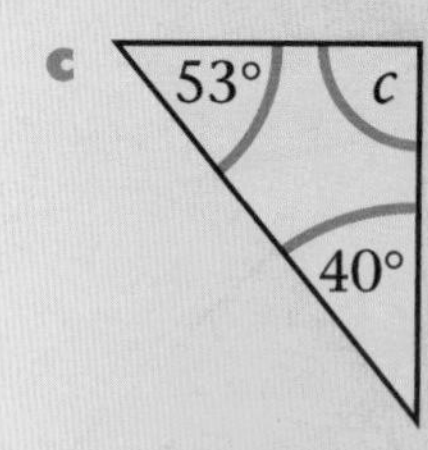

d

e

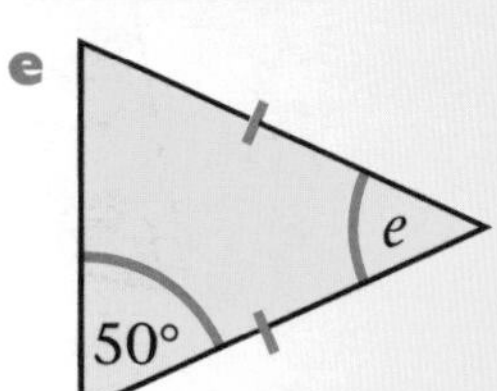

f

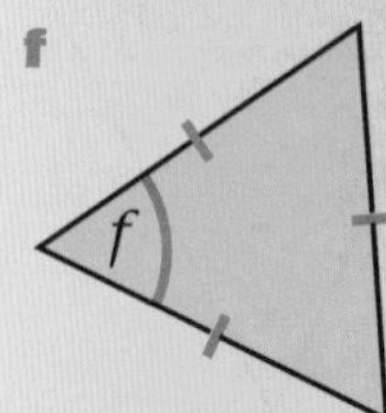

Challenging Exercises

8 Copy this sketch and mark a pair of each of the following angles.

a vertically opposite angles
b alternate angles
c corresponding angles
d angles on a straight line

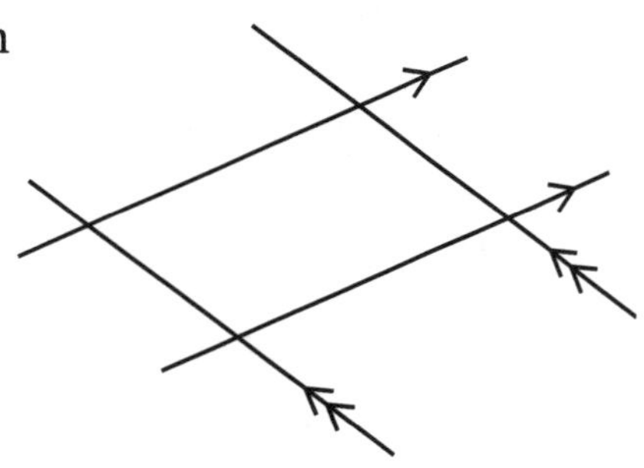

9 Find angle *a* in this rectangle.

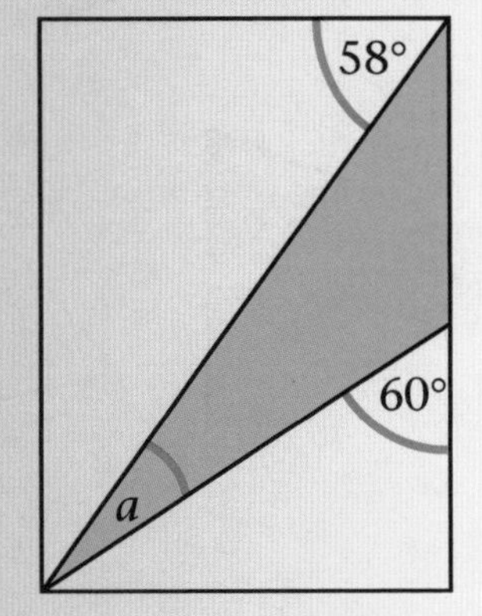

10 Draw a triangle ABC and extend one side as shown in the diagram.

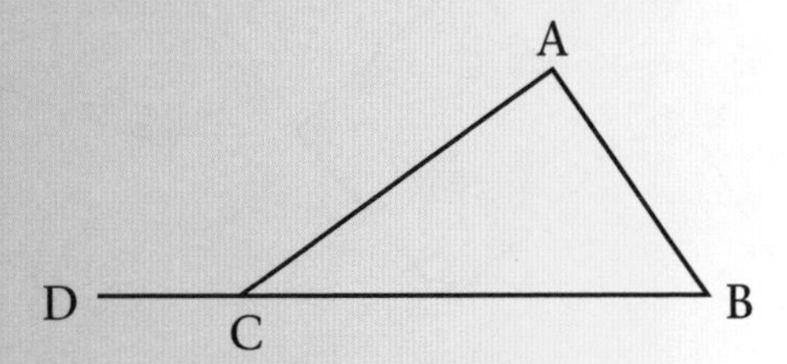

Measure $B\hat{A}C$ and $A\hat{B}C$.
Add them together.
Measure angle $A\hat{C}D$.
What do you notice? Can you come to any conclusions about the exterior angle of a triangle? Explain.
Draw another triangle and check your results.

8 Triangles and Quadrilaterals

Essential Exercises

1 Copy these triangles and mark them 'equilateral', 'isosceles' or 'right-angled'.

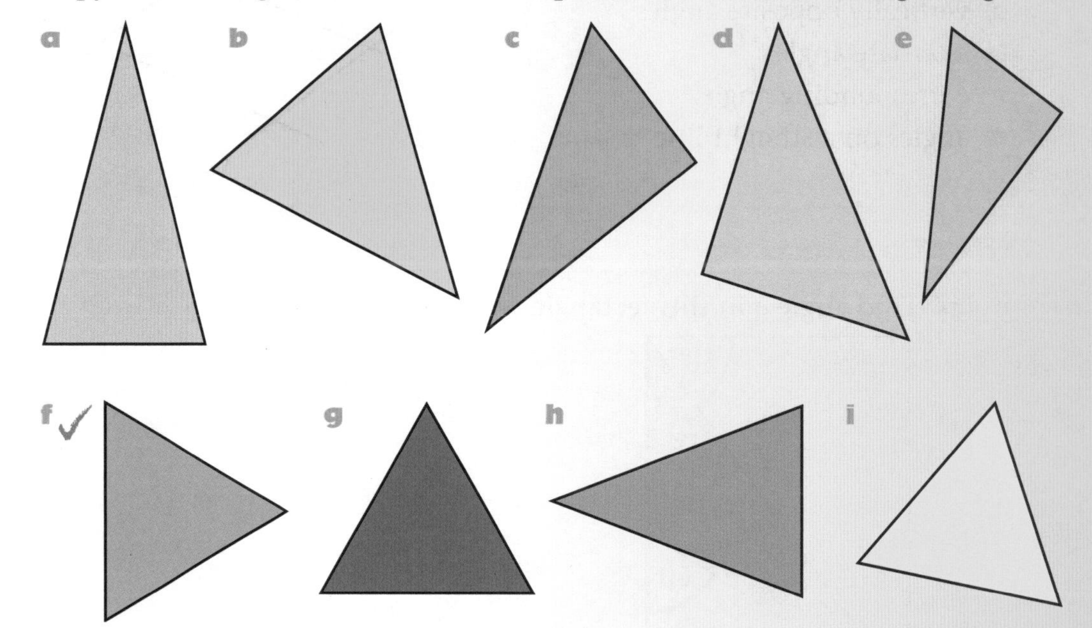

2 Copy these quadrilaterals and mark them 'kite', 'rhombus', 'parallelogram', 'arrowhead' (delta) or 'isosceles trapezium'.

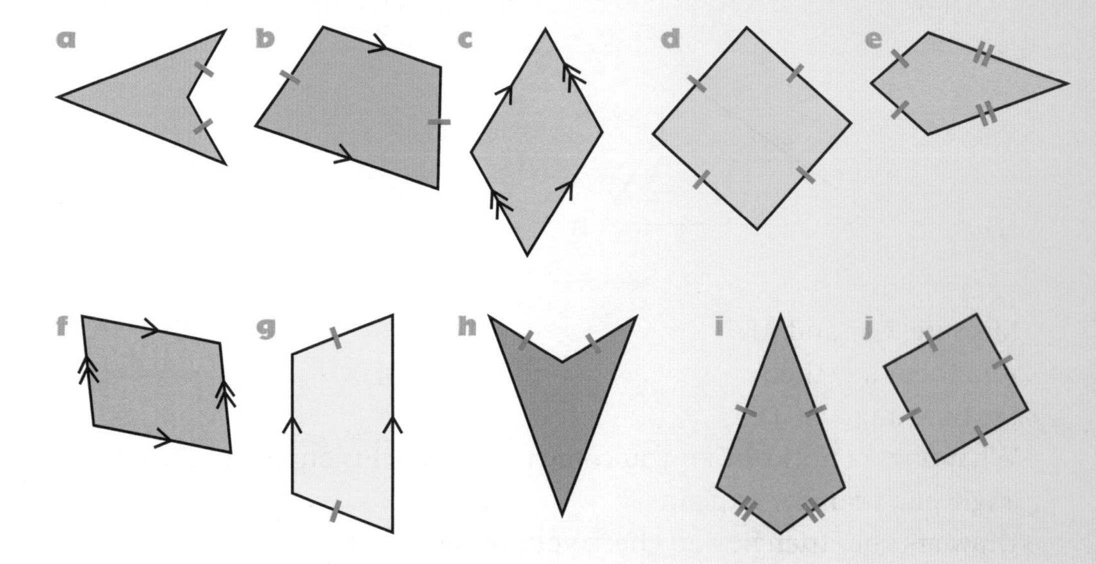

3 Copy this table and write in the name of the triangle for each set of properties.

	Name	Sides	Angles	Lines of symmetry	Order of rotational symmetry
a		3	3	0	0
b		3 equal	3 equal	3	3
c		2 equal	2 equal	1	0
d		3	3 acute	0	0
e		3	1 obtuse	0	0
f		3	1 right angle	0	0

Could triangle **d** have line symmetry? Could it have rotation symmetry? Give your reasons. Repeat for triangles **e** and **f**.

4 Copy this table and write in the name of the quadrilateral for each set of properties.

	Name	Sides	Angles	Lines of symmetry	Order of rotational symmetry
a		4 equal	4 right angles	4	4
b		2 pairs equal, opposite parallel	4 right angles	2	2
c		4 equal, opposite parallel	2 pairs equal and opposite	2	2
d		2 pairs equal, opposite parallel	2 pairs equal and opposite	0	1
✓ e		2 adjacent pairs equal	1 pair equal and opposite	1	0
f		1 pair parallel	4 different	0	0
g		1 pair parallel 1 pair equal	2 pairs equal	1	0
h		2 adjacent pairs equal	1 interior reflex	1	0

Draw each of these quadrilaterals with its diagonals. Write down what you notice about the intersection of the diagonals for each shape.

Consolidation Exercises

5 Calculate the missing angles in the following triangles.

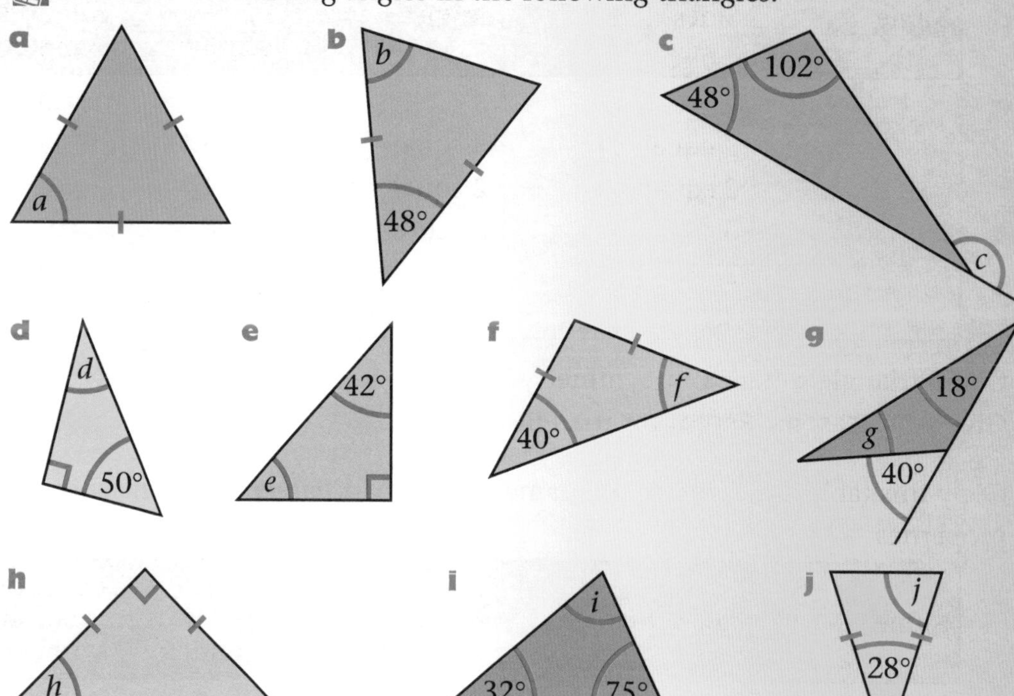

6 Calculate the missing angles in these quadrilaterals.

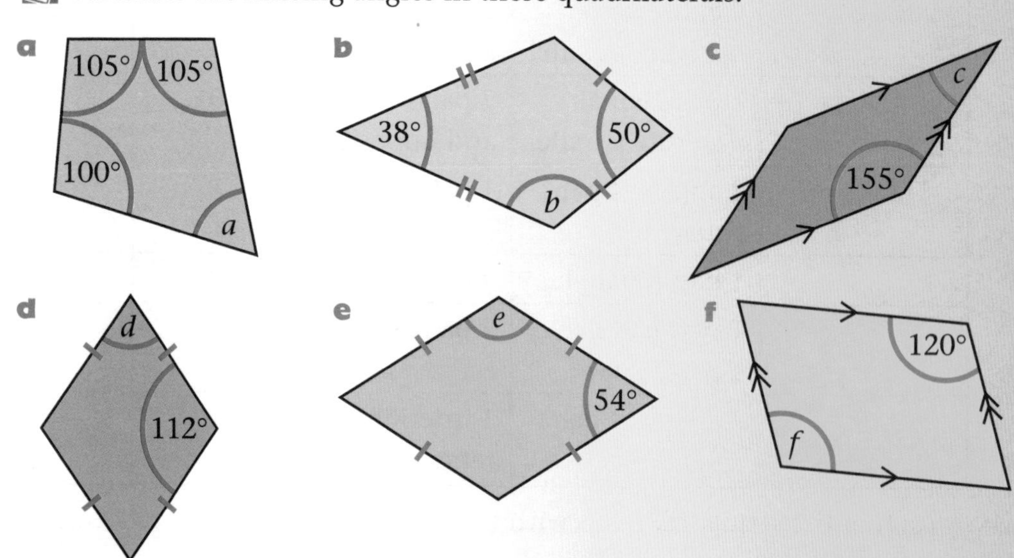

Challenging Exercises

7 Find the missing angles in each of the following diagrams.

✓ **a**

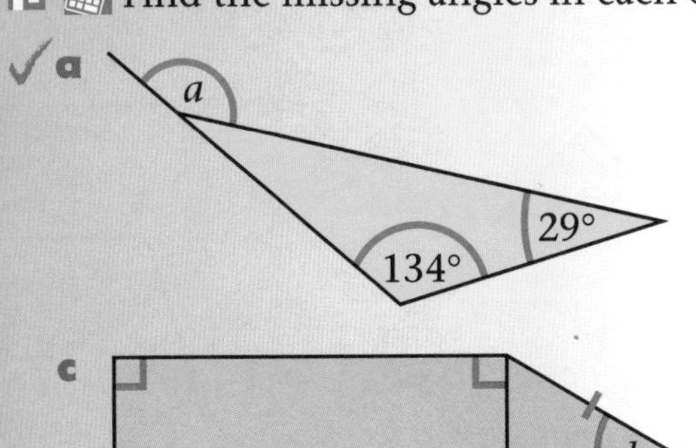

b

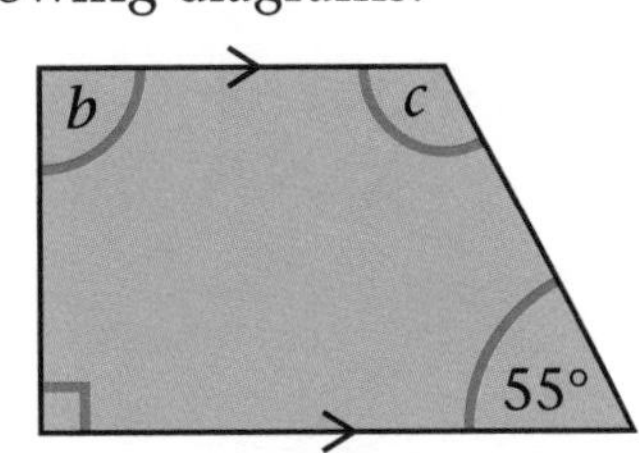

c

d

d

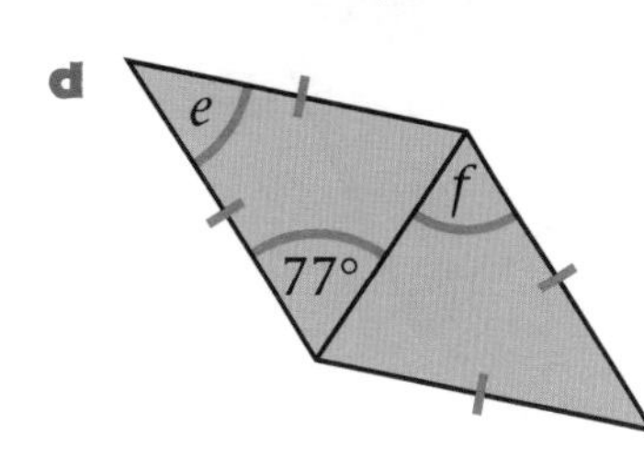

8 Draw any quadrilateral. Label it PQRS. Draw the diagonal PR.
Can you use the angle sum of a triangle to find the angle sum of a quadrilateral?

9 Draw any rhombus. Label it CDEF.

a Can you say that a rhombus is a parallelogram? Why?

b Can you draw a parallelogram that is not a rhombus? Explain.

10 Which of these regular shapes cannot be used to tile a floor?
Explain your answer.

a

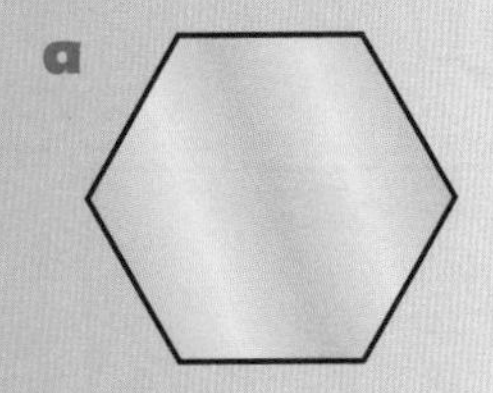

b

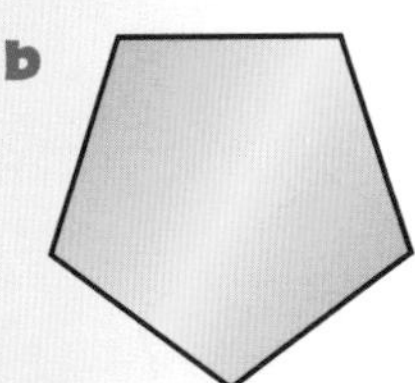

e

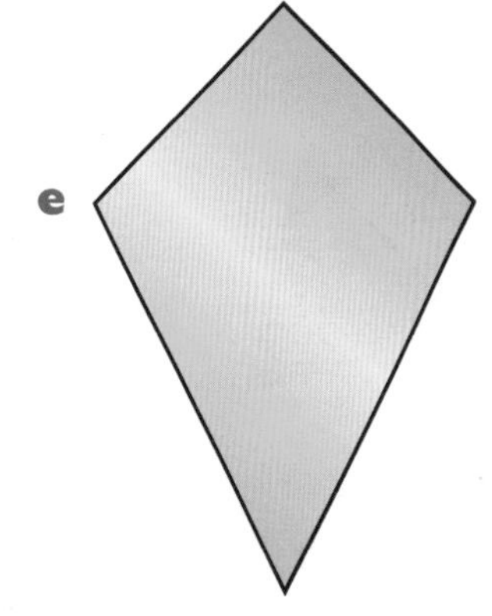

c

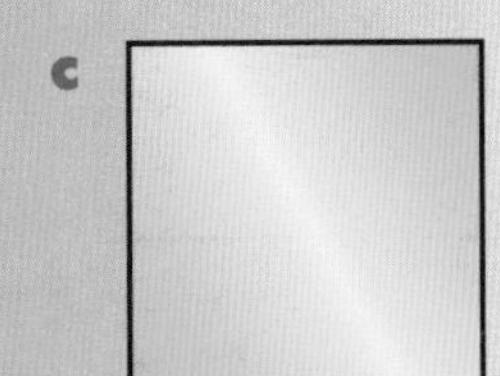

d

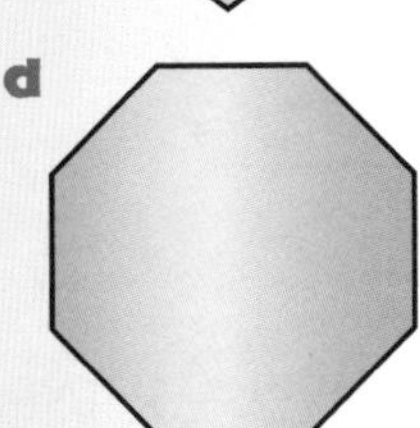

Choose a shape that can be used to tile a floor. Draw at least 10 tiles fitting together. Colour the tiles so that no 2 touching tiles have the same colour.
What is the smallest number of colours you can use?
Now make a tessellation using 2 of the usable shapes.

Congruent Shapes

Essential Exercises

1 Which shapes below are congruent?

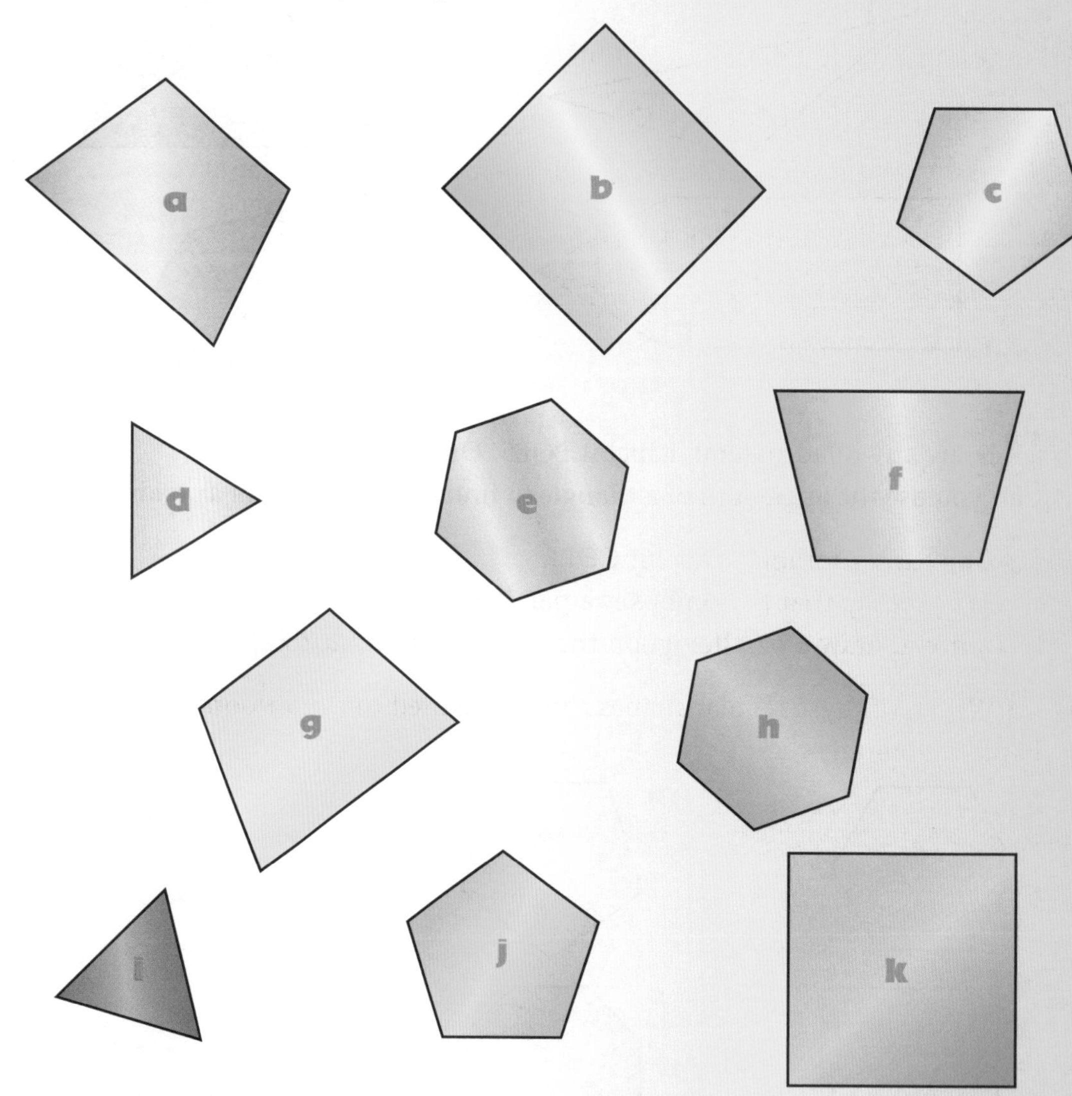

2 Draw an equilateral triangle on squared paper.
Draw a second, congruent, equilateral triangle, touching the first along one side. What shape has been formed? Why?
Keep adding equilateral triangles and each time comment on the shape you have formed.

Consolidation Exercises

3 Draw and name the triangles given below. State the order of rotation symmetry. Then see whether they will tessellate. Explain what you find.

- **a** a triangle having 1 line of symmetry
- **b** a triangle having 3 lines of symmetry
- **c** a triangle having no lines of symmetry

4 Draw and name the quadrilaterals given below. State the order of rotation symmetry. Then see whether they will tessellate. Explain what you find.

- **a** a quadrilateral having only 1 line of symmetry
- **b** a quadrilateral having 4 lines of symmetry
- **c** a quadrilateral having no lines of symmetry
- **d** a quadrilateral having 2 lines of symmetry

Is quadrilateral **d** the only quadrilateral with 2 lines of symmetry?

Challenging Exercises

5 **a** Draw one of the triangles from question **3** on squared paper. Copy it at least 6 times. Cut them out and see whether they tessellate.
Now repeat this for the other triangles. What do you notice?

b Draw one of the quadrilaterals in question 4 on squared paper. Copy it at least 6 times. Cut them out and see whether they tessellate.
Now repeat this for the other quadrilaterals.
What do you notice?

6 The angle at the vertex of a regular hexagon is 120°.
Use 3 diagonals to make 4 triangles.
Calculate the angles in each triangle.
Trace the hexagon and cut it into the 4 triangles.
Can you fit them together to make other shapes?
Trace the hexagon again and mark the centre.
Draw a line from the centre to each vertex.
How many triangles have you formed?
Cut them out and fit them together to make other shapes.

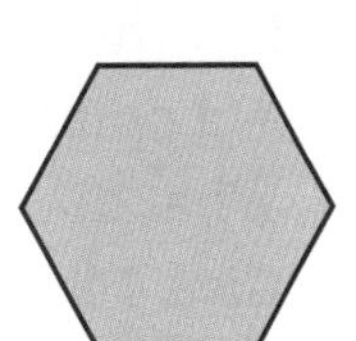

Solid Shapes

Essential Exercises

1 How many unit cubes do you need to make the following solid shapes?

a

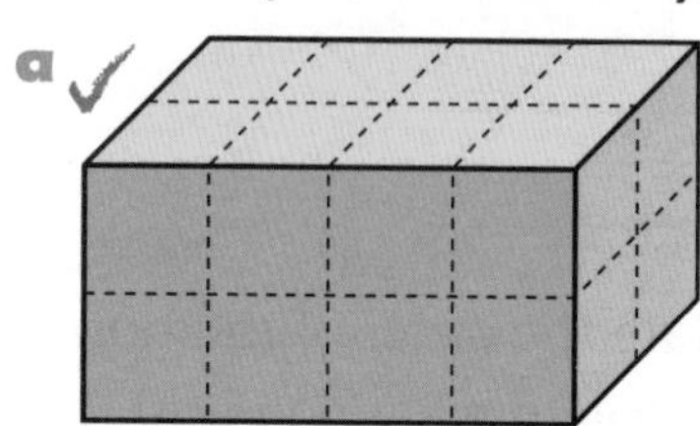

b

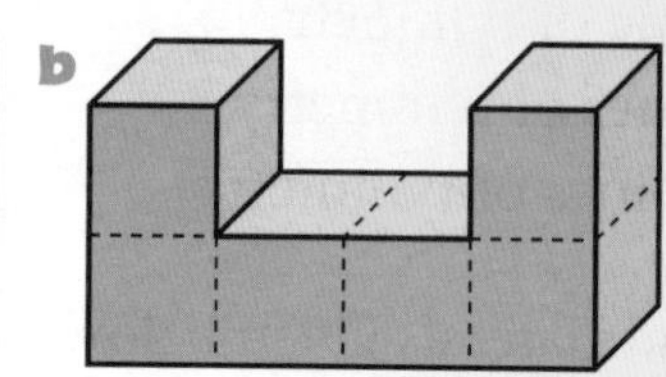

c

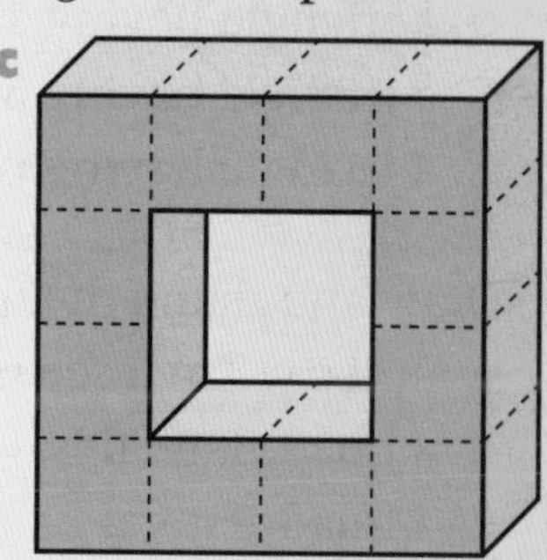

d

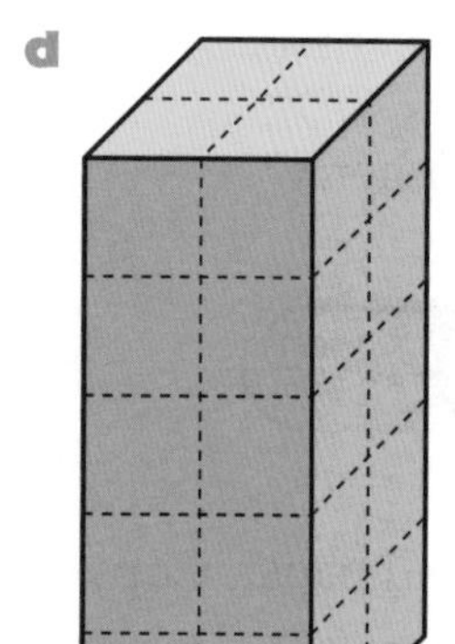

e

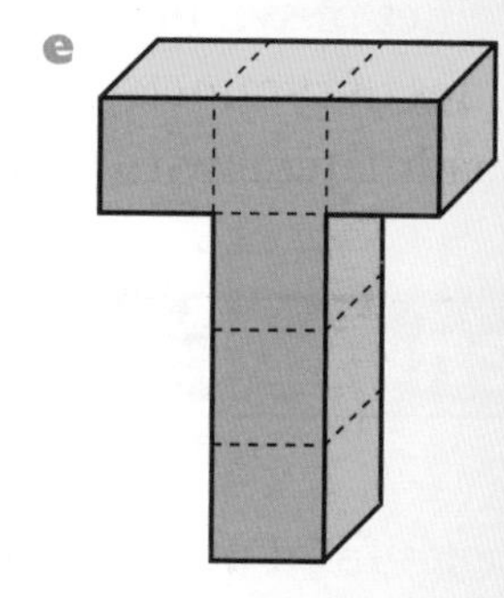

f

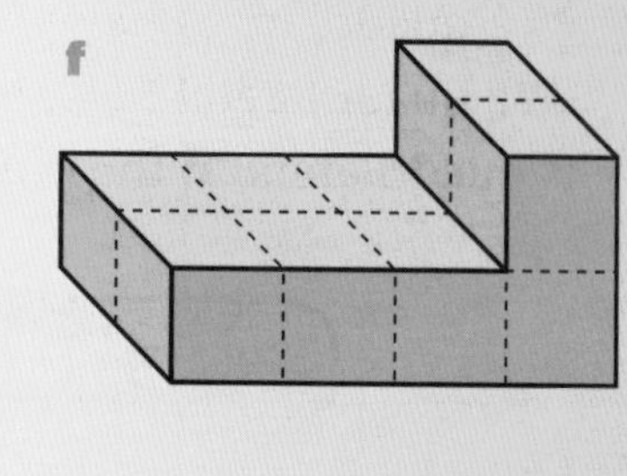

2 Look at this cuboid.

- **a** Give an example of edges meeting at a point.
- **b** Can you find another example? What is it?
- **c** How many more examples of edges meeting at a point are there?
- **d** What do we call the point where edges meet?
- **e** Give 4 lines that are parallel.
- **f** Are there any other groups of parallel lines? If so, name them.
- **g** Name 2 pairs of lines that are perpendicular to one another.
- **h** Name more pairs of lines that are perpendicular to one another.
- **i** What do we call ABCD?
- **j** How many of **i** does a cuboid have?

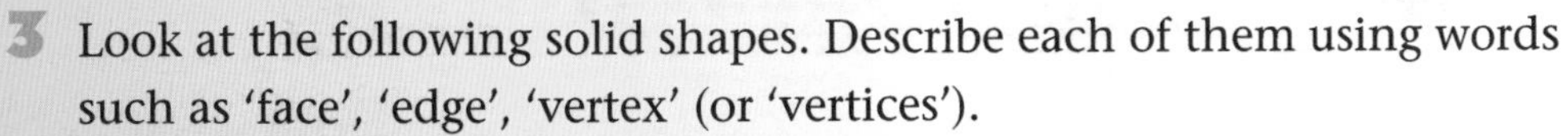

3 Look at the following solid shapes. Describe each of them using words such as 'face', 'edge', 'vertex' (or 'vertices').

a

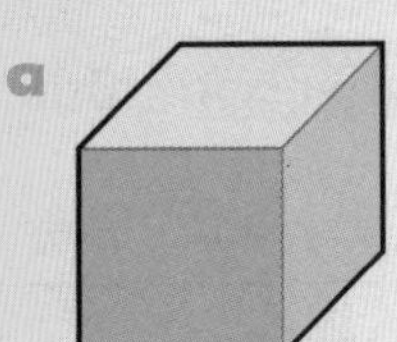

b ✓

c

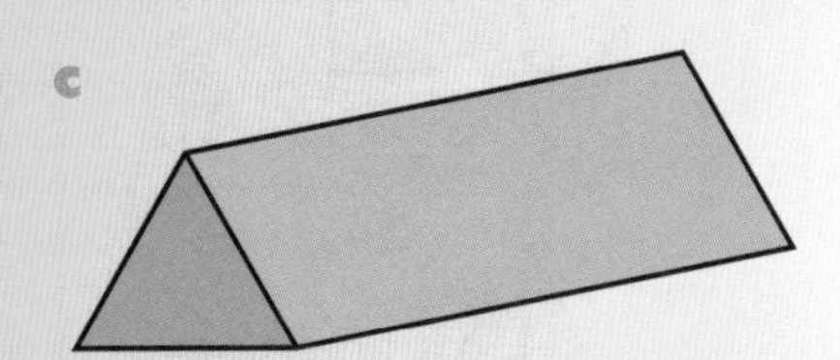

d

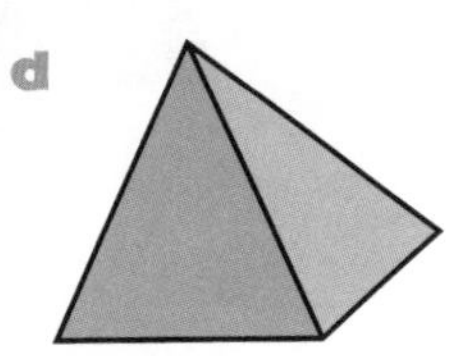

e

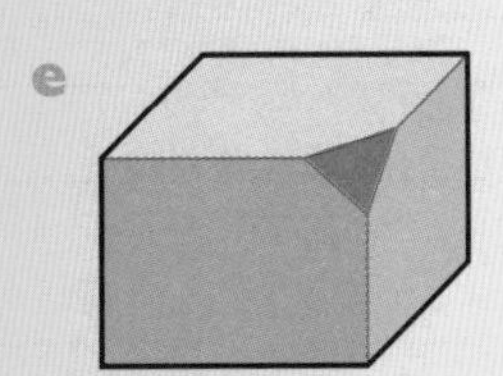

f

4 Use cuboids to draw solid shapes formed from the following capital letters.

a E
b F
c H
d T
e L

Sketch the net needed to make a model of one of the above shapes.

5 Draw the front and side elevations of the solid shapes listed below. Then draw the plan view for each.

a sphere
b cuboid
c cone
d triangular prism

Consolidation Exercises

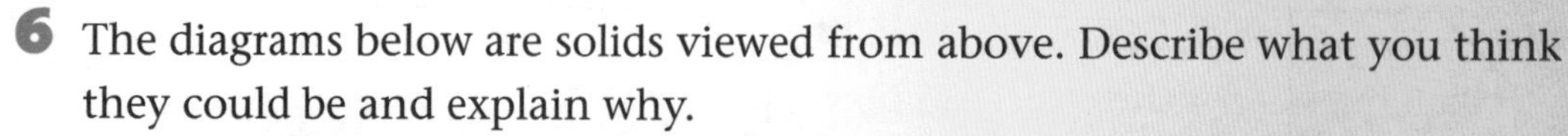

6 The diagrams below are solids viewed from above. Describe what you think they could be and explain why.

a 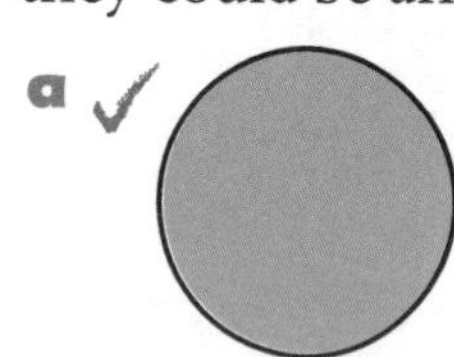

b 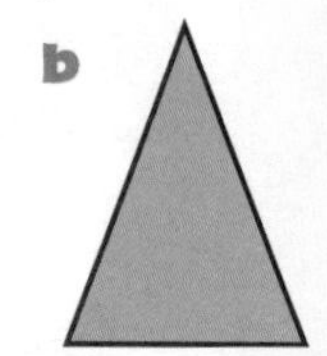

c 

d 

e 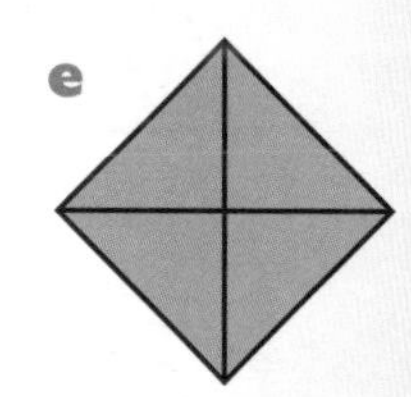

f 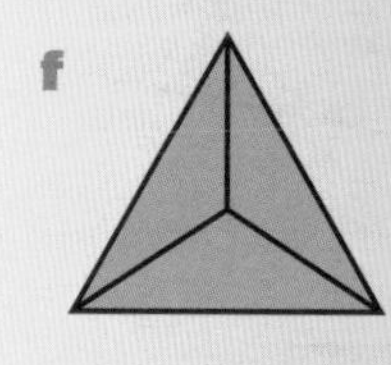

One of the diagrams could be 2 different solids. Which is it and what are they?

7 What solids can be constructed from the following elevations?

a front, side, plan

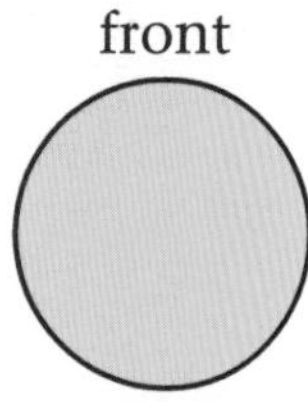

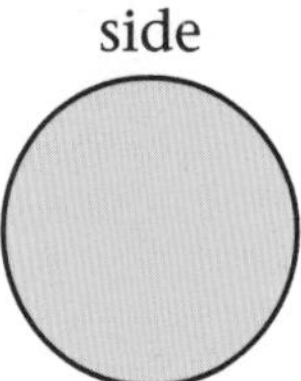

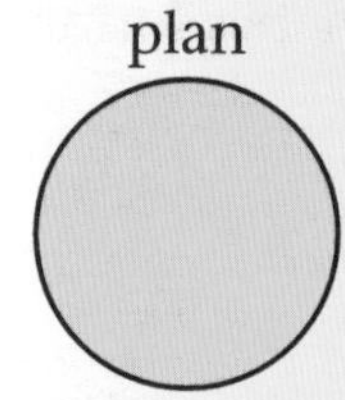

b front, side, plan

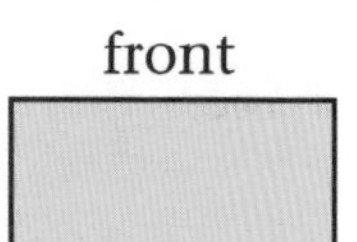

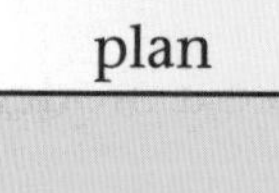

c front, side, plan

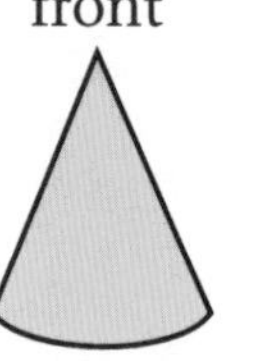

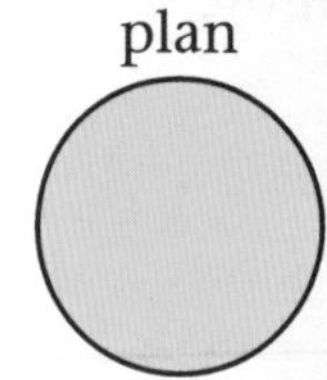

d front, side, plan

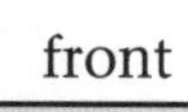

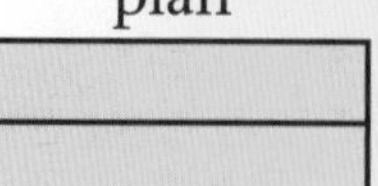

Challenging Exercises

8 **a** A die has 6 faces numbered 1 to 6. Opposite faces add up to 7. Sketch a net for the cube and number the faces.

b Here are 2 views of a similar cube.
The letters opposite each other on this cube make 3 two-letter words.
What are they?

9 Use isometric paper to draw the following.

a a cube

b a cuboid

c a triangular prism

10 The sketch shows a solid made from unit cubes.

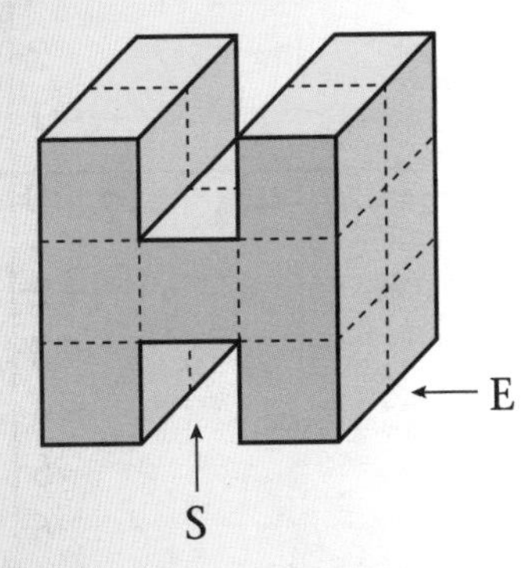

a Draw elevations from directions E and S.

b How many cubes have been used?

c White cubes were used, but the finished solid was painted green. How many cubes have:

i 1 green face

ii 2 green faces

iii 3 green faces

iv 4 green faces.

Transformations

Essential Exercises

1 ✓ Reflect shape A in the x-axis and label the transformed shape B.
Reflect shape B in the y-axis and label the transformed shape C.
What transformation will map A onto C?

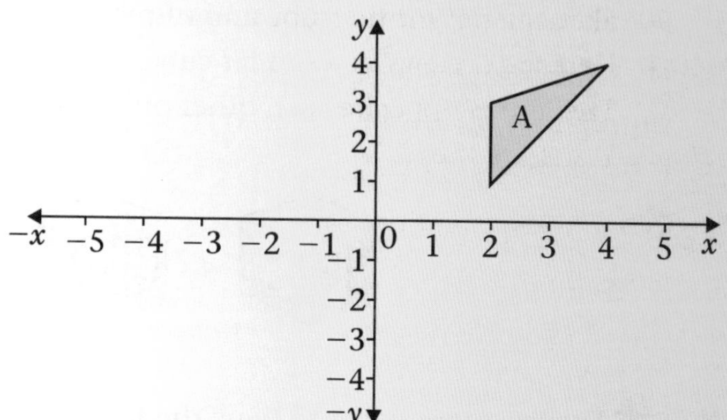

2 Draw a shape.
Rotate your shape about one vertex.
Continue to draw and rotate your shape to form a tessellation.

3 Draw the images of shape A translated by the following vectors.

a $\begin{pmatrix} 4 \\ 0 \end{pmatrix}$

b $\begin{pmatrix} 0 \\ -3 \end{pmatrix}$

c $\begin{pmatrix} 6 \\ -10 \end{pmatrix}$

d $\begin{pmatrix} 2 \\ 1 \end{pmatrix}$

e $\begin{pmatrix} 8 \\ -9 \end{pmatrix}$

f $\begin{pmatrix} -2 \\ 1 \end{pmatrix}$

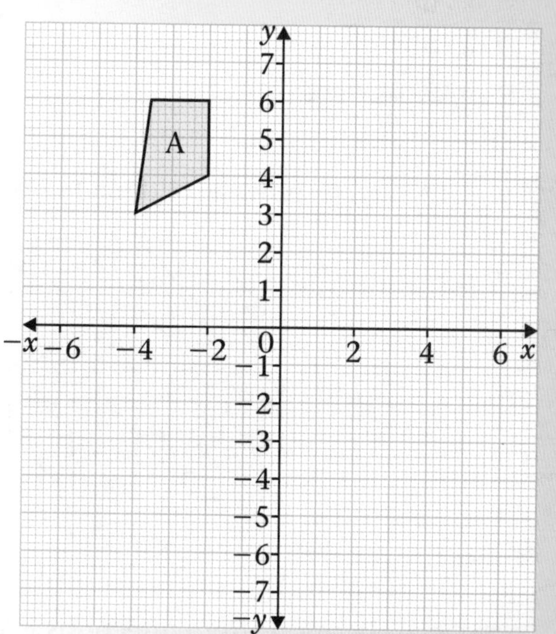

4 Draw a capital letter W on squared paper.
Reflect it in a horizontal line drawn as shown. What letter is formed?
Now reflect the W in a vertical line and continue along the line to the end.
Reflect this line of Ws along the horizontal to the end.

W

Consolidation Exercises

5 Rotate shape A clockwise through 90° about the origin to form shape B.

Now rotate shape B clockwise through 90° about the origin to form shape C.

What transformation moves A to C?

Now rotate shape C clockwise, through 90° about the origin to form shape D and rotate shape D clockwise through 90° about the origin to form shape E.

What do notice about A and E?

Explain the connection between the shapes.

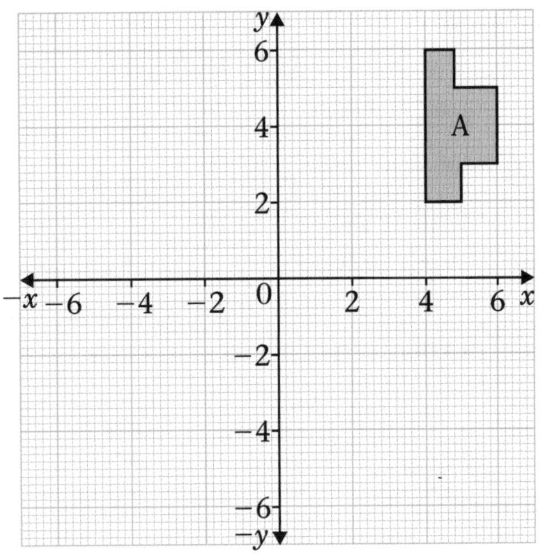

6 Give the vector that translates each lettered shape onto its shape (for example, A to A′) shown in the diagram.

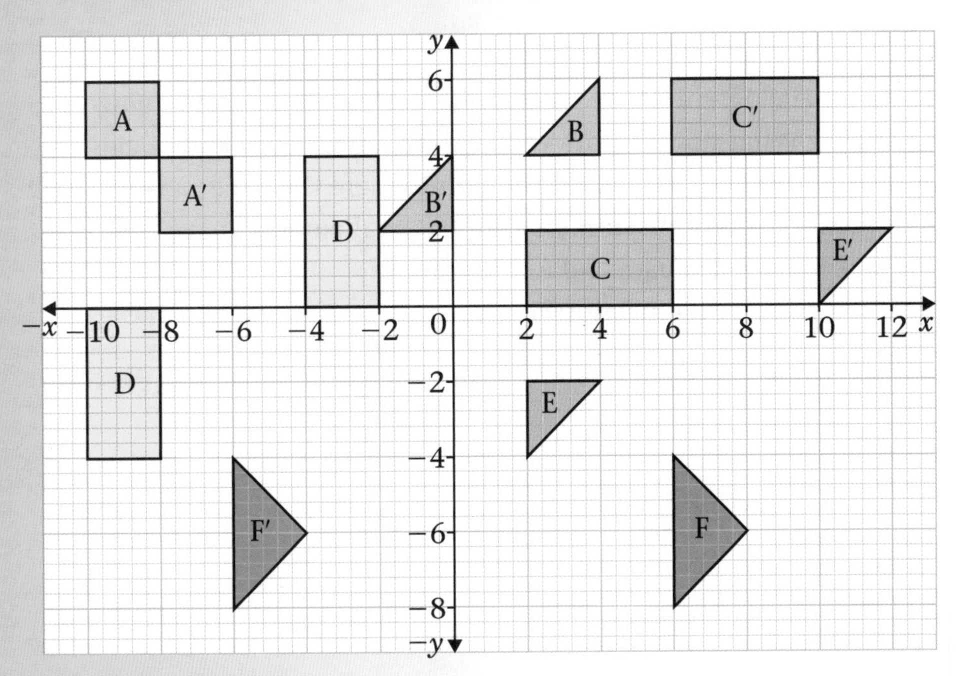

Challenging Exercises

7 Draw the same triangle in different positions on squared or dotted paper. Label your original triangle A. Now describe the transformations from A to the other triangles.

8 Reflect the given shape A in the line $x = -1$ to give shape B.
Reflect shape B in the line $x=1$ to give shape C.
What do you notice about shapes A and C?
Continue reflecting the shapes in $x=3$ and $x=5$.
Explain the connection between the shapes.

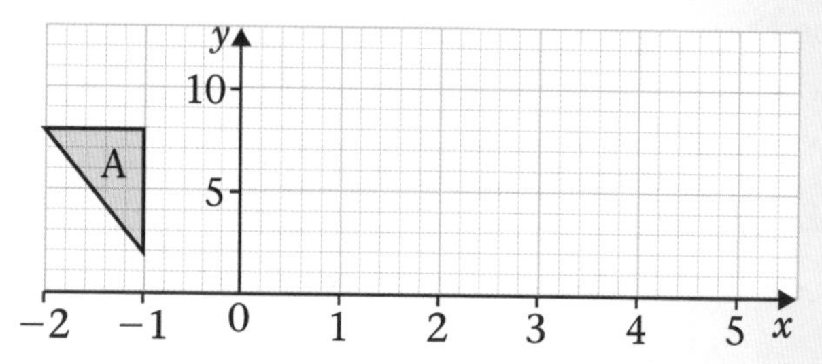

9 ✓ What happens if you rotate an isosceles triangle through 180° about the mid-point of the shortest side? What shape is formed? Mark any equal sides and angles. Explain why they are equal.

10 a Draw a parallelogram. Draw its diagonals. Measure the sides, diagonals and angles. What do you notice? Mark any equal sides and angles. Rotate the parallelogram about the point where the diagonals intersect. What order of rotation symmetry does a parallelogram have?

b Now repeat **a** for a square and a rhombus.
Do you notice any connections between these 2 polygons?

Enlargements

Essential Exercises

1 Calculate the scale factor that enlarges the following.

a A onto B
b A onto C
c B onto A
d B onto C
e ✓ C onto A
f C onto B

A 3 mm
3 mm

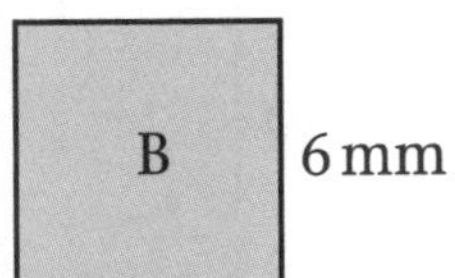

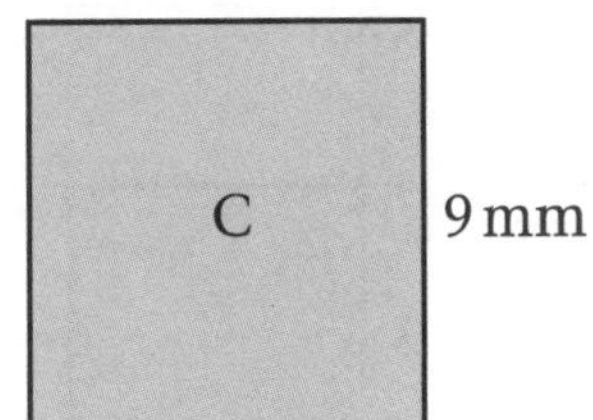

2 Enlarge the given shape by a scale factor 3 and centre of enlargement at the origin.

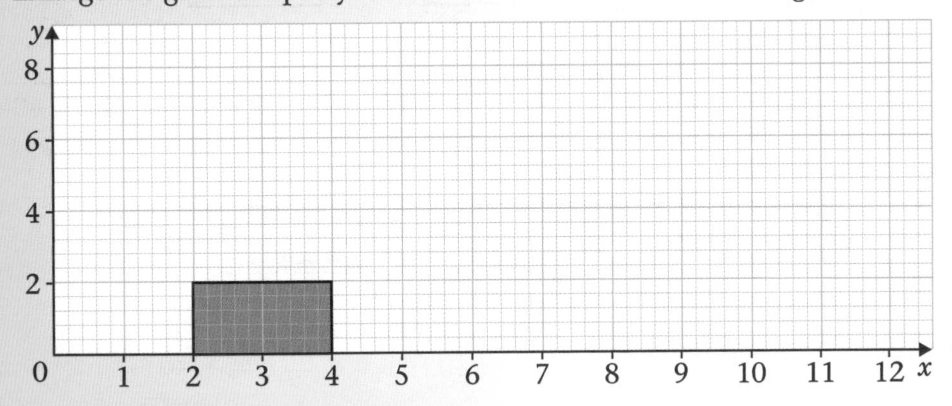

Consolidation Exercises

3 Enlarge the following shapes by the given scale factor.

a scale factor 2

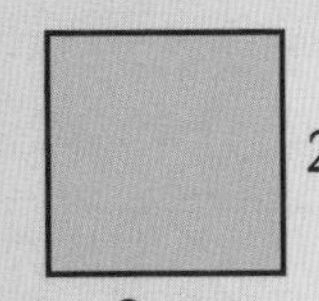

b scale factor 2

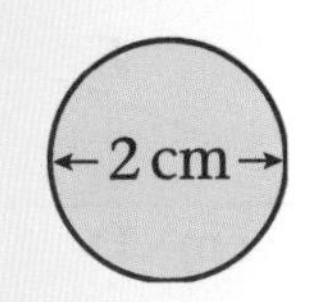

c scale factor 2

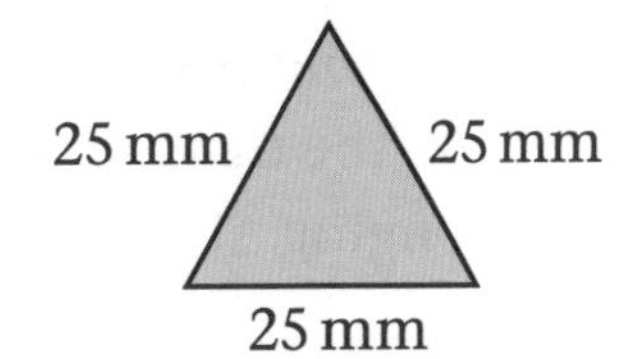

d scale factor 3

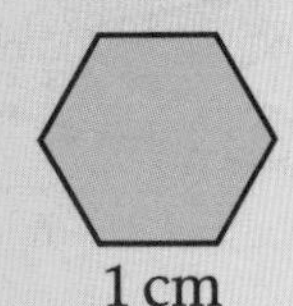

e scale factor 3

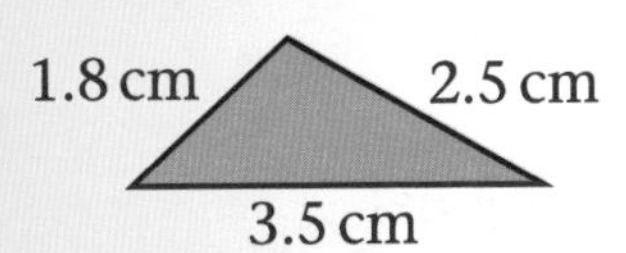

f scale factor 3

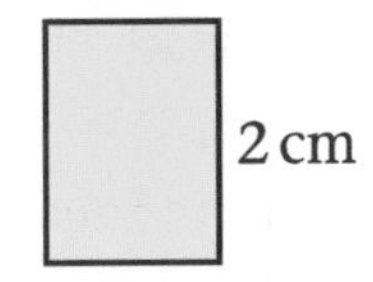

8

4 Describe fully the following enlargements.

a

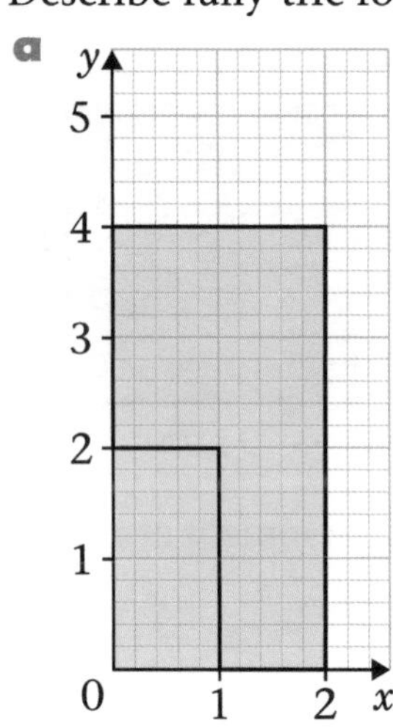

b

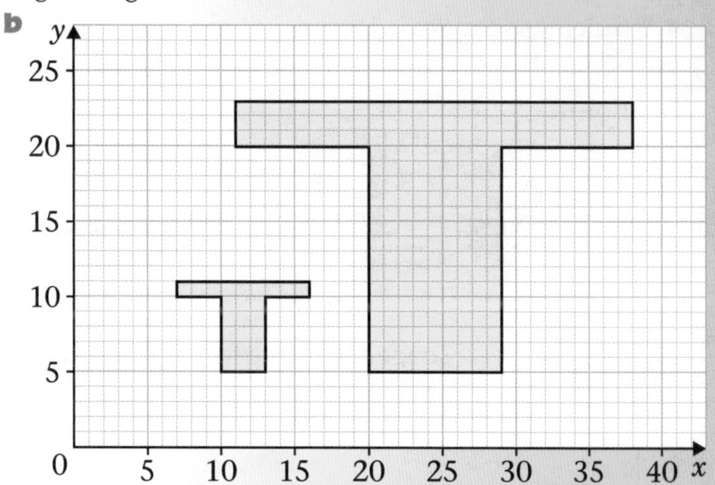

Challenging Exercises

5 Choose a capital letter.
Draw it on squared paper.
Mark a point outside the letter. This is your centre of enlargement.
Enlarge your letter by choosing a whole number for your scale factor.

6 ✓ Look at the diagram.
Compare the triangles ABC and ADE.
Are they congruent or similar?
Give your reasons. Describe fully the transformation changing ADE into ABC.

C
3 cm
E
A
B
2 cm D
6 cm

7 Draw an enlargement of this arrowhead with scale factor 2 and centre C.
Compare the angles in the original drawing with your enlargement. What do you notice?

C •

Drawing to Scale

Essential Exercises

1 Copy and complete the following table of plan lengths, scales and actual lengths.

	Plan length	Scale	Actual length
a	15 cm	1 : 100	
b		1 : 50	100 cm
c		1 : 25	500 cm
d	2.5 cm	1 : 30	
e ✓	9 cm	1 : 15	
f		1 : 20	200 cm

2 Measure the following and draw them using an appropriate scale.

- **a** the door of your classroom
- **b** computer keyboard
- **c** computer monitor – front view
- **d** a classroom window
- **e** a desk
- **f** a cupboard

Consolidation Exercises

3 A model of a house is being constructed before it is built. The scale is 1 : 100.

- **a** What does 1 cm on the plan represent in metres?
- **b** One room in the house measures 4 metres by 5 metres. What does it measure on the plan?
- **c** Draw the plan of this room.
- **d** The kitchen measures 6.5 cm by 2 cm on the plan. What are the actual dimensions of the kitchen?
- **e** What is the area of the kitchen?
- **f** Draw the plan of the kitchen. Decide where the window and door should be placed.

Challenging Exercises

4 This is the plan of a one bedroomed flat drawn to a scale of 1 cm : 1 metre.

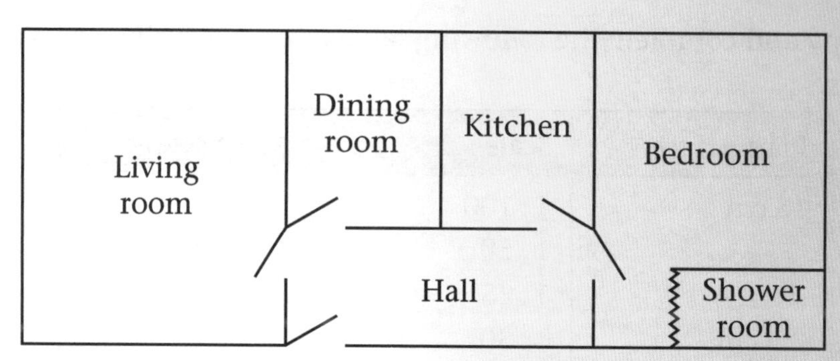

a What are the dimensions of the following rooms?
  i living room
  ii bedroom
  iii kitchen
  iv shower room

b What is the area of each of these rooms?

c The living room needs carpet. It costs £22 per square metre.
How much will the living room carpet cost?

5 Draw a plan of your bedroom. Remember to include furniture.
Choose an appropriate scale for your plan.

6 Draw lines to represent the following distances using the scales given in brackets. Remember to write the actual measurements on each line.

a 25 m (1 : 500)
b 150 m (1 : 100)
c 300 m (1 : 3000)
d 500 m (1 : 5000)
e 4 km (1 : 40 000)
f 6.5 km (1 : 50 000)

Coordinates

Essential Exercises

1 Draw axes with both x-axis and y-axis marked from -6 to $+6$.
Plot the points $(-2, 6)$ and $(2, 6)$.
Join the points.
Plot 4 further points to form a hexagon. What are the coordinates of these points?
Use your original line to find the perimeter of the hexagon.

2 A triangle is formed by plotting the points A$(-4, 0)$, B$(-6, 1)$, C$(0, 2)$. It is enlarged by a scale factor of 3 about the centre of enlargement $(0, 0)$.
What are the coordinates of the vertices of the enlarged triangle?

3 Plot the following points and then find the coordinates of the mid-point of the line joining them.

- **a** A$(-4, 4)$, B$(-2, 6)$
- **b** C$(1, 6)$, D$(2, 3)$
- **c** ✓ E$(4, 4)$, F$(6, 5)$
- **d** G$(2, -1)$, H$(1, -6)$
- **e** I$(-4, -2)$, J$(-2, -6)$
- **f** K$(-2, 3)$, L$(-2, -1)$

Consolidation Exercises

4 Follow these instructions.

- **a** Make each of the lines in question **3** into a right-angled triangle.
- **b** Write down the coordinates of the third vertex.
- **c** Find the area of each triangle.
- **d** Make each of these triangles into a rectangle.
- **e** Write down the coordinates of the fourth vertex.
- **f** Find the area of each rectangle using your answer to **c** above.
- **g** Is there another way of finding the area of each rectangle? Explain using one of the rectangles.

Challenging Exercises

5 On squared paper draw axes with x-axis marked from -3 to 5 and y-axis marked from 0 to 7.

- **a** Mark the 3 points $(-2, 7)$, $(0, 5)$, and $(4, 1)$.
- **b** ✓ What do you notice about each pair of coordinates?
- **c** What do you notice about the position of each point?
- **d** Can you find a rule for each point?
- **e** Now mark another point obeying your rule.

6 Draw axes with both x-axis and y-axis marked from -5 to $+5$.
Plot the points $(-3, -2)$, $(0, -1)$ and $(-2, -4)$ to form a triangle.
What are the coordinates of the vertices of the triangle after the following transformations?

- **a** Reflection in the y-axis.
- **b** Translation by the vector $\begin{pmatrix} -1 \\ 3 \end{pmatrix}$.
- **c** Rotation through 180° about the origin.
  Does it make any difference if the triangle is rotated clockwise or anticlockwise? Explain your answer.

Constructions

Essential Exercises

1 Use a ruler to draw the following.

- **a** a line AC measuring 8 cm
- **b** the mid-point M of line AC
- **c** at M, draw a line BD, perpendicular to AB with MB and MD measuring 4 cm each
- **d** join AB, BC, CD and DA

What shape have you formed?

2 Draw the following triangles using ruler and protractor. You may need to draw them to scale. If so, remember to write down your chosen scale.

- **a** PQ = 5 cm, PR = 4 cm, $\hat{P} = 45°$. Measure QR.
- **b** DE = 8 cm, DF = 5.5 cm, $\hat{D} = 62°$. Measure EF.
- **c** ✓ AB = 12 cm, AC = 16 cm, $\hat{A} = 90°$. Measure BC.
- **d** AB = 14 cm, $\hat{A} = 57°$, $\hat{B} = 48°$. Measure the third angle.
- **e** DE = 9 cm, $\hat{D} = 120°$, $\hat{E} = 25°$. Measure the third angle.
- **f** PQ = 7.5 cm, $\hat{P} = 40°$, $\hat{Q} = 105°$. Measure the third angle.

You should be able to work out if your measured angles in **d**, **e** and **f** are correct. How? Why?

3
- **a** Draw any triangle. Measure the length of each side and the size of each angle.
- **b** Now write instructions for someone else to construct your triangle.
- **c** Perhaps your triangle is a scale drawing. Suggest a scale and write down the real lengths. Do the size of the angles change? Explain your answer.

Consolidation Exercises

4 Use a ruler, protractor and compasses for the following.

- **a** Draw a line measuring 7.5 cm.
- **b** At one end, A, draw an angle of 80°.
- **c** With centre A and radius less than the length of your line, draw an arc to cross both arms of the angle. Mark these points B and D.
- **d** With the same radius, and using B and D as centres, draw 2 crossing arcs within the angle.
- **e** Write C at the point of intersection.
- **f** Now measure AB, BC, CD and DA. Explain your findings.
- **g** Measure $A\hat{B}C$ and $A\hat{C}B$. What do these, and your results from **f**, tell you about $\triangle$ ABC?
- **h** What can you deduce about $\triangle$ BCD?

5 Using only ruler and compasses construct the following triangles and quadrilaterals. You may need to draw them to scale. If so, remember to write down your chosen scale.

- **a** Triangle XYZ: XY=50 mm, YZ = 70 mm, XZ = 30 mm. Measure $\hat{X}$.
- **b** Triangle DEF: DE = 12 cm, EF = 16 cm, DF = 8 cm. Measure angle $\hat{E}$.
- **c** Triangle ABC: AB = 10.5 cm, BC = 7.3 cm, AC = 8 cm. Measure $\hat{A}$.
- **d** Quadrilateral ABCD: AB = AD = 3 cm, BC = CD = 2 cm, $\hat{A}$ = 55°. Measure the length of BD.
- **e** Quadrilateral WXYZ: WX = 4 cm, XY = 2.5 cm, WZ = 1.5 cm, $\hat{W}$ = 78°, $\hat{X}$ = 52°. Measure YZ and $\hat{Z}$ and $\hat{Y}$.
- **f** Quadrilateral DEFG: DE = 4 cm, FG = 2 cm, DG = 2.5 cm, $\hat{D}$ = 67°, $\hat{G}$ = 128°. Measure EF and $\hat{E}$ and $\hat{F}$.

You should be able to check if your measured angles in **e** and **f** are correct. How? Why?

Challenging Exercises

6 Construct nets for the following solids.

- **a** A tetrahedron of edge 4 cm.
- **b** A die with edge 3 cm. Number the faces making sure that opposite faces add up to 7.

7 Use a ruler and compasses for the following.

- **a** Draw a line AC measuring 8 cm.
- **b** With centre A, draw an arc of radius 5 cm above and below the line AC.
- **c** Repeat using C as centre so that the arcs intersect above and below the line. Label these points B and D.
- **d** Join the points of intersection. Write M at the point of intersection of AC and BD.
- **e** Measure AM, BM, CM and DM. What do you notice?
- **f** Now measure AB, BC, CD and DA. What do you notice?
- **g** What shape have you drawn?

8 Use a ruler and compasses for the following.

- **a** Draw a line AC measuring 10 cm.
- **b** Mark a point B somewhere above the line.
- **c** With centre B, draw an arc to cross the line AC, with radius greater than the distance of B from the line. Mark the points of intersection, of the arc and line, X and Y.
- **d** With the same radius and centres X and Y, draw 2 intersecting arcs below the line. Mark D at the point of intersection of the arcs.
- **e** Join BD and write M at the point of intersection of AC and BD.
- **f** Measure $A\hat{M}B$.
- **g** What can you say about the lines AC and BD?

9 Use a ruler and compasses for the following.

- **a** Draw a line AC measuring 10 cm.
- **b** Mark a point M so that AM = MC.
- **c** Draw 2 arcs, centre M, to cross AC either side of M.
- **d** With a greater radius than in **c**, and using the points of intersection from **c**, draw pairs of crossing arcs above and below AC.
- **e** Label the points where these pairs of arcs cross B and D. Join these points.
- **f** Measure $A\hat{M}B$.
- **g** What can you say about the lines AC and BD?
- **h** Look at the question above and compare your findings.

Simple loci

Essential Exercises

1 Here is a plan of the area around Susan's house.

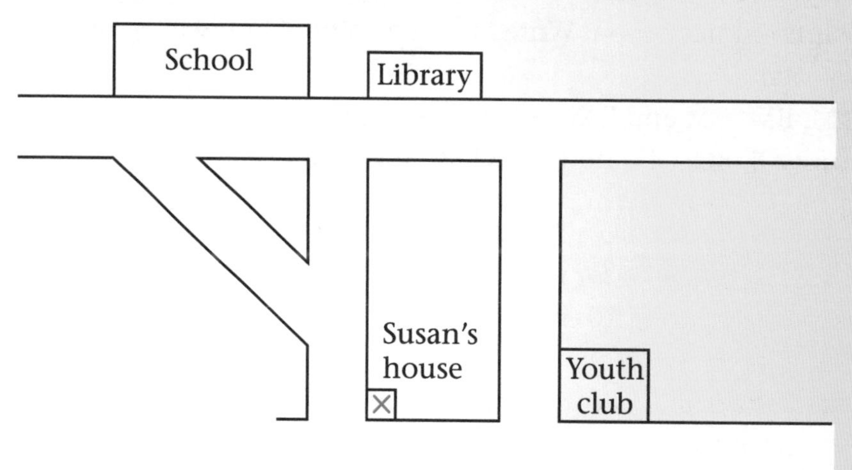

Describe:

- **a** Susan's route to school
- **b** the route from school to the library
- **c** the route from the library to the youth club
- **d** the route from the youth club to her home.

2 Draw the path traced by the following:

- **a** the tip of the minute hand of a clock
- **b** a dog tied by its lead to a ring, which can slide up and down a pole, in the middle of a garden
- **c** a handle on a door
- **d** a ball thrown up in the air
- **e** ✓ the end of a car windscreen wiper
- **f** the seat of a swing in the park.

Consolidation Exercises

3 Draw a cross in the centre of your page.
Place a dot at a distance of 5 cm from the cross.
Continue to place more dots at the same distance from the cross.
What path or locus do the dots make?

4 Ship A and ship B are positioned as shown in the diagram.
Ship C sails so that it is always the same distance from A and from B.
Mark its path using dots.
How would you describe this path?

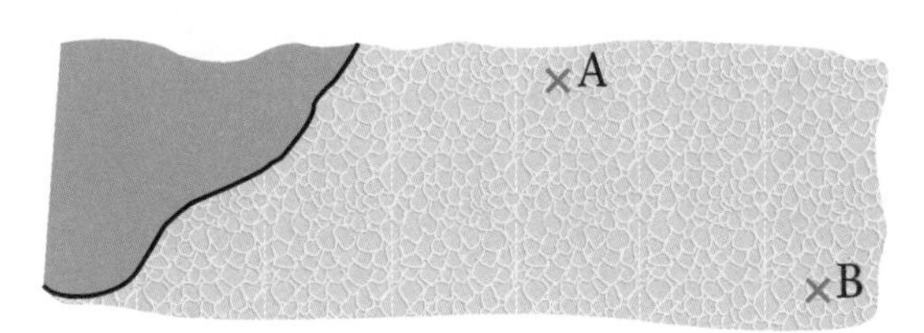

5 What is the locus of the top of Jack's head as he walks at a distance of 1 metre from a hedge?
Draw a diagram to illustrate this.

Challenging Exercises

6 This is the diagram of a garden.
The edge of the lawn is 1 metre from the garden walls.
Copy the diagram and mark the edge of the lawn.
How would you describe this?

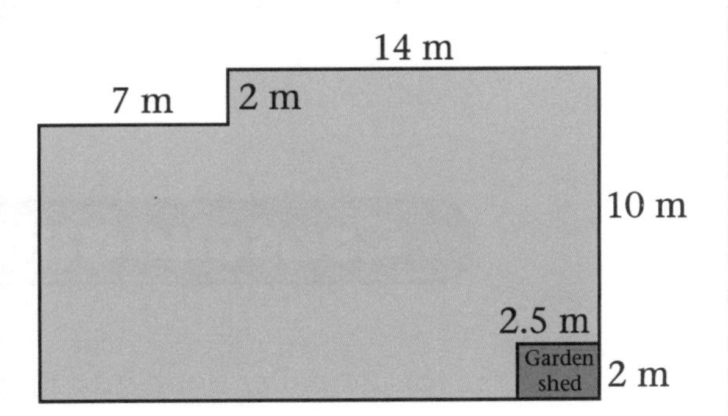

7 This diagram shows the plan of Ayesha's bedroom.
Power points (✗) must be placed by the bed, for a bedside lamp, and by the desk for a lamp and computer. A third power point is needed equidistant from the other two.
Copy the plan and draw the locus of possible positions for the third power point.

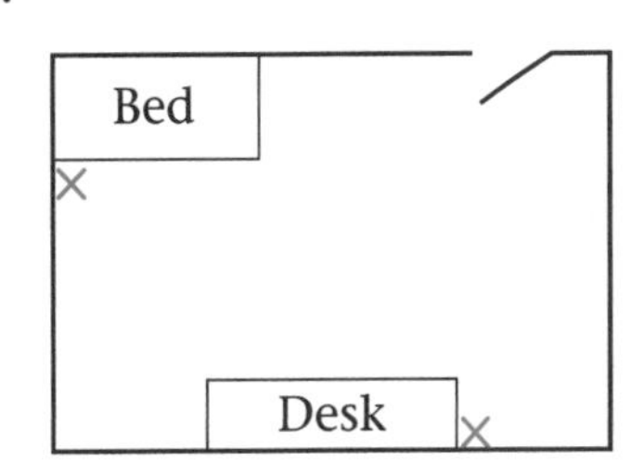

Using Units

Essential Exercises

1 Copy and complete the following conversion table.

	Metric	Imperial
a	2 m	... ft
b	... km	10 miles
c	... g	3 oz
d	5 kg	... lb
e	1 *l*	... pts
f ✓	... *l*	1 gallon

2 Answer the following questions about time.

- **a** How many days are there in a week?
- **b** How many hours are there in a week?
- **c** How many minutes are there in a day?
- **d** How many seconds are there in a day?
- **e** How many days before your next birthday?
- **f** How many minutes of Maths lessons do you have in a week?

Consolidation Exercises

3 Change these smaller units into larger units.

- **a** change 750 g into kilograms
- **b** change 500 ml into litres
- **c** change 230 cm into m
- **d** change 750 m into kilometres
- **e** change 425 kg into tonnes
- **f** change 1250 cm^3 into litres

4 Find the difference between the following times, in hours and minutes.

- **a** 01 35 and 05 15
- **b** 11 45 and 23 05
- **c** 09 10 and 18 00
- **d** 00 25 and 13 40
- **e** ✓ 07 30 and 21 15
- **f** 12 55 and 20 15

Challenging Exercises

5 Work out the following areas in the unit given in brackets.

a a field measuring 200 m by 350 m (hectares)
b a square table with side 100 cm (m^2)
c a piece of wood measuring 1500 mm by 150 mm (cm^2)
d ✓ a triangle with base 35 mm and height 50 mm (cm^2)
e a rug measuring 2.5 m by 60 cm (m^2)

6 This is a table of distances measured in miles.

Cambridge					
326	Edinburgh				
144	190	Leeds			
232	104	96	Newcastle		
132	448	245	360	Portsmouth	
58	373	196	278	74	London

a Giving all your answers in kilometres, how far is it from:
  i Cambridge to London
  ii Edinburgh to Portsmouth
  iii ✓ London to Leeds
  iv London to Newcastle?

b Mrs Wood has to drive from Edinburgh to Portsmouth, via Leeds and London. What is the total distance, in kilometres, of her journey?

7 Estimate the following measures.

a The height of a door is __________ m.
b The height of a double-decker bus is __________ m.
c A large bag of sugar weighs __________ kg.
d The mass of a small car is __________ t.
e The capacity of a wine glass is __________ ml.
f The area of a tennis court is __________ m^2.
g Average walking speed is __________ km/h.

BEARINGS

Essential Exercises

1 What are the four main compass points?

a N___ **b** S___ **c** E___ **d** W___

2 What are the four compass points between the main points?

a N___ E___ **b** S___ E___ **c** S___W___ **d** N___W___

3 What is the size of the smaller angle between:

a N and E
b N and S
c N and W
d E and W
e N and SE
f ✓ SE and NW
g S and NE
h S and SW.

Consolidation Exercises

4 Draw a diagram showing all the compass points mentioned in question 3.

5 This is a scale map of an island. There are three towns, B, C and D, on the island.

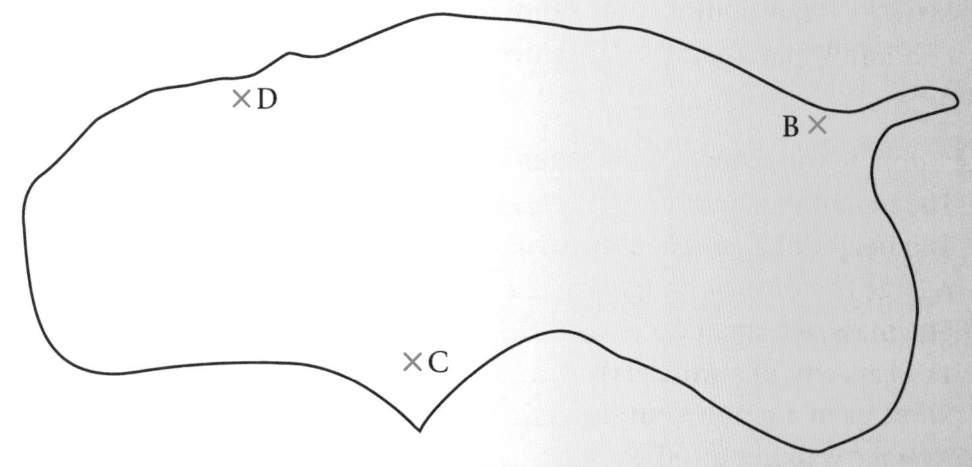

a What is the bearing of B from C?
b What is the bearing of B from D?
c ✓ What is the bearing of C from D?
d What is the bearing of D from B?
e What is the bearing of C from B?
f What is the bearing of D from C?

6 These are drawings (not to scale) of journeys from town X to town Y. Calculate the bearings of a journey from Y to X. Show any working.

a

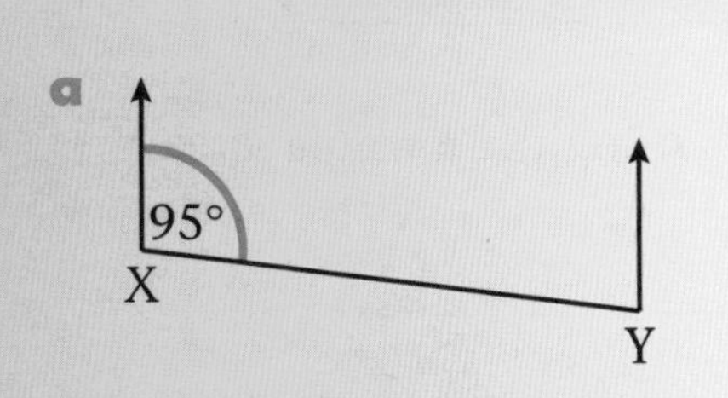

b

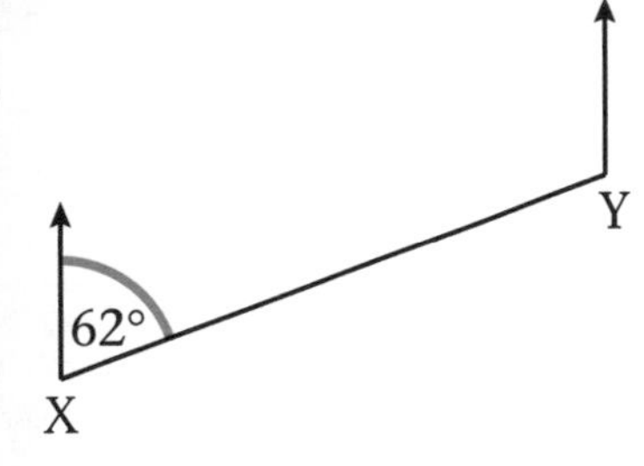

c

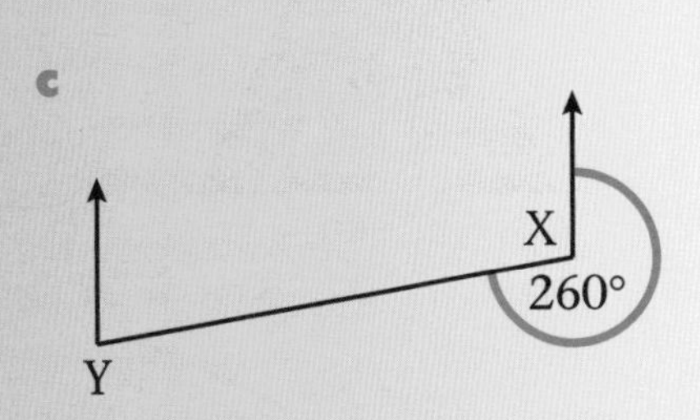

d

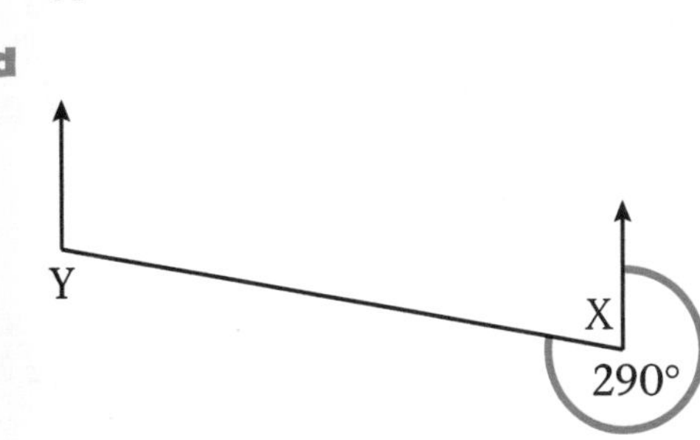

Challenging Exercises

7 Use scale drawings to illustrate each of the following.

a A ship sails from port A for a distance of 50 sea miles on a bearing of 110°.

b Town B is 75 km due south of town A. Town C is 150 km from A on a bearing of 070°.

c A ship is anchored 120 km from the port on a bearing of 225°.

8 Use scale drawings to answer the following.

a A ship sails 25 km from port A on a bearing of 085° and then 30 km due east to port B. It then sails directly back to A. How far is the return journey and on what bearing does the ship need to sail to return to A?

b An aircraft flies from an airport, H, on a bearing of 285° for 300 km to airport M. It then has to fly to airport G, on a bearing of 300°, for 200 km. What is the total distance flown? What is the bearing of H from G?

9 A bird flies from its nest on a bearing of 050° to a tower 50 km away. It then flies on a bearing of 160° to a roof 20 km away. Use a scale drawing to find the bearing and journey distance for the bird's return to its nest.

8 Areas

Essential Exercises

1 Calculate the area of the following triangles using the formula $\text{area} = \frac{b \times h}{2}$

a

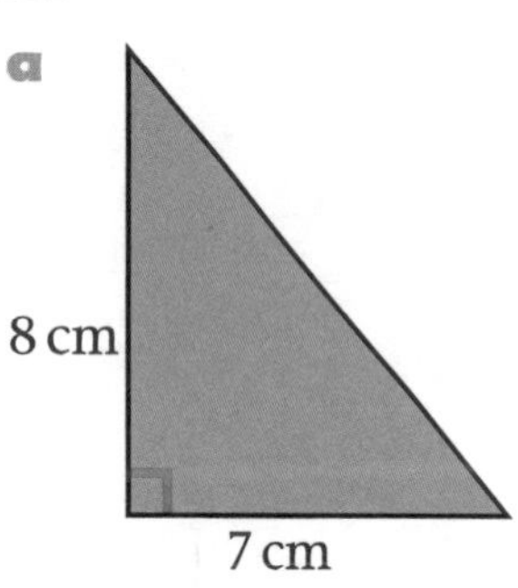

b

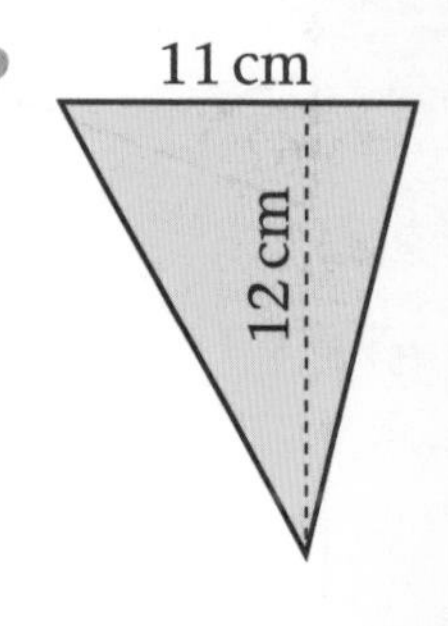

c

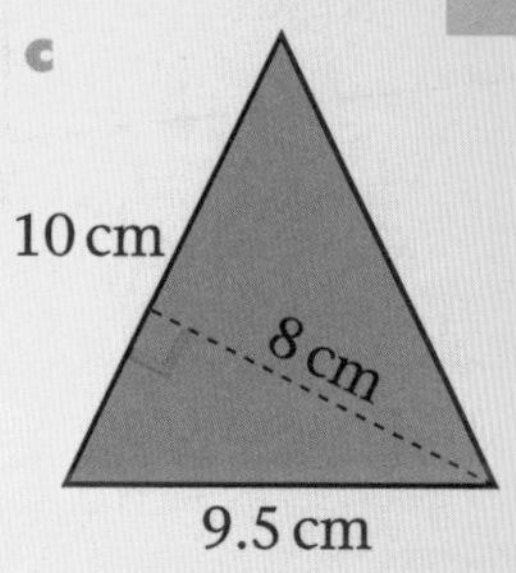

d

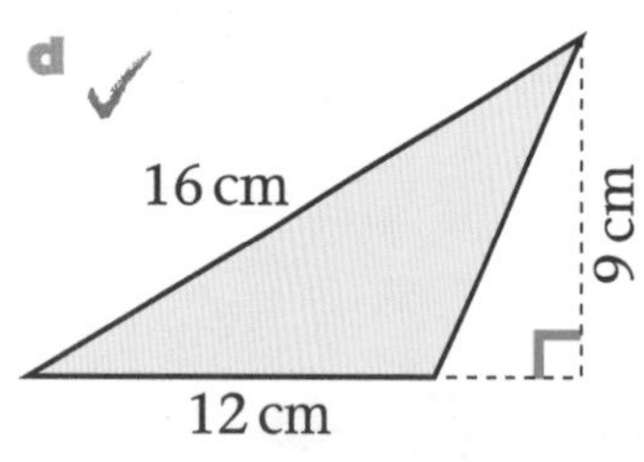

e

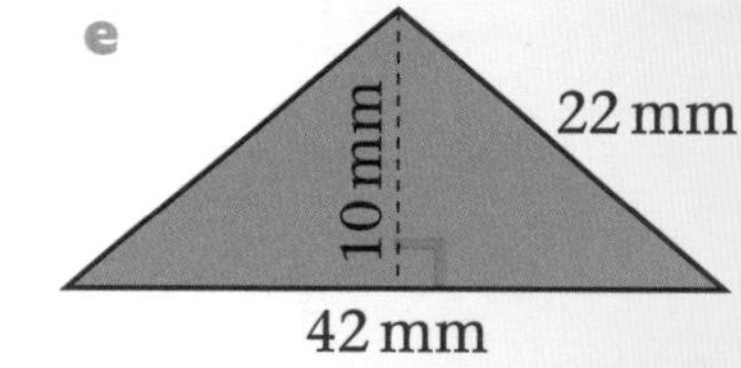

f

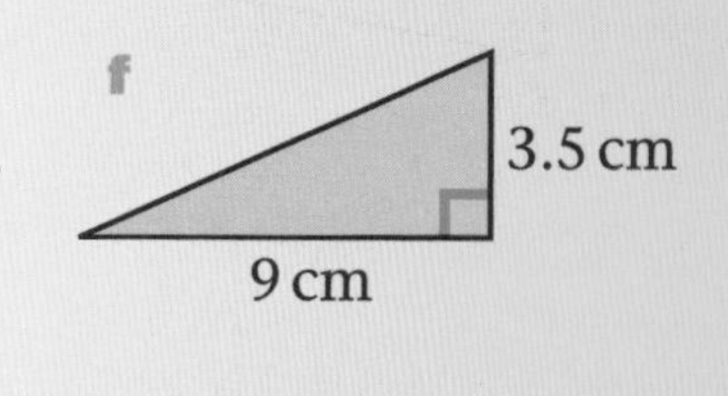

2 Calculate the area of the following parallelograms using the formula $\text{area} = b \times h$

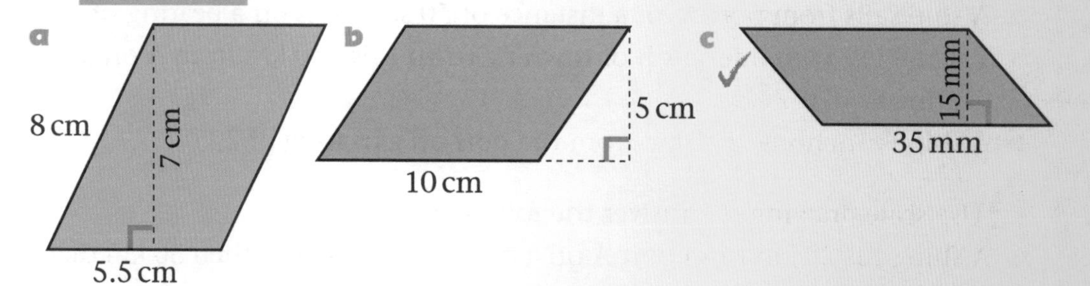

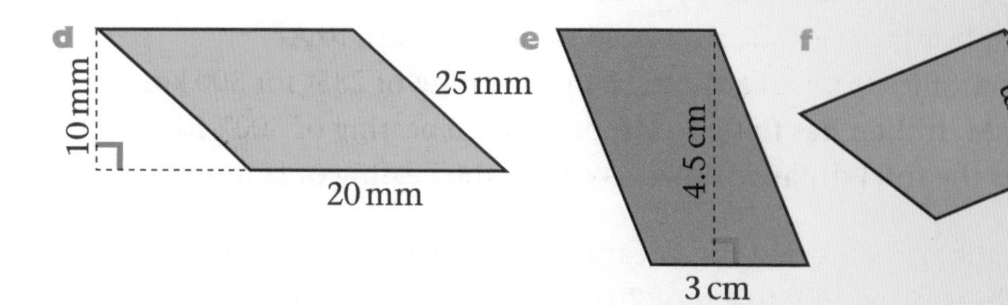

3 Calculate the area of each trapezium using the formula

$$\text{area} = \frac{h(a \times b)}{2}$$

a 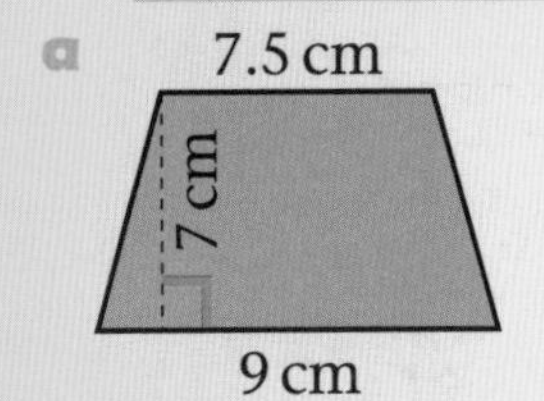

b 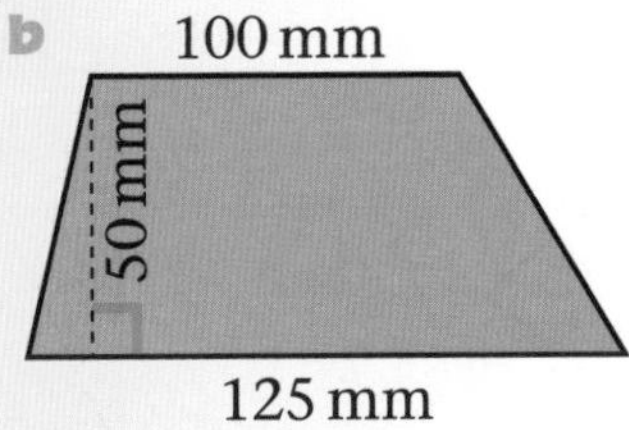

c 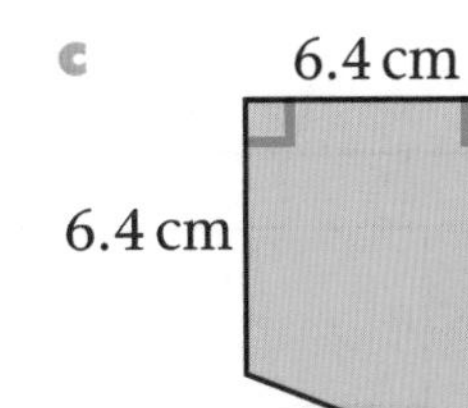

d 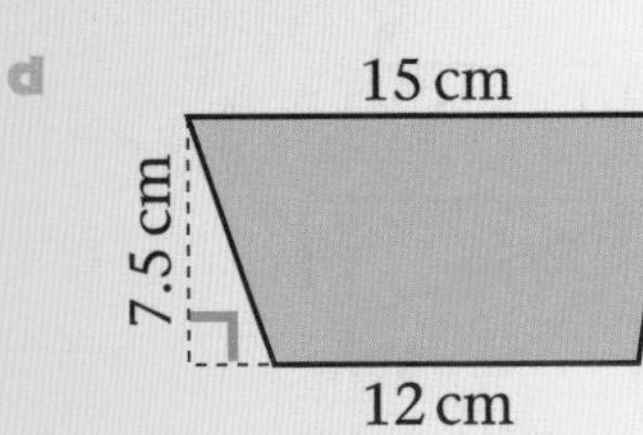

e 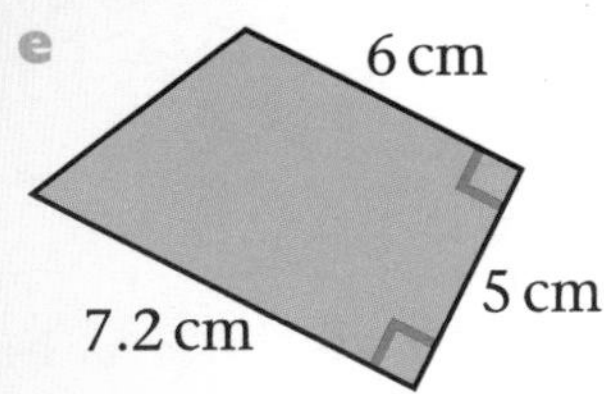

f 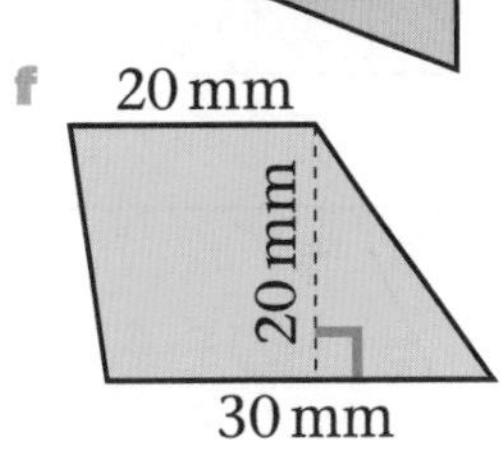

Consolidation Exercises

4 Calculate the missing dimension for the following shapes.

a 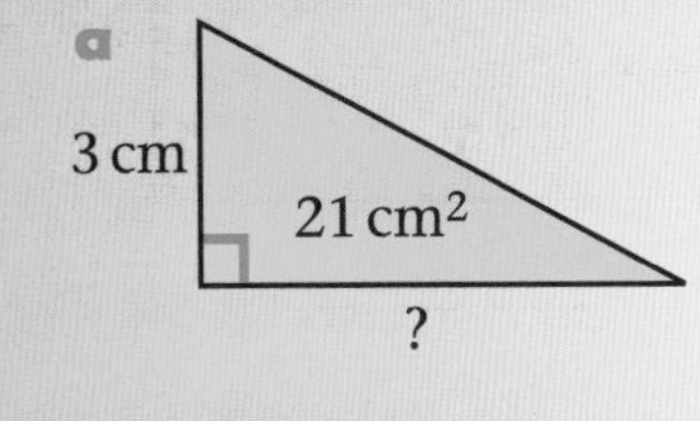

b 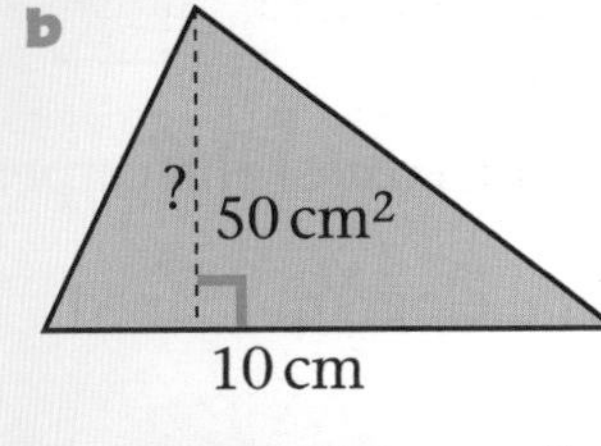

c 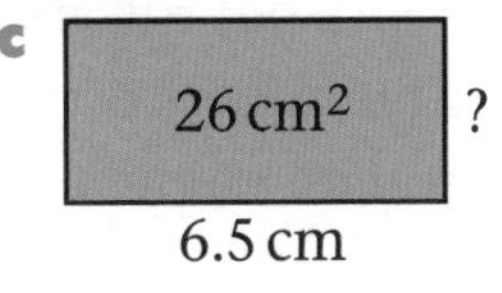

d 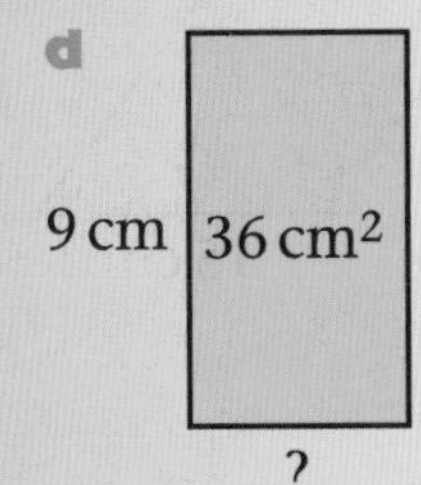

e 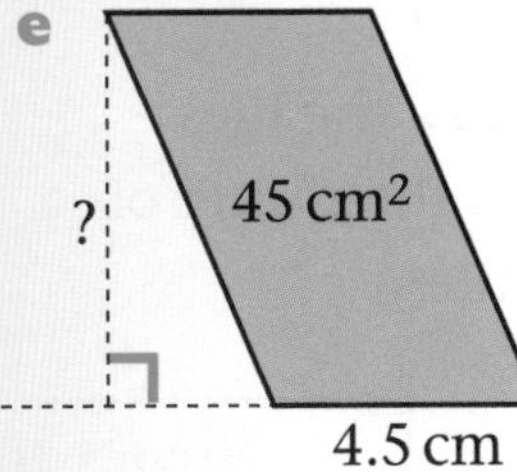

f 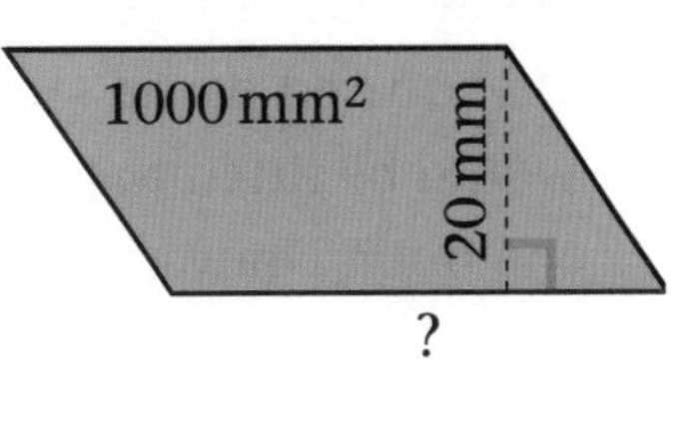

g 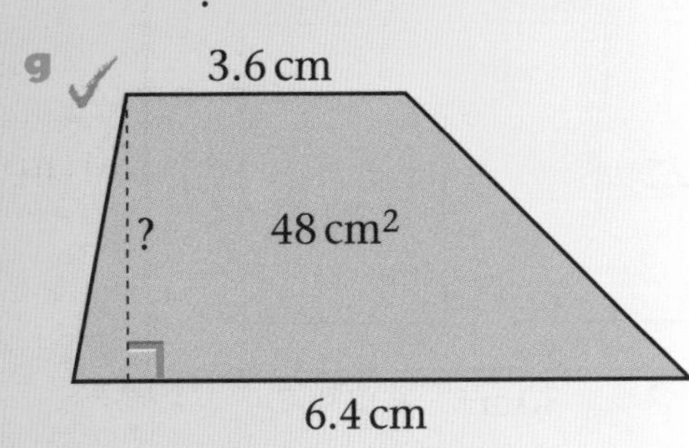

h 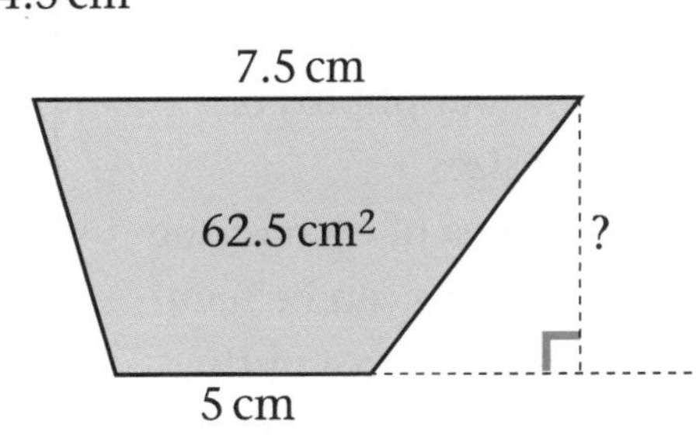

5 Calculate the shaded areas in each of the following.

a

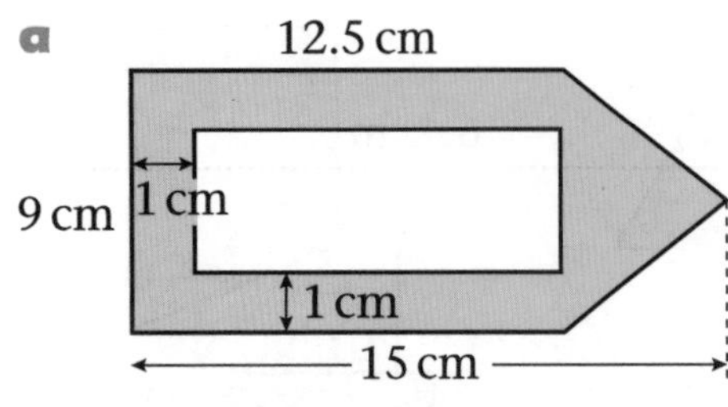

b

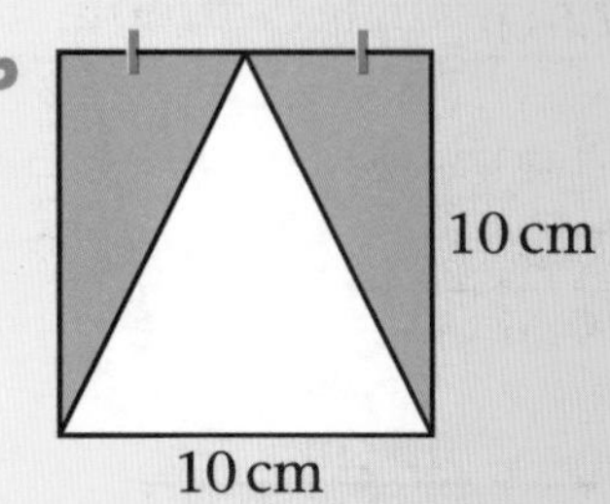

c

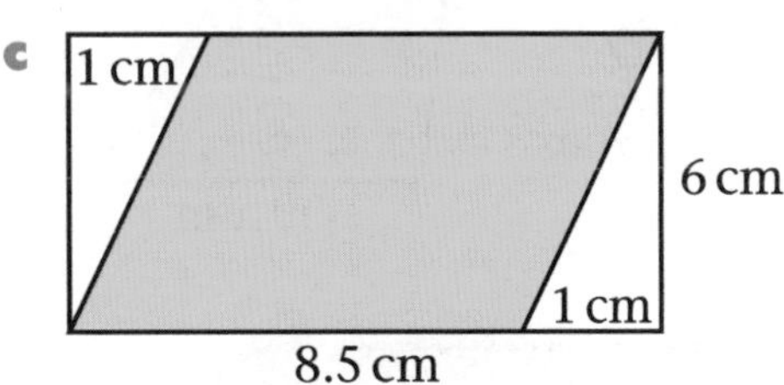

d

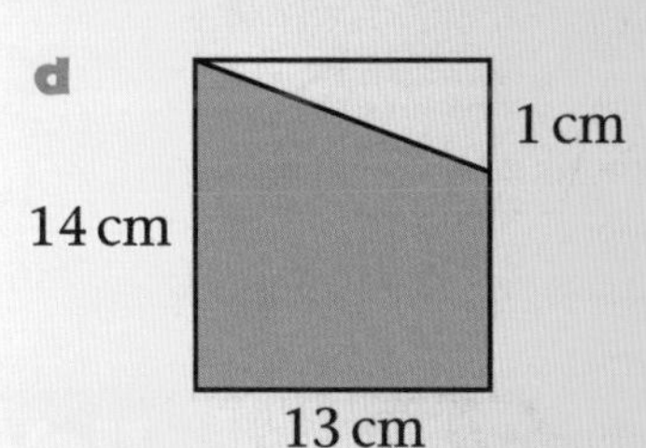

6 The diagram shows a plan of a room that is to be carpeted.

a Work out the area of carpet needed.

b The carpet costs £21.50 a square metre. Calculate the cost of the carpet.

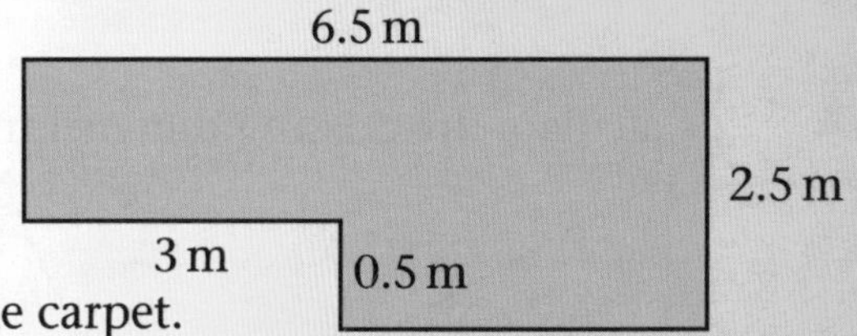

7 A floor is tiled with parallelogram-shaped tiles shown in the diagram.

a What is the area of each tile?

b On squared paper, show how the tiles would be fitted together in the corner of the floor. Draw at least 6 tiles.

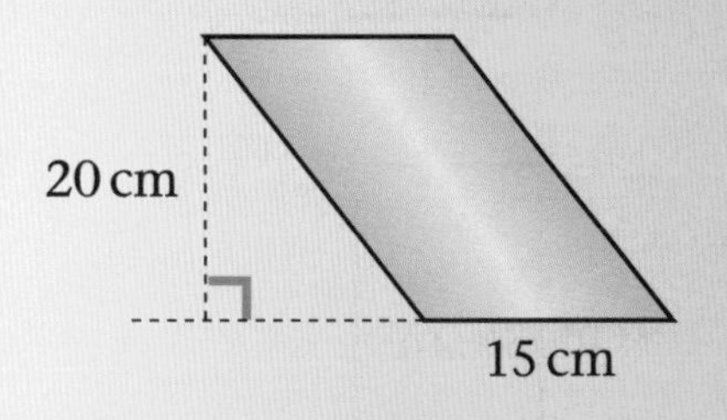

8 The diagram shows a photograph frame that has room for four photos of different sizes.

a What area of each of the four photos can be seen?

b What is the area of the remaining shaded part?

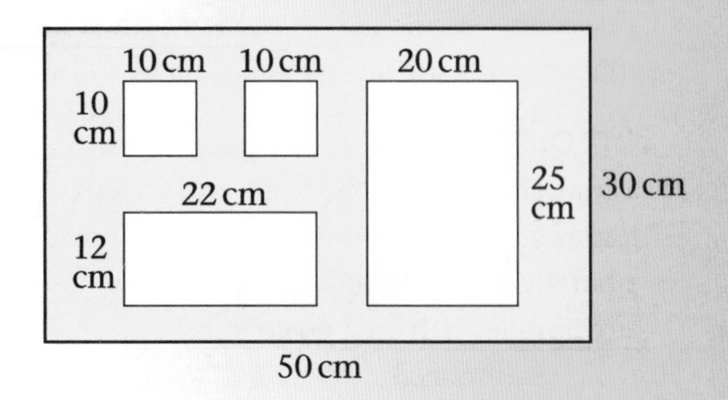

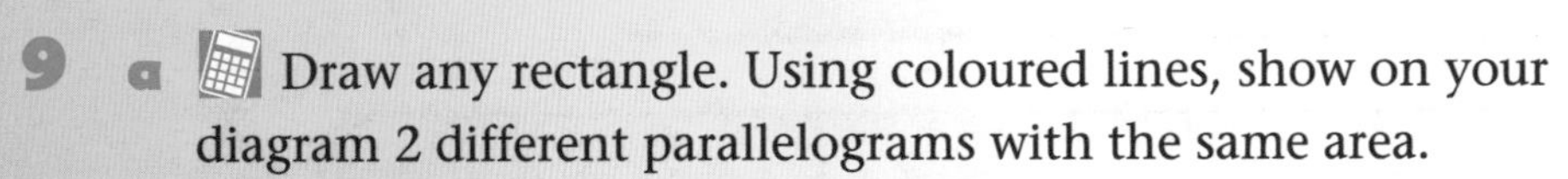

9 **a** Draw any rectangle. Using coloured lines, show on your diagram 2 different parallelograms with the same area.

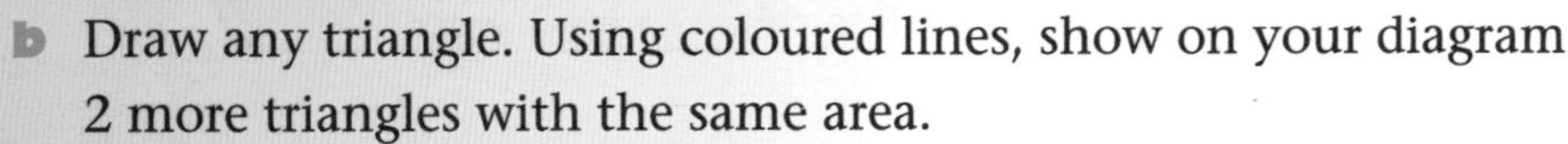

b Draw any triangle. Using coloured lines, show on your diagram 2 more triangles with the same area.

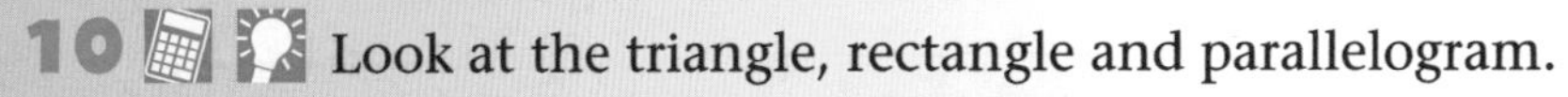

10 Look at the triangle, rectangle and parallelogram.

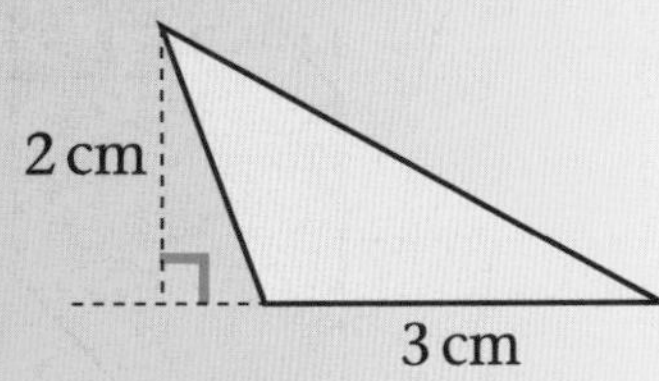

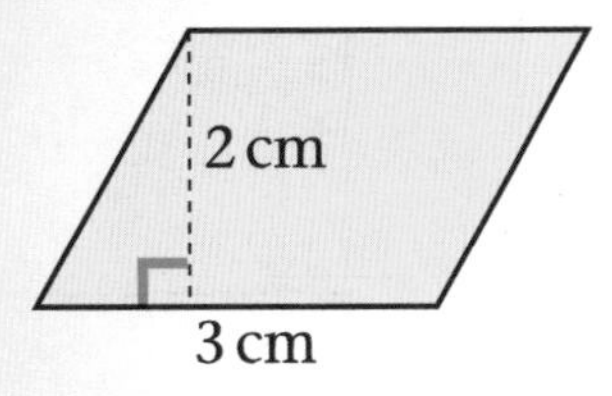

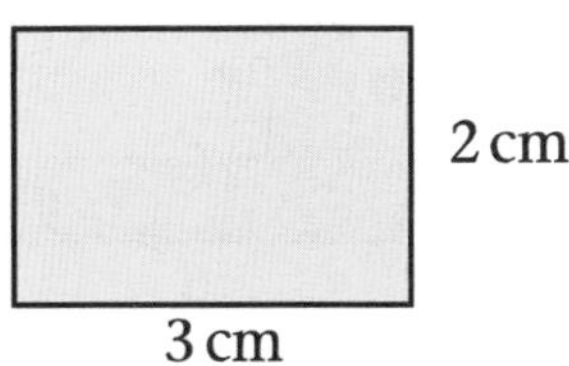

Using the formula for area for each of them, show the connection between their areas.

Challenging Exercises

11 Using squared paper, draw 4 different quadrilaterals.
Find the area of each quadrilateral.

12 A garden has the dimensions 50 m by 17 m.
What is the area of the garden?
How much fencing is needed for the garden?
Flower beds, width 1 m, are planted down each long side of the garden and the rest is lawn. What is the area of the lawn?

13 A field is triangular shaped with sides 500 m, 400 m and 300 m.

a Calculate the area of the field in hectares and the perimeter of fencing needed.

b Draw a scale diagram of the field.

c The farmer would like to have a 4-sided field. By drawing, show 2 different shaped fields the farmer could have.

14 On squared or dotted paper draw these shapes.

a a triangle with area 28 mm^2 and a right angle

b a triangle with area 40 cm^2 and an obtuse angle

c a parallelogram with area 126 cm^2

d a rectangle with area 60 cm^2

How many different rectangles can you find with an area of 60 cm^2?

8 VOLUME AND SURFACE AREA

Essential Exercises

1 Give the volume of these cuboids in terms of the unit cubes.

a

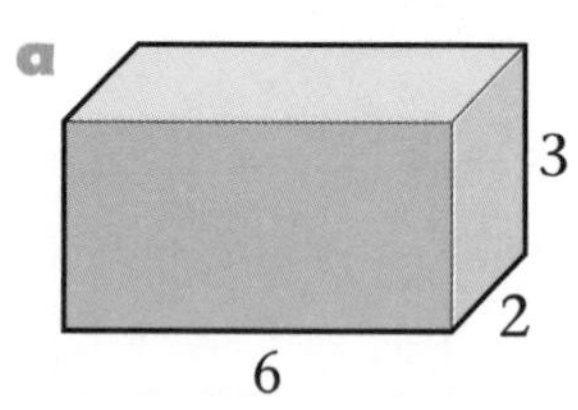

b

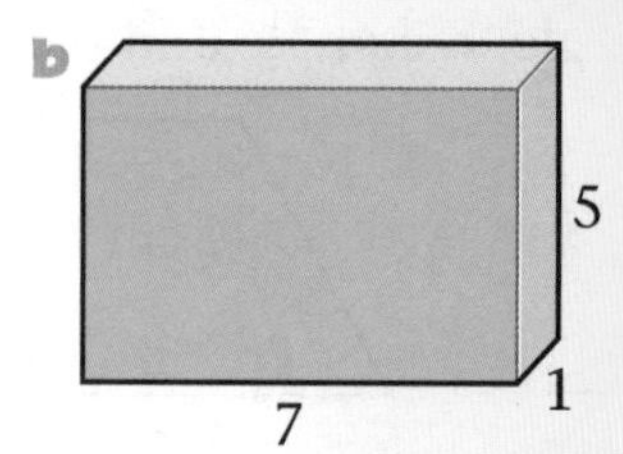

c

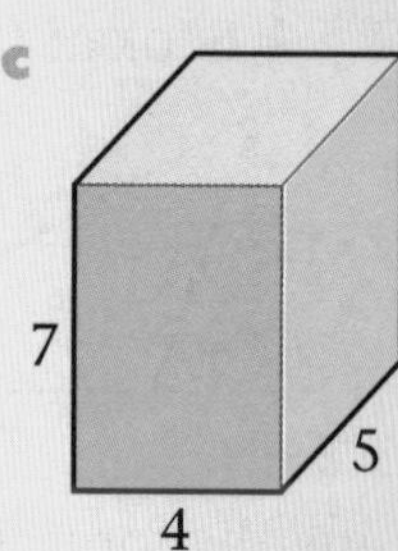

d

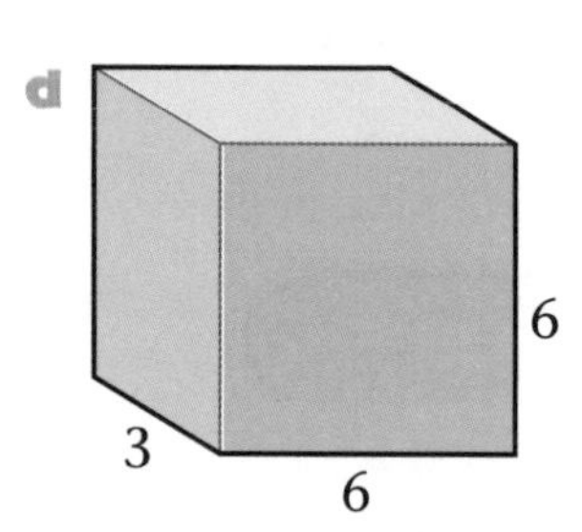

e

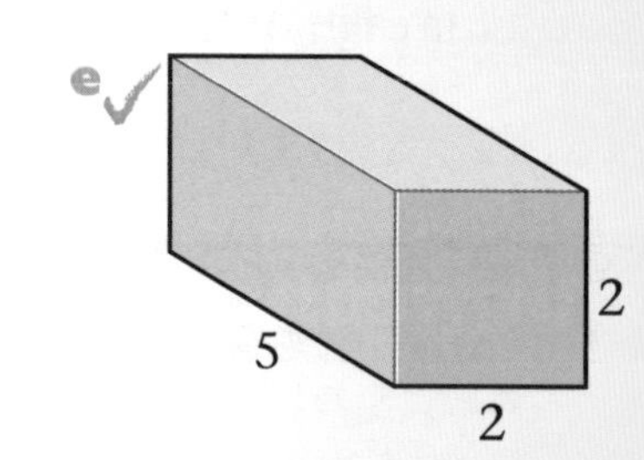

f

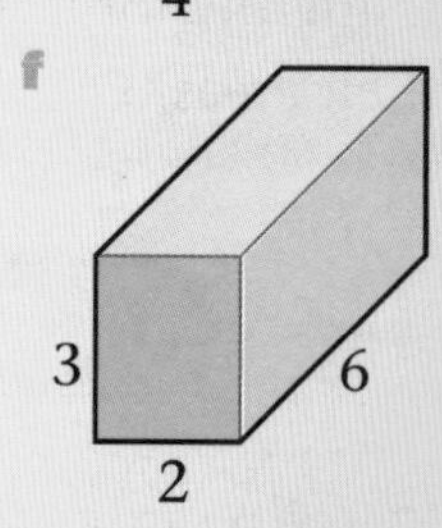

2 Calculate the volume and surface area of these cuboids.

Volume = $l \times b \times h$
Surface area = $2(l \times b + b \times h + h \times l)$

a

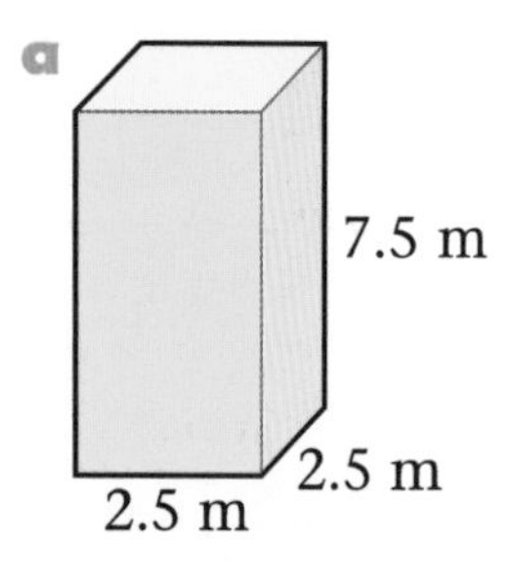

b

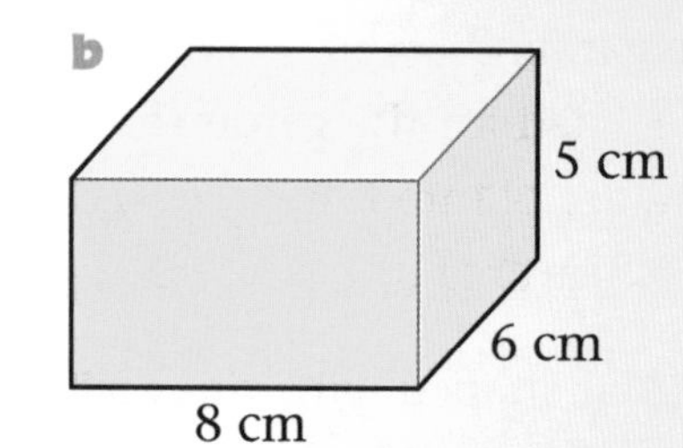

c

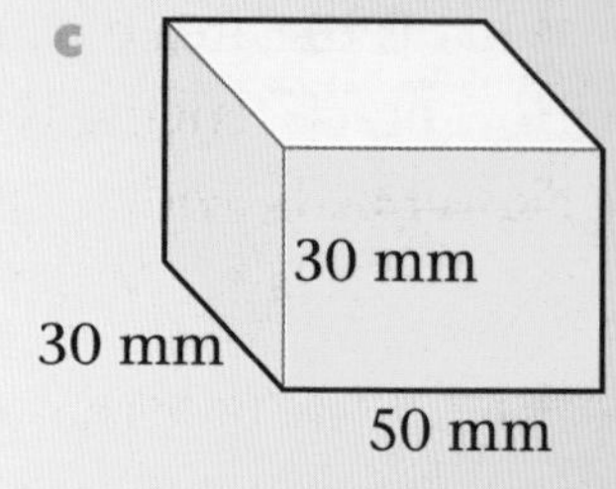

d

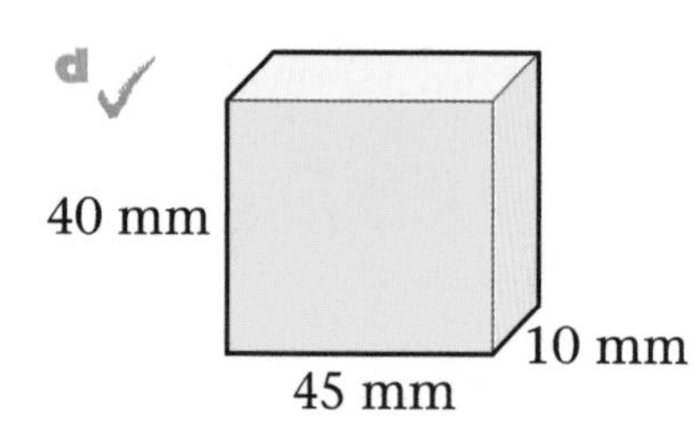

e

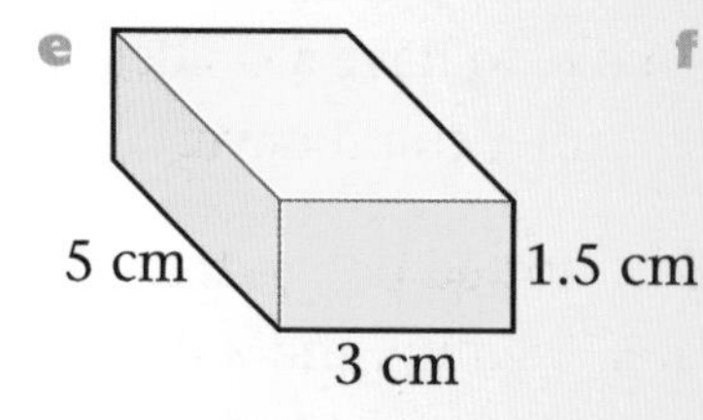

f

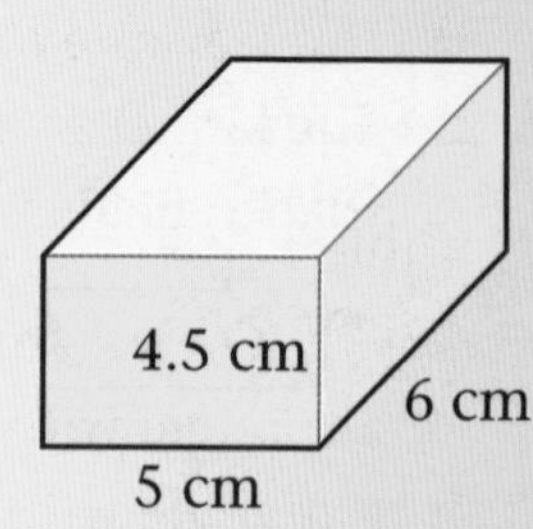

3 Estimate the volume of the following giving the units usually used.

a a brick **b** a matchbox **c** a shoe box

d a bar of soap **e** a box of tissues **f** a CD

Consolidation Exercises

4 Copy and complete the table.

	Length	Breadth	Height	Volume
a	5 mm	8 mm	4.5 mm	
b		3.7 cm	3.5 cm	129.5 cm^3
c	25 m		10 m	3750 m^3
d	9 cm	9 cm		243 cm^3
e	7.5 cm	5 m	2.5 m	
f		4 cm	5 cm	270 cm^3
g	3.5 cm	3.5 cm		122.5 cm^3
h	42 mm		7 mm	4704 mm^3

5 Split these solid shapes into cuboids to calculate their volume.

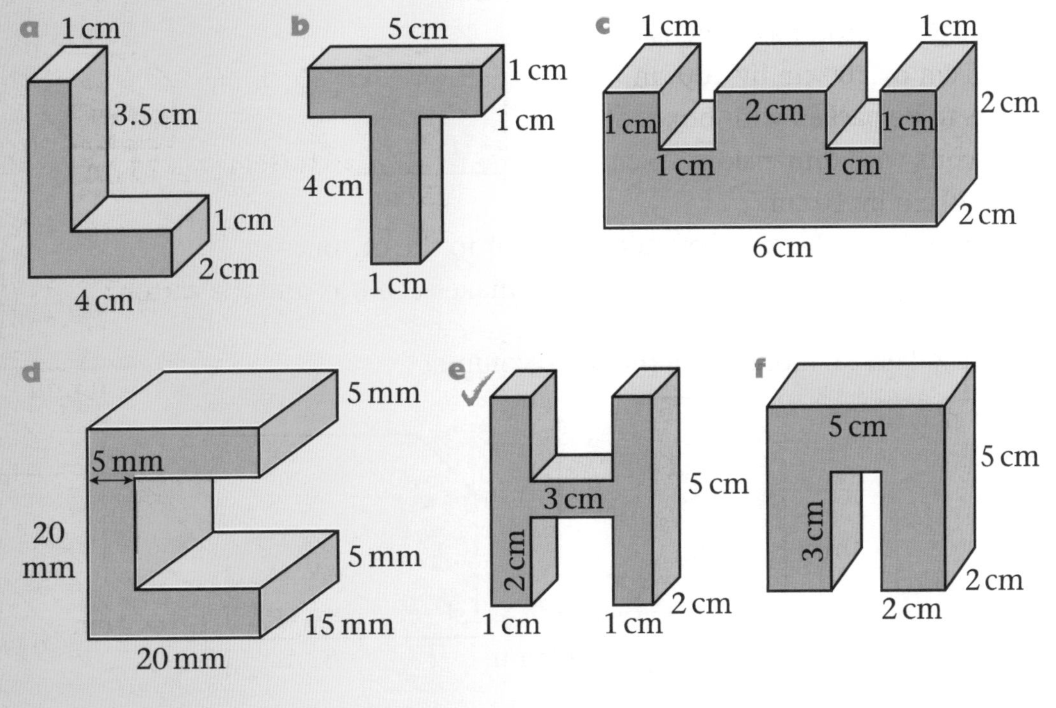

Calculate the surface area of each shape.

6 What is the surface area of this box?
Find the length of each edge.

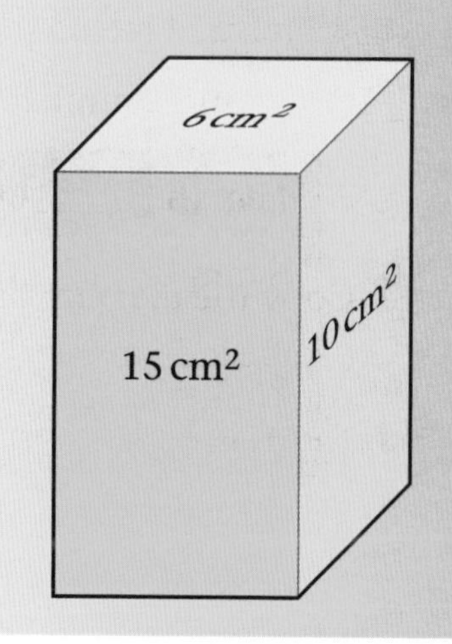

Challenging Exercises

7 A carton has dimensions 125 cm by 100 cm by 100 cm. It is to be packed with boxes of biscuits with dimensions 25 cm by 20 cm by 10 cm.

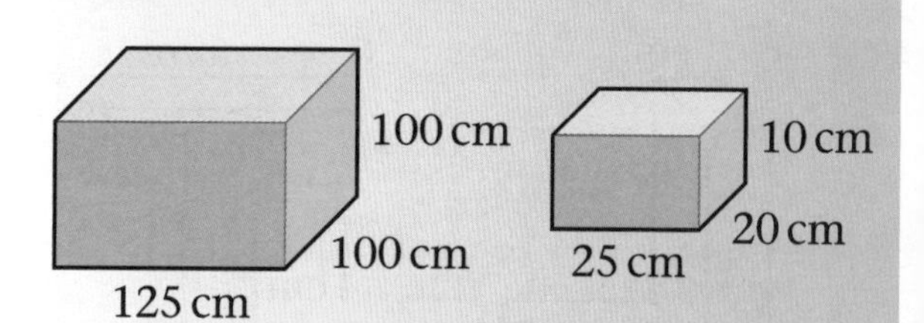

a How many boxes of biscuits will fit into the carton?

b What is the area of card needed to make each box and the carton?

8 These cuboids have the same volume.

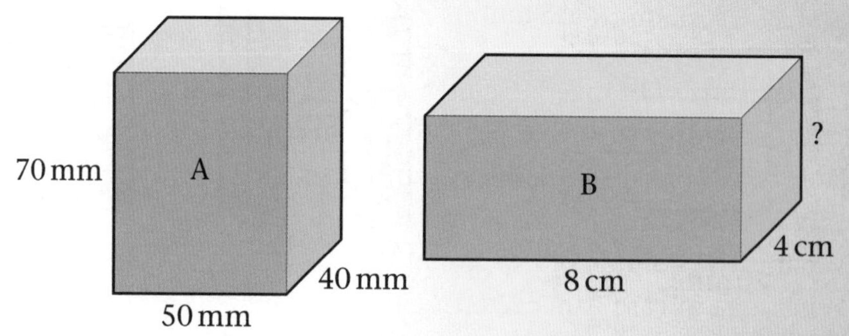

a Calculate the volume of A.

b What is the height of B?

c Calculate the surface area of each cuboid.

9 The diagram shows the cross-section of the strip of wood at the bottom of a patio door.

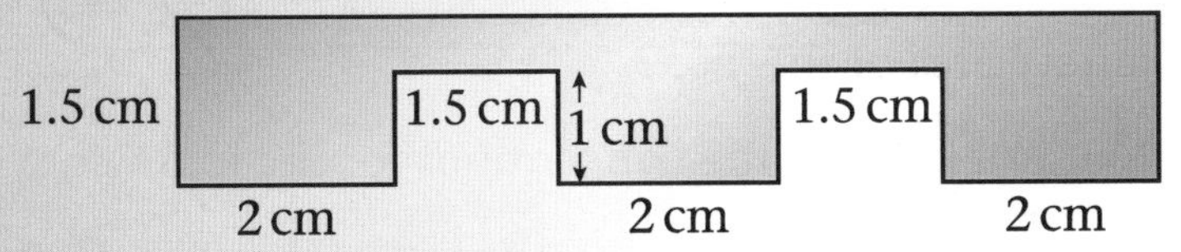

a Copy the diagram and use dotted lines to show how you can divide it into rectangles.

b What is the area of the cross-section?

c The wood is 2 m long. Calculate the volume of wood.

10 A garden of a new house needs to have a patio and garden shed built.

Soil needs to be removed, to a depth of 60 cm to lay their foundations.

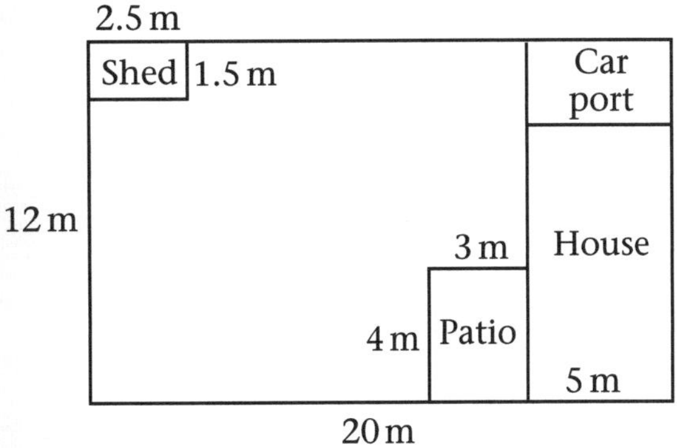

a What is the total area of the garden?

b What is the volume of soil to be removed for the foundations of the patio?

c What is the volume of soil to be removed for the foundations of the shed?

d What is the area of garden left after building the patio and shed?

e Copy the diagram. Draw in a flower bed and calculate the area of lawn needed to cover the rest of the garden.

Give answers in appropriate units.

11 Cartons of orange juice measure 17.5 cm by 10 cm by 6 cm. The manufacturer wishes to pack 20 cartons into each container.

a How much orange juice is in each carton?

b What are the dimensions of the container?

c What is the volume of the container?

d What area of card is needed for each container?

e He wishes to pack 3 containers into each crate.

i What are the dimensions of the crate?

ii What is the volume of the crate?

Names and Properties

Essential Exercises

1 Draw diagrams to illustrate labelling conventions for the following:

- **a** parallel lines
- **b** the vertices of a triangle and the opposite sides
- **c** the vertices of a polygon
- **d** an angle
- **e** a right angle
- **f** equal sides.

2

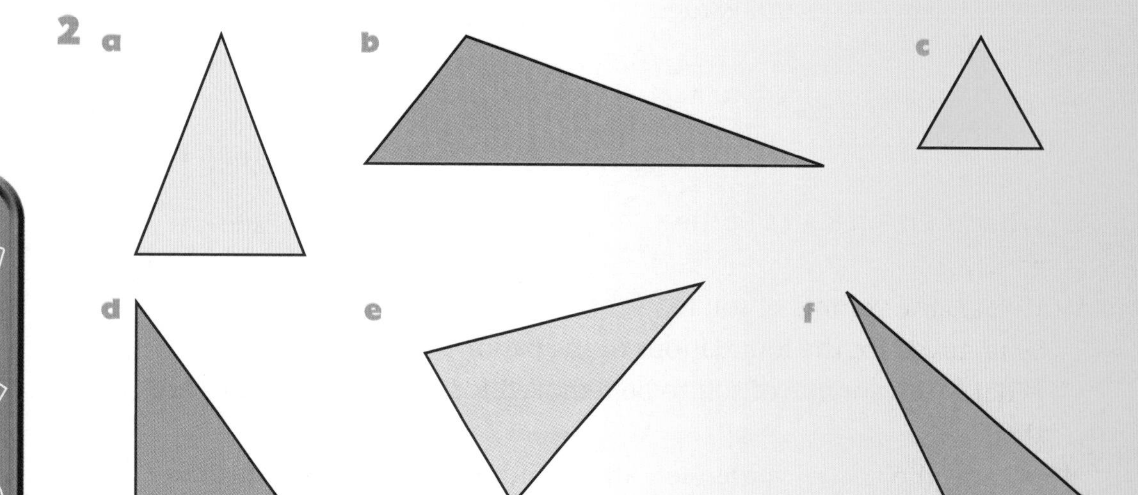

Copy the six triangles above and write the correct name under each one.

3 Find the polygon! What is the name of each of these?

- **a** A quadrilateral with one pair of parallel sides.
- **b** A triangle with no equal sides or angles.
- **c** An eight-sided shape.
- **d** A quadrilateral with one pair of equal sides and an included obtuse angle.
- **e** ✓ A quadrilateral with two pairs of equal adjacent sides.
- **f** A seven-sided shape.

Consolidation Exercises

4 Write down the missing words from the following statements.

a A __________ is a closed shape with straight sides.

b A __________ is a quadrilateral with 4 equal sides and 4 equal angles.

c A regular __________ is a shape with all sides and angles the same.

d A degree is a unit for measuring __________.

e A complete __________ is divided into 360 degrees.

f A transformation mapping a 2D shape (P) onto (P′) across a mirror line is a __________. PP′ is at right angles to the mirror line or line of __________. P and P′ are equidistant from this line.

5 a What is the angle sum of a triangle?

b How do you find the exterior angle of a regular polygon?

c How do you find the interior angle of a regular polygon?

d ✓ What do you know about the diagonals of a square?

e Which other quadrilaterals have diagonals with the same property as d?

f What do you know about the opposite sides of a parallelogram?

Challenging Exercises

6 **Learning about transformations.**

a reflection b rotation c translation d enlargement

Here are some properties of different transformations. Do they describe a, b, c or d? They may apply to more than one.

i The object and image are congruent.

ii The object and image are similar.

iii The transformation is described by a vector.

iv The transformation is described by an angle.

v The transformation takes place from a centre.

vi The transformation takes place relevant to a line.

9 Polygons

Essential Exercises

1 Calculate the exterior angles for the following regular polygons:

a triangle – what do we call a regular triangle?
b quadrilateral – what do we call a regular quadrilateral?
c pentagon
d hexagon
e heptagon
f octagon
g ✓ decagon
h dodecagon

$$\text{exterior angle} = \frac{360°}{\text{number of sides}}$$

2 The following are the exterior angles of regular polygons.

a 30°
b 36°
c 45°
d 60°
e 72°
f 90°
g 120°

interior angle = 180° – exterior angle

Find: **i** the interior angle of each polygon
ii the number of sides of each polygon.

3 The following are the interior angles of regular polygons.

a 60°
b 90°
c 108°
d 120°
e 135°
f 144°
g 150°

Find: **i** the exterior angle of each polygon
ii the number of sides of each polygon.

Consolidation Exercises

4 What is the sum of the interior and the exterior angle of a polygon?
Using your answer, calculate the interior angle of each polygon mentioned in question **1**.
Now calculate the interior angle sum of each polygon.

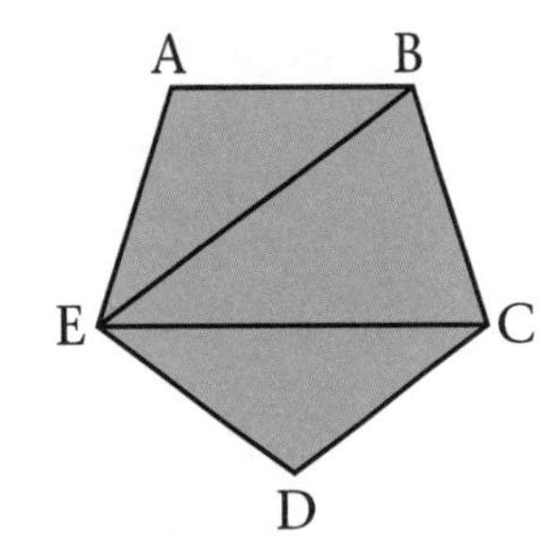

5 ABCDE is a regular pentagon.
Find the following angles:
a $E\hat{D}C$ **b** ✓ $D\hat{E}C$ **c** $B\hat{E}C$ **d** $E\hat{B}C$.

Challenging Exercises

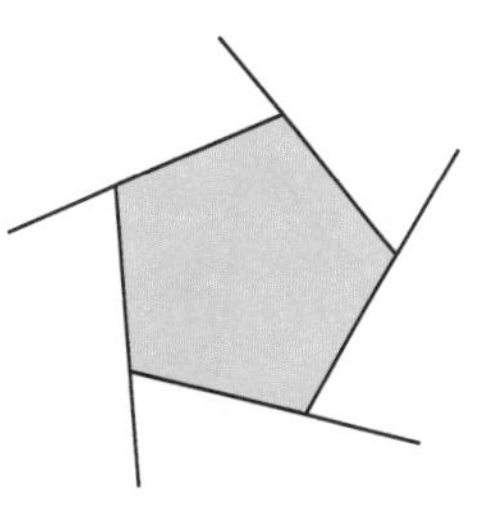

6 **a** Measure each exterior angle of this regular pentagon. What is their sum?
b Now draw any irregular pentagon. Extend each side to form exterior angles. Measure each exterior angle and add them. What is their sum? What do you notice?
c Explain your answers to **a** and **b**.
d What conclusion have you come to about the sum of exterior angles of regular and irregular pentagons?

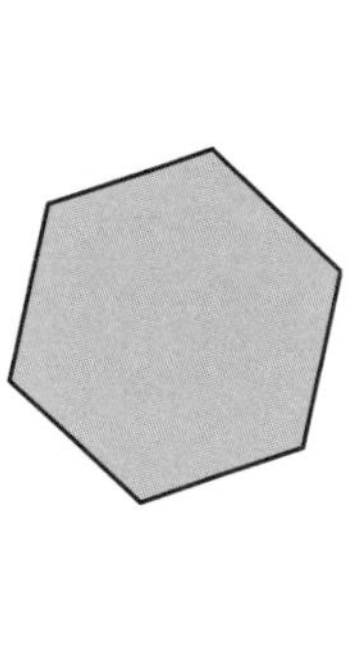

7 **a** Measure each interior angle of this regular hexagon and add them. What is their sum?
b Now draw any irregular hexagon. Measure each interior angle and add them. What is their sum? What do you notice?
c Divide your hexagon into triangles by drawing diagonals. How many triangles have you made?
d What is the angle sum of each triangle?
e Can you connect your answers to **b** and **d**?
f What conclusion have you come to about the sum of interior angles of regular and irregular hexagons?

Angles, lines and Pythagoras

Essential Exercises

1 Calculate the angles marked with a letter in the following diagrams.

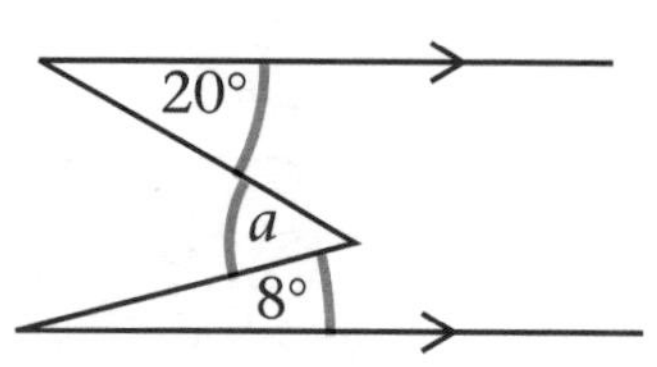

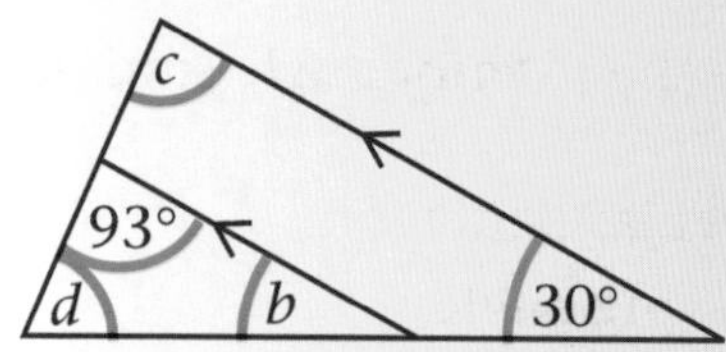

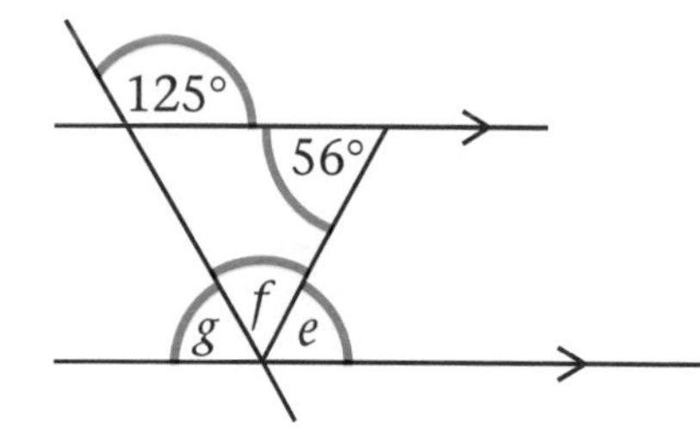

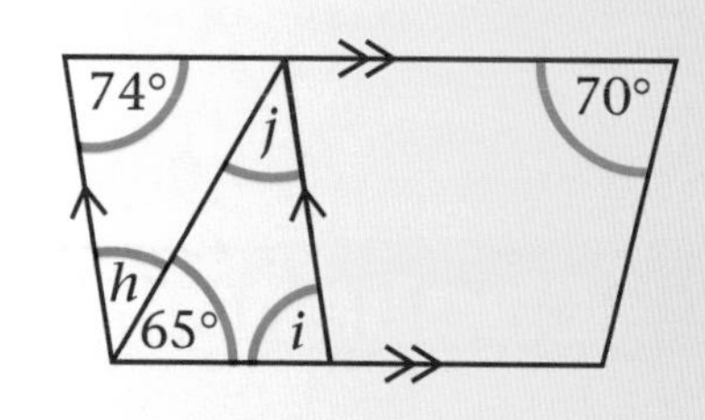

2 Find the length of the hypotenuse in each of the following triangles.

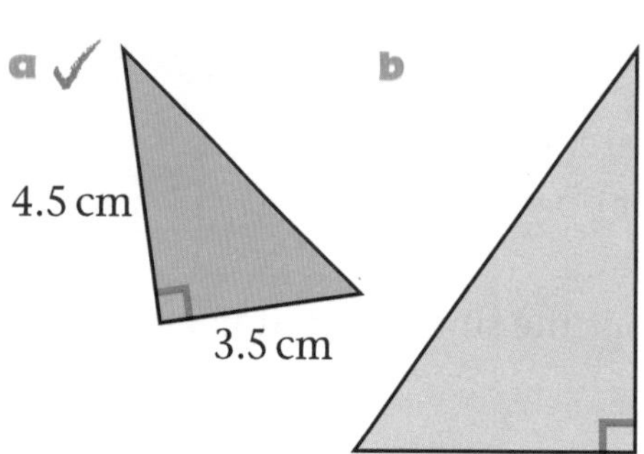

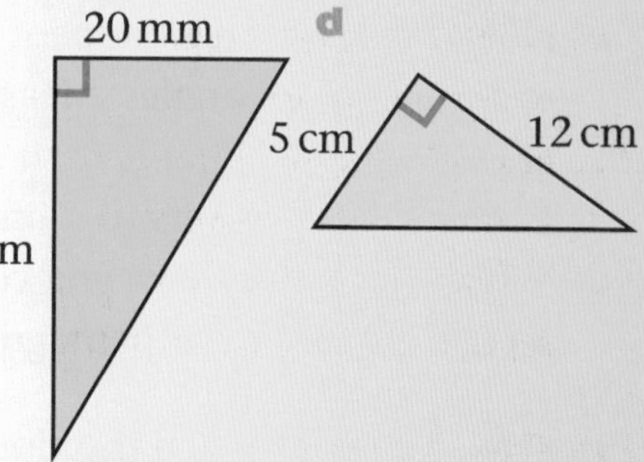

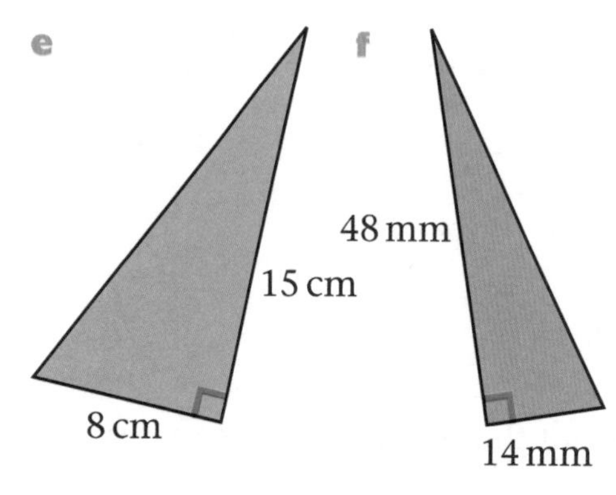

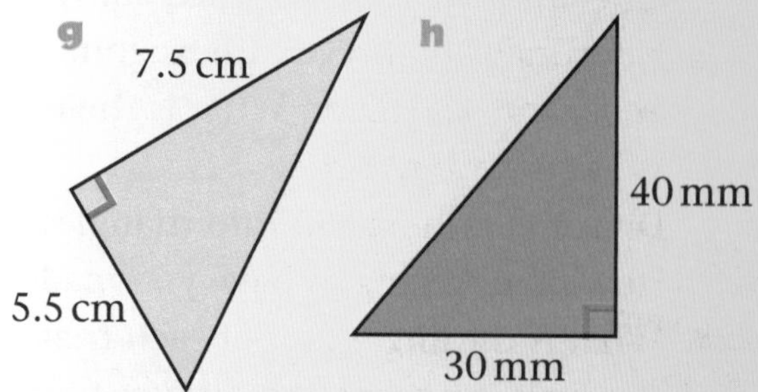

3 Find the radius of these circles.

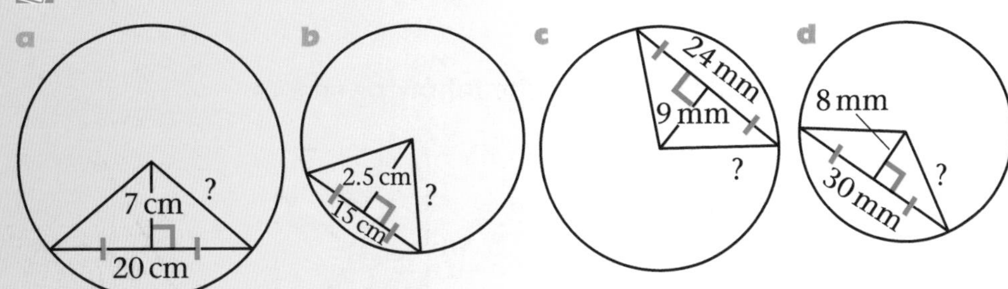

Consolidation Exercises

4 Calculate the angles marked with letters in the following diagrams.

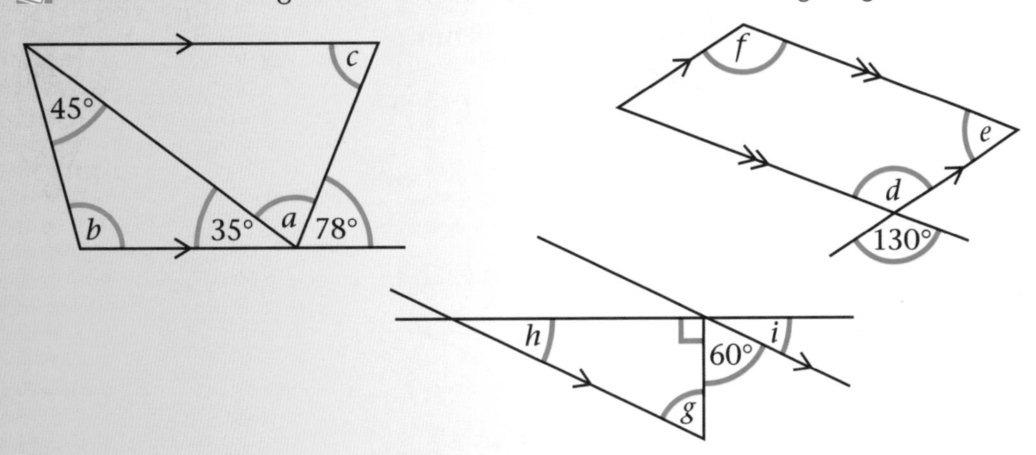

5 Find the missing side lengths in these triangles.

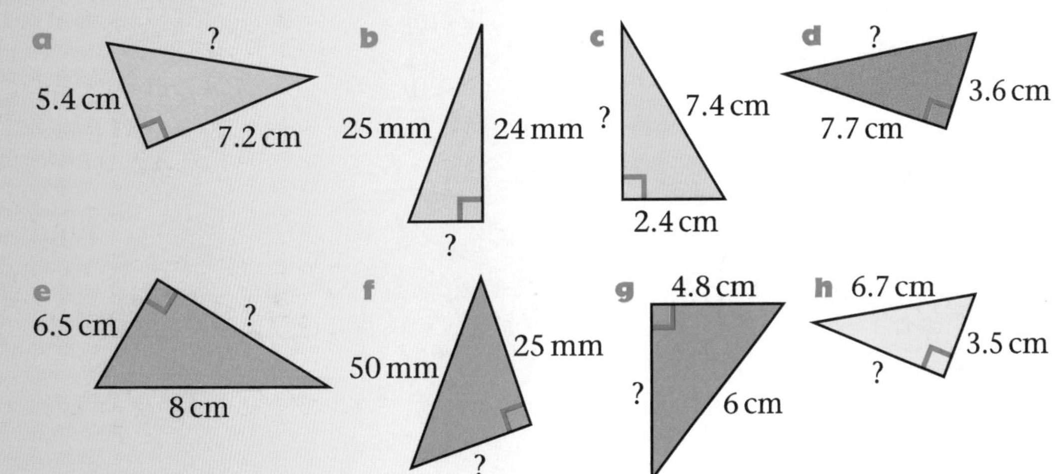

6 Find the missing side lengths of the following shapes.

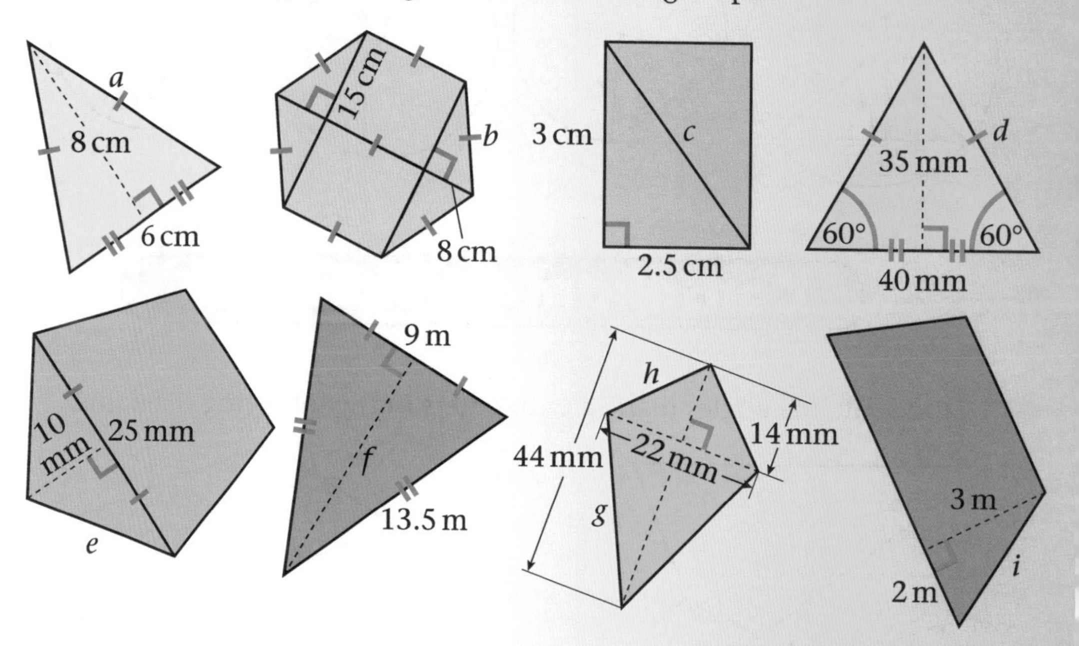

7 Find the length of the chord CD in each of these circles.

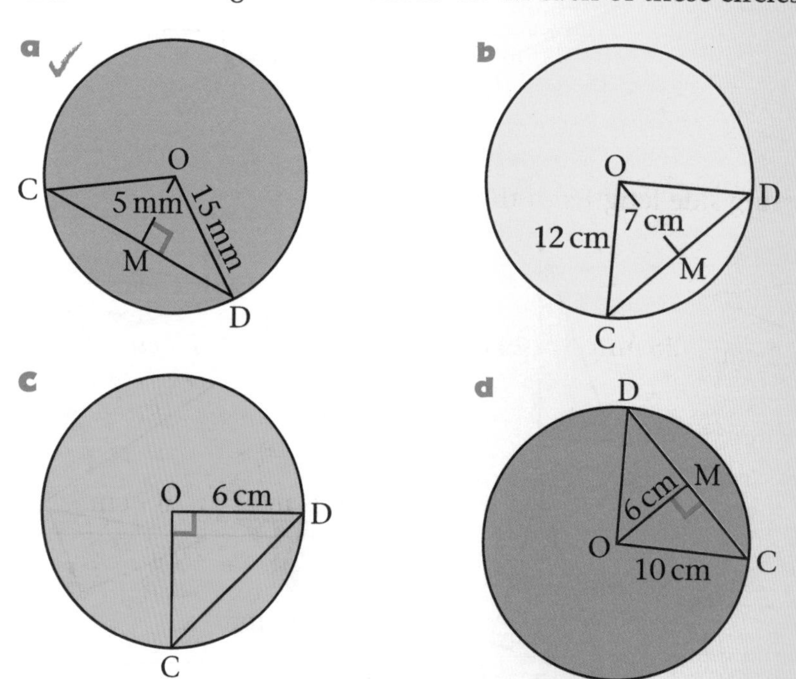

8 Calculate the length of the diagonal, or missing side, of the following rectangles.

a

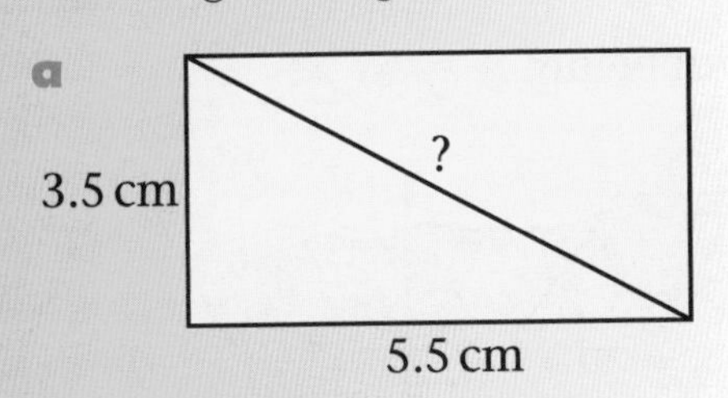

b

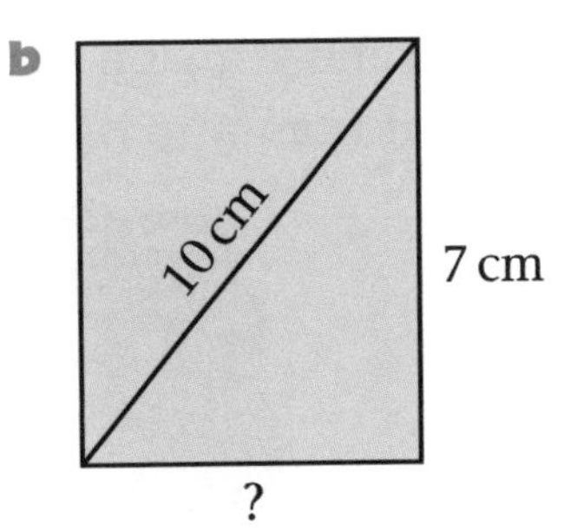

c

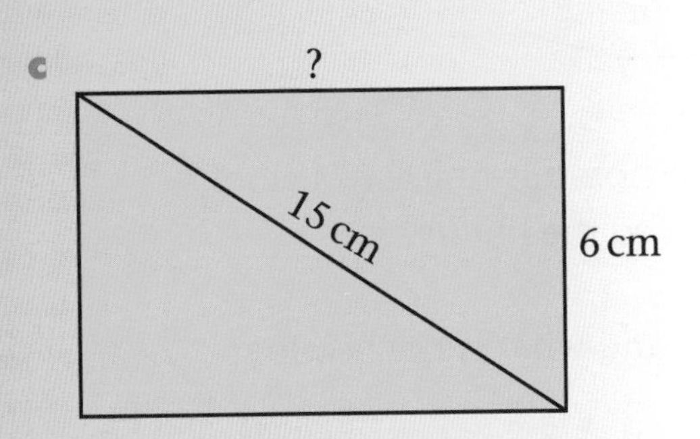

d

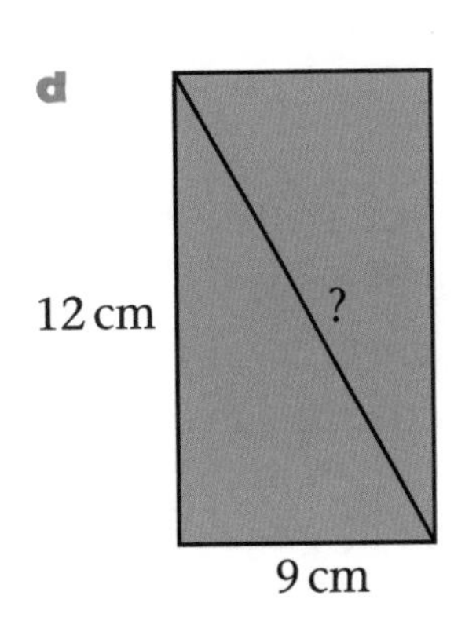

e

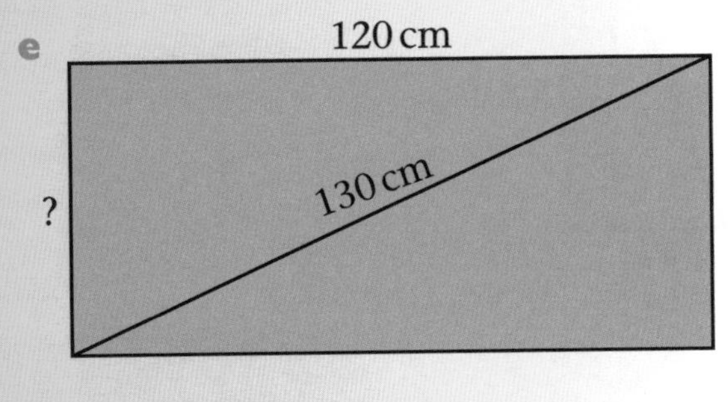

f

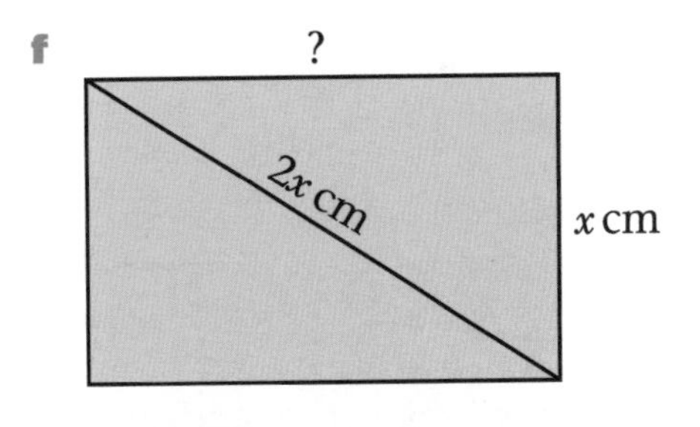

g

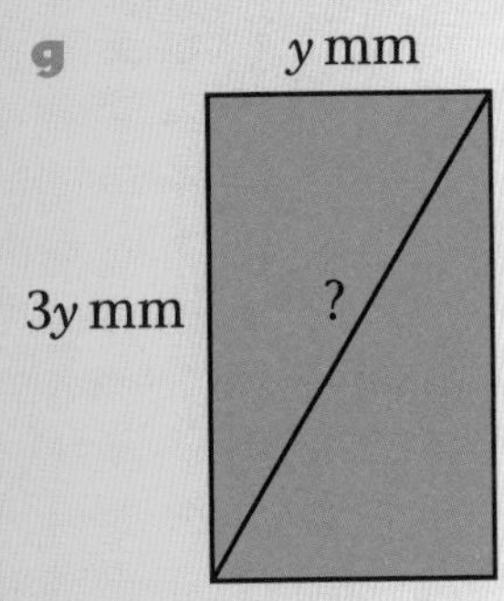

h

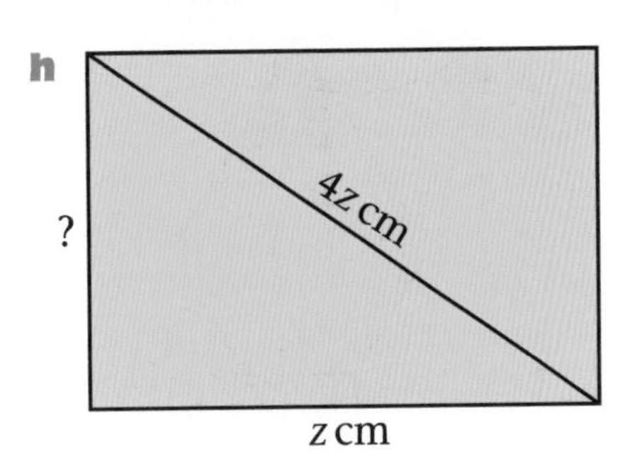

Challenging Exercises

9 A, B and C are on the island drawn below.
How far is it from A to B?

10 A boy walks 325 m due north from his house to school.
After school he walks 455 m due east to the library.
Draw a sketch of his journey.
How far does he have to walk home and what is the bearing?

11 The diagram shows a ladder is leaning up against the side of a house.

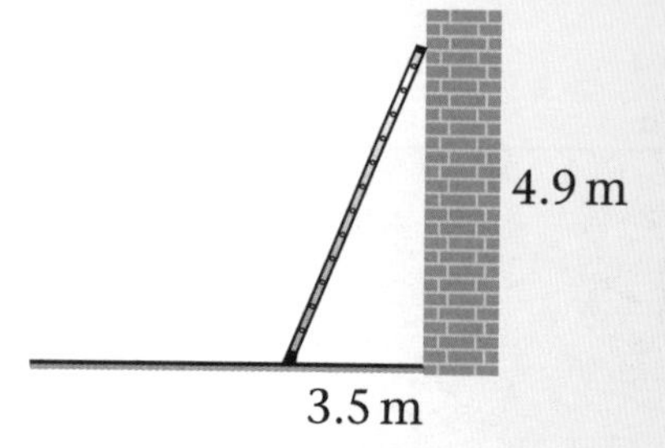

How long is the ladder?

12

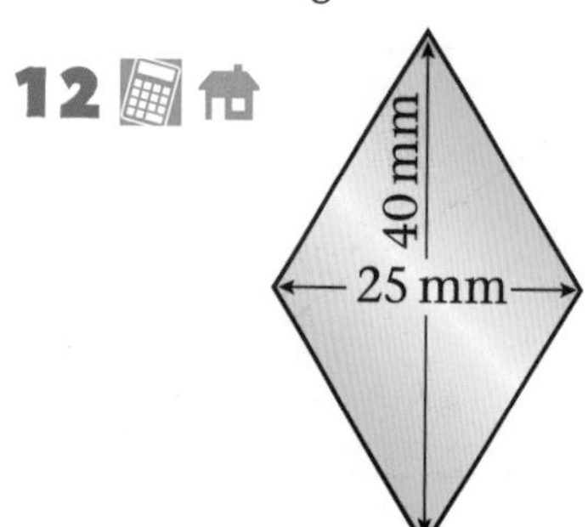

a How long is a side of this rhombus?
b What is the perimeter?

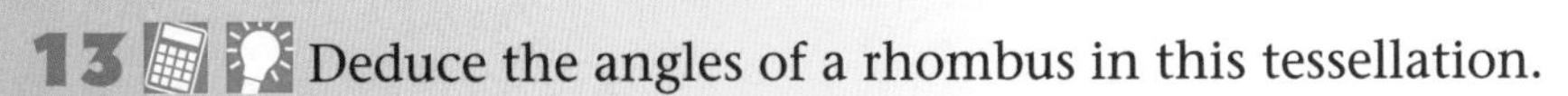

13 Deduce the angles of a rhombus in this tessellation.

What other shapes can you see in the tessellation?

14 ✓ The diagram shows a flagpole which is kept vertical by 2 guide wires.

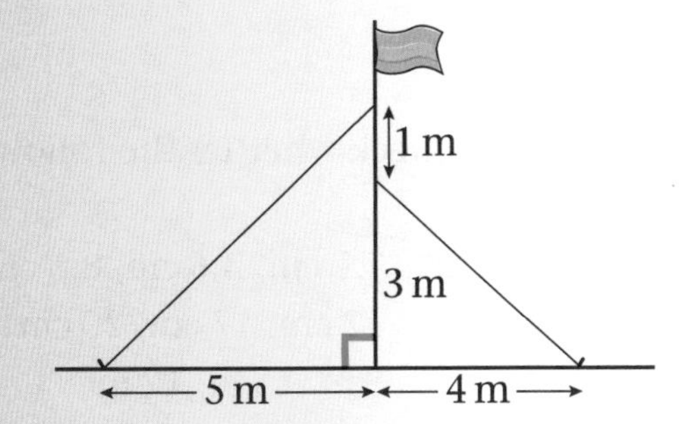

Find the length of each guide wire.

15 This is the cross-section of the end of a desk.

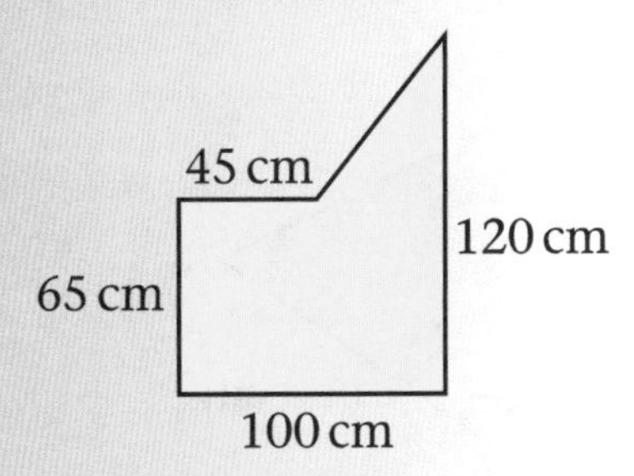

Find:

a the length of slope of the top

b the area of the total cross-section.

16 These are the front and side elevations of a house.

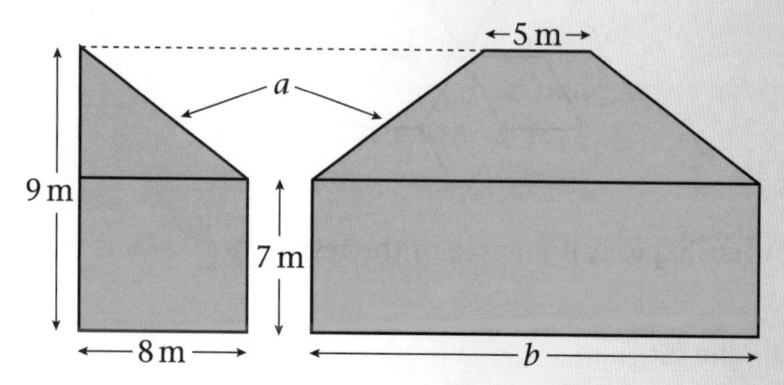

a How long is the slope of the roof?

b What is the width of the house?

17 Using Pythagoras' theorem, check whether the following triangles are right-angled.

a 24 mm, 7 mm, 25 mm

b 7.7 cm, 3.6 cm, 8.5 cm

c 13 cm, 22 cm, 25 cm

d 12 cm, 17 cm, 20 cm

e 16 mm, 63 mm, 65 mm

f 8 m, 15 m, 17 m

g 15 cm, 71 cm, 72 cm

h 11 cm, 60 cm, 61 cm

18 PQRS is a quadrilateral.

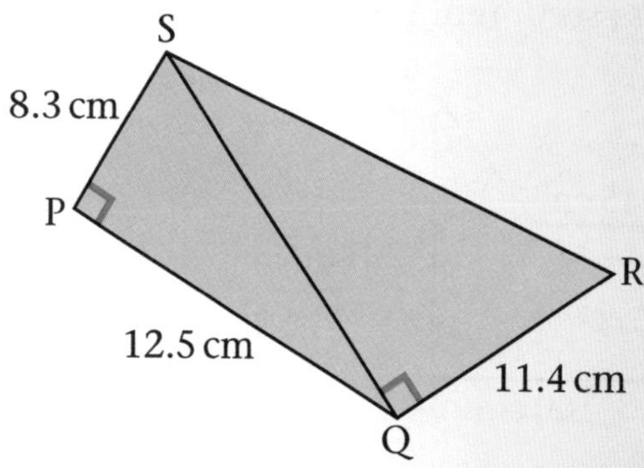

Find:

a QS

b RS

c the perimeter of PQRS.

Give answers to 1 d.p.

Congruent Triangles

Essential Exercises

1 Write down the words or numbers missing from the following statements.

a Triangles are congruent if:

i ______________ sides are equal

ii ______________ sides and the included ______________ are equal

iii ______________ angles and a corresponding ______________ are equal

iv a ______________ angle, hypotenuse and ______________ are equal.

b Triangles are not congruent if:

i three ______________ are equal

ii two ______________ and a non-included ______________ are equal.

2 Look at these pairs of triangles and decide whether they are congruent. Give your reasons.

a

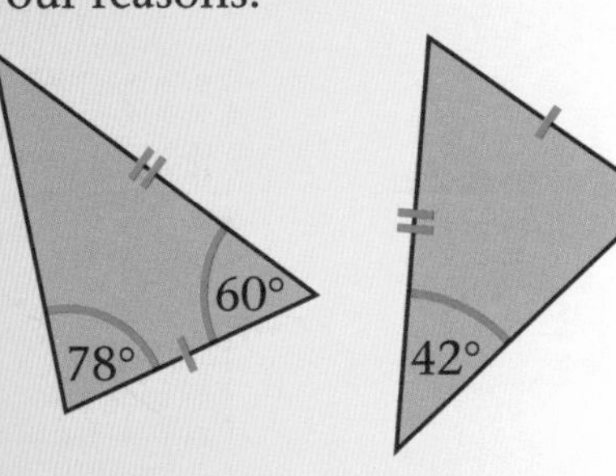

b

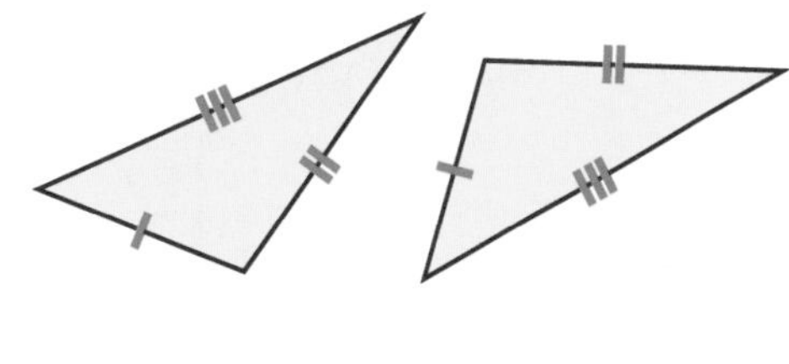

c

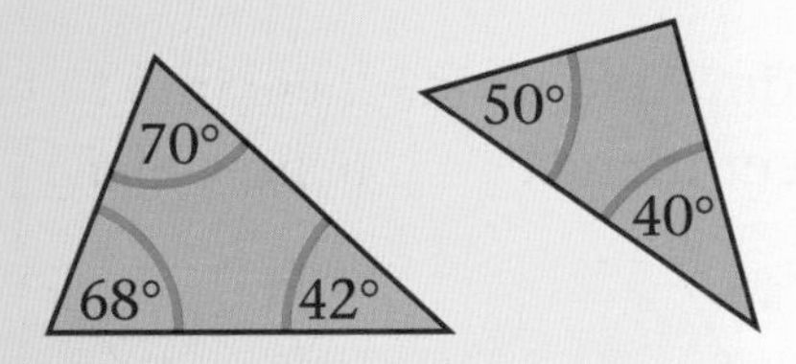

d

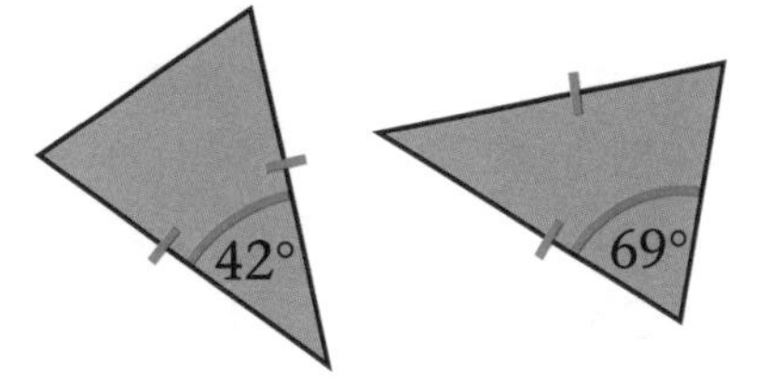

e

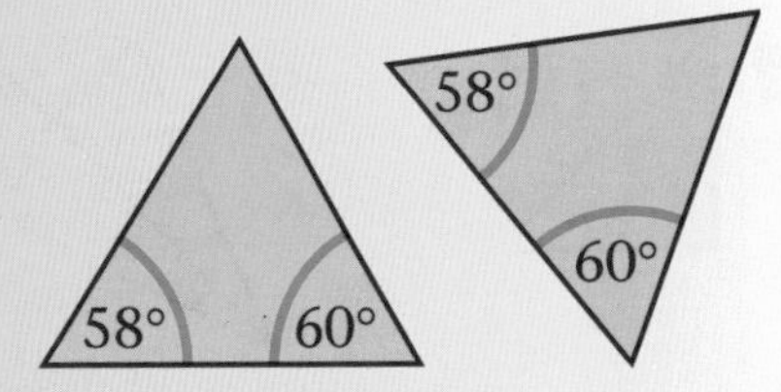

Consolidation Exercises

3 Work out the missing angles and sides in these pairs of congruent triangles.

a

Q
3.5 m
2 m
P
T
4 m
R
4 m
2 m
?
S

b

A
B
65°
65°
?
7.5 cm
D
5 cm
?
E
C

c ✓

A
30 mm
B
E
?
F
33°
?
40 mm
?
50 mm
?
?
C
D

d

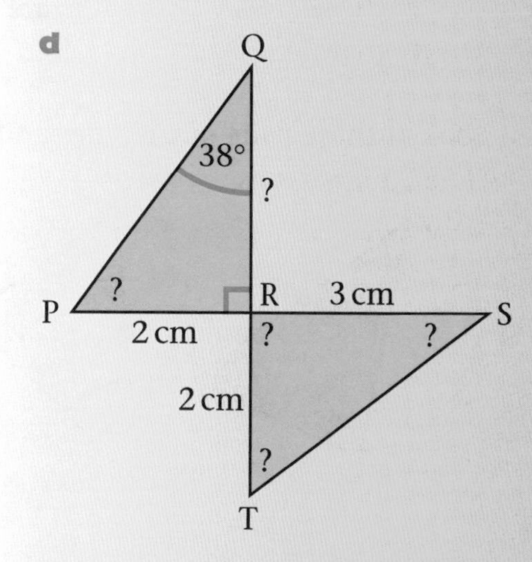

4 Look at these figures. Diagonals have been drawn to divide them into triangles. Which figures now include pairs of congruent triangles? State how many pairs.

a

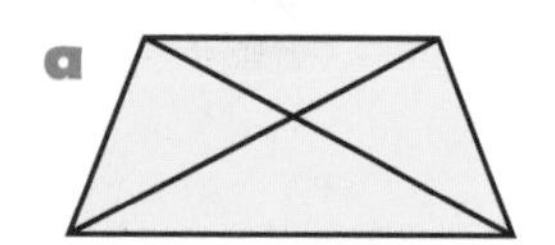

b

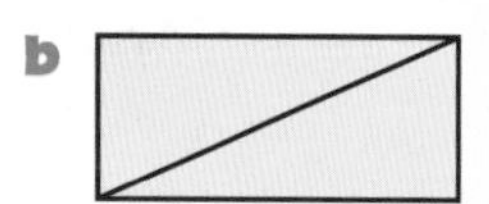

c

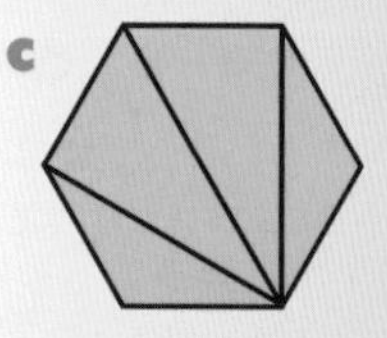

d

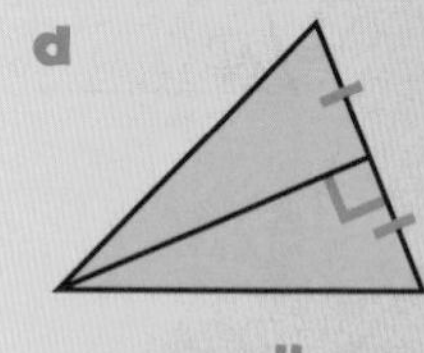

e

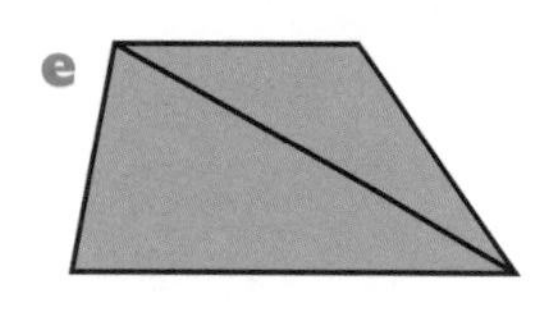

f

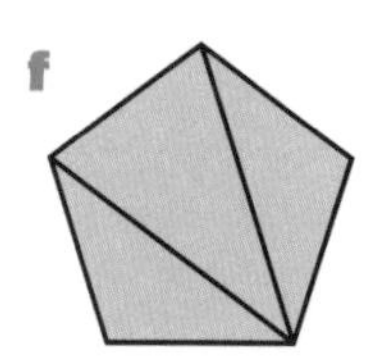

g

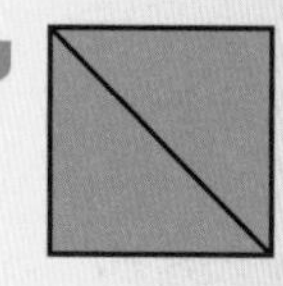

h

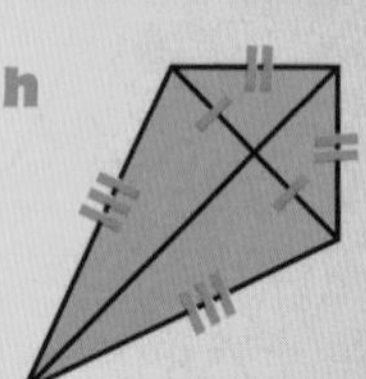

Challenging Exercises

5 A transformation maps A onto B and onto C.

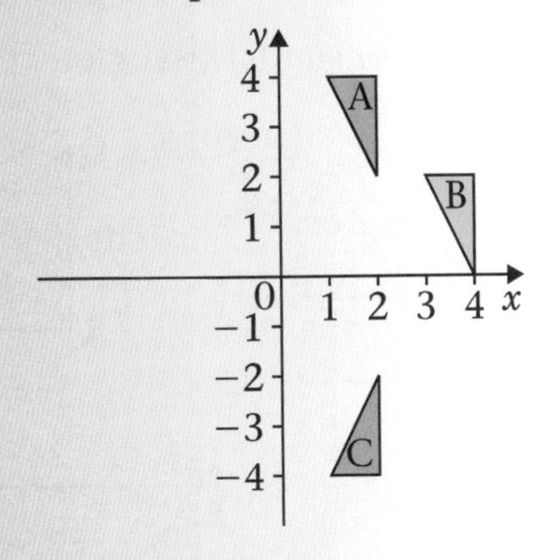

a What are the transformations?

b What can you say about shapes A and B?

c What can you say about shapes A and C?

6

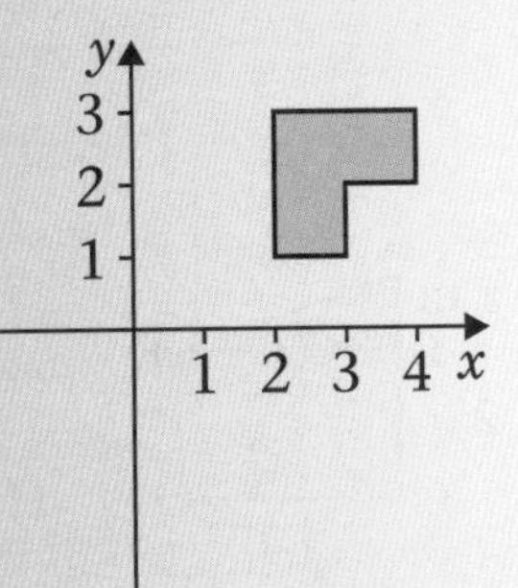

a Use three different transformations to form congruent images of the object shown in the diagram.

b Describe fully your transformations.

Similar Shapes

Essential Exercises

1 Find the missing sides in these pairs of similar triangles.

a

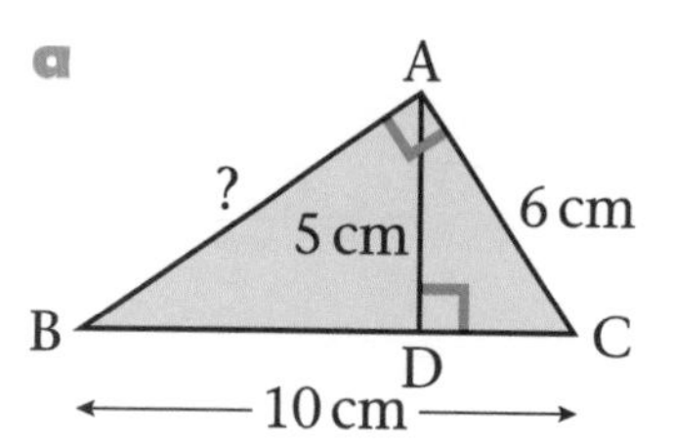

b

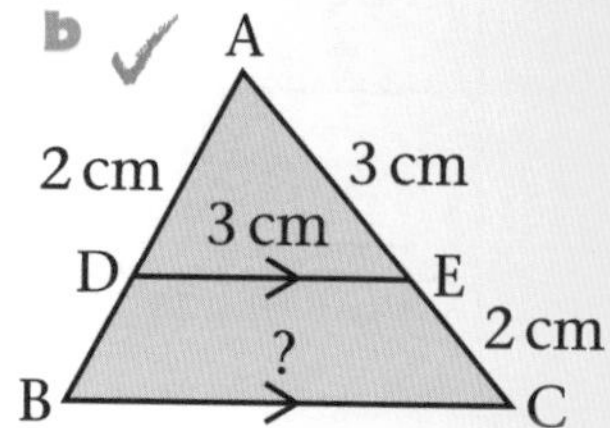

c

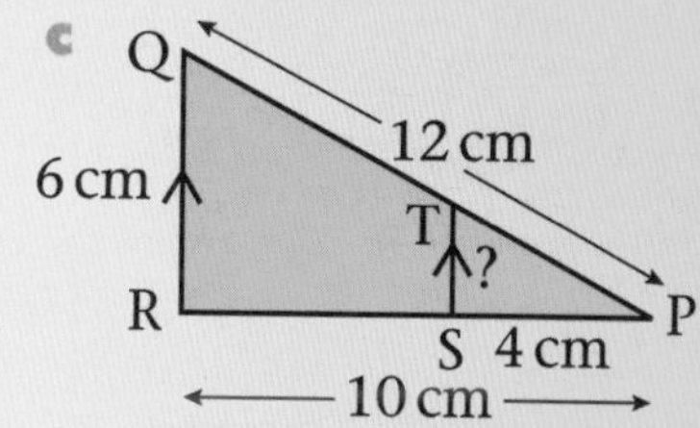

d

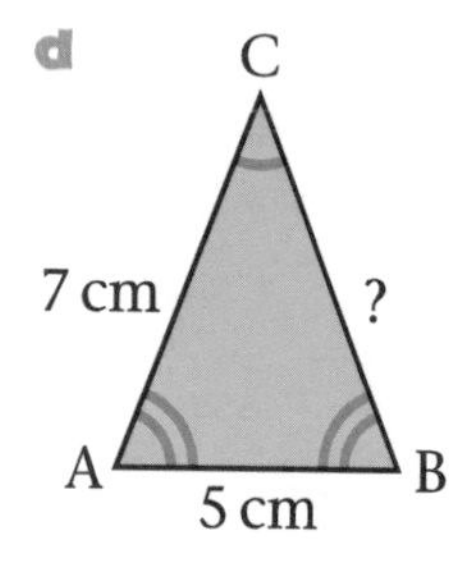

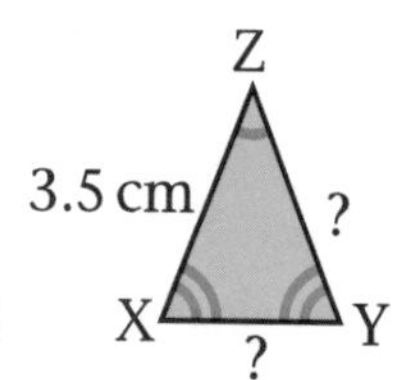

e

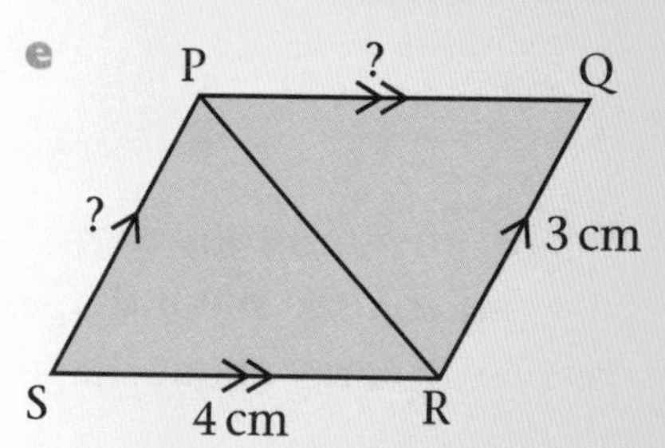

2 Find the missing lengths in these figures.

a

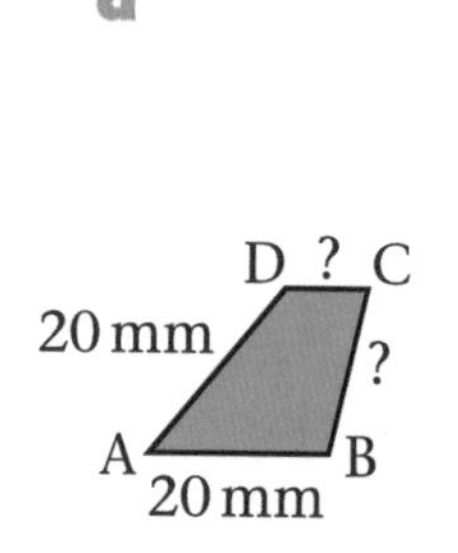

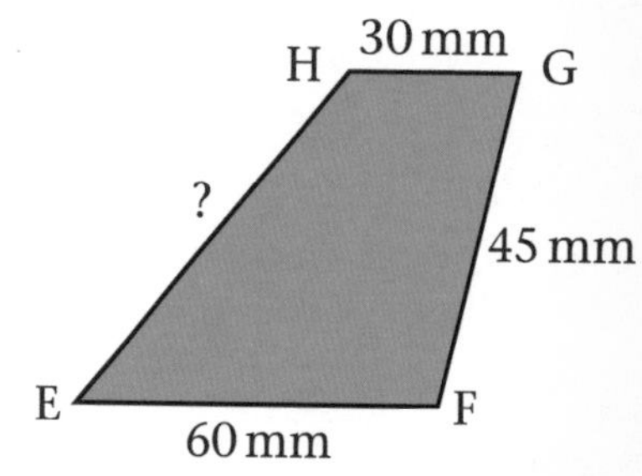

b

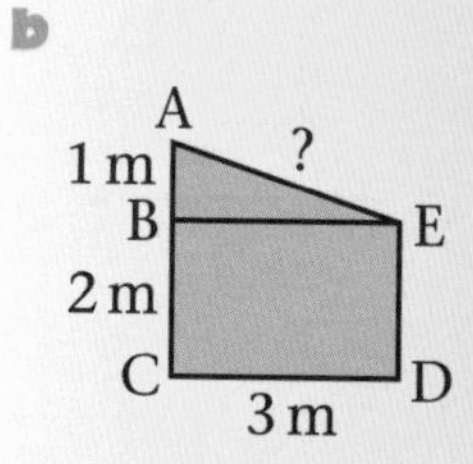

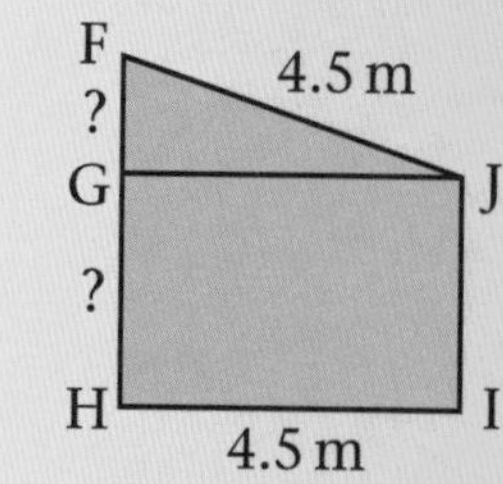

c

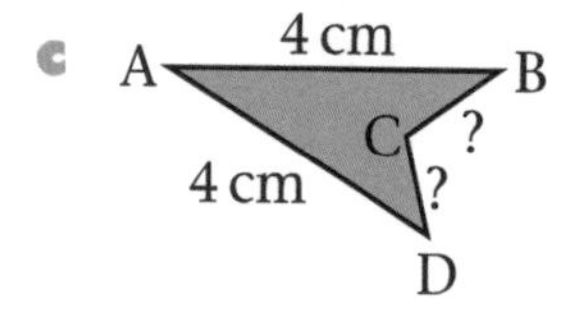

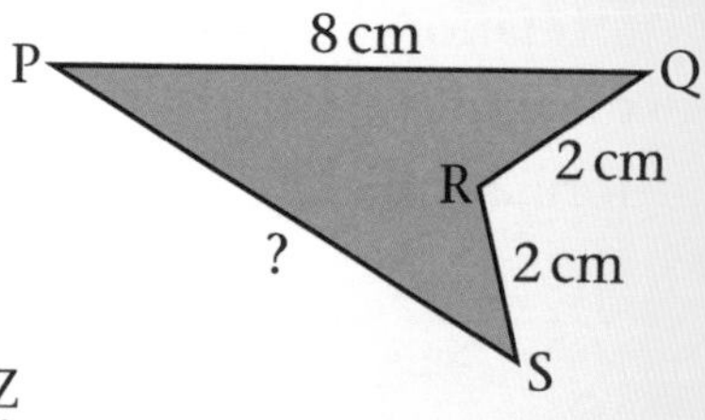

d

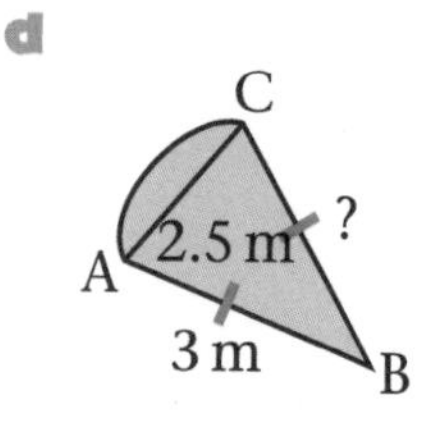

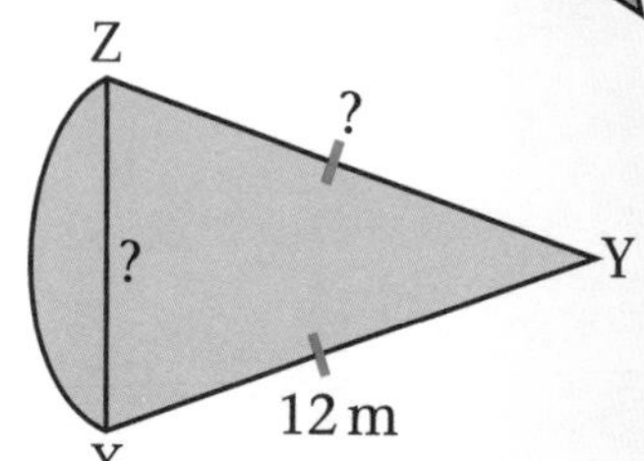

Consolidation Exercises

3 What is the scale factor or ratio that enlarges figure A to B in the following?

a

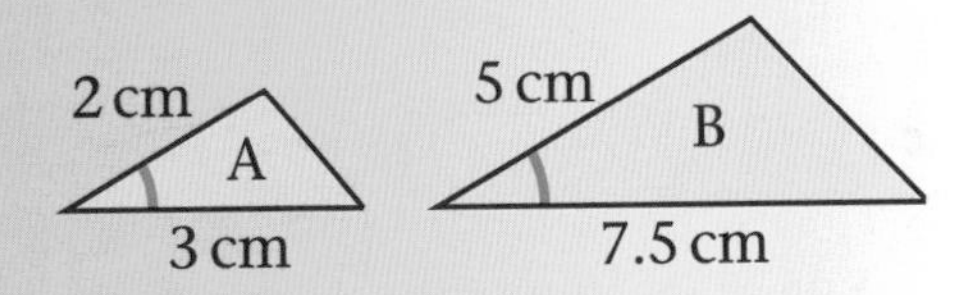

b

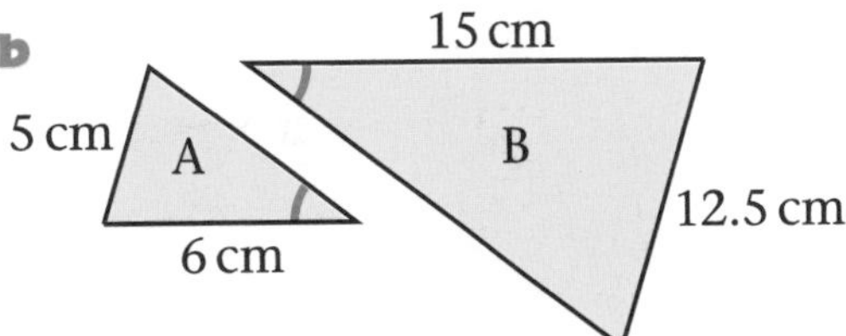

c ✓

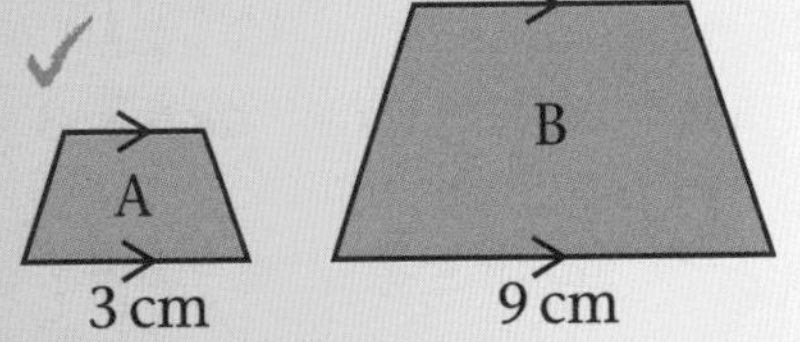

d

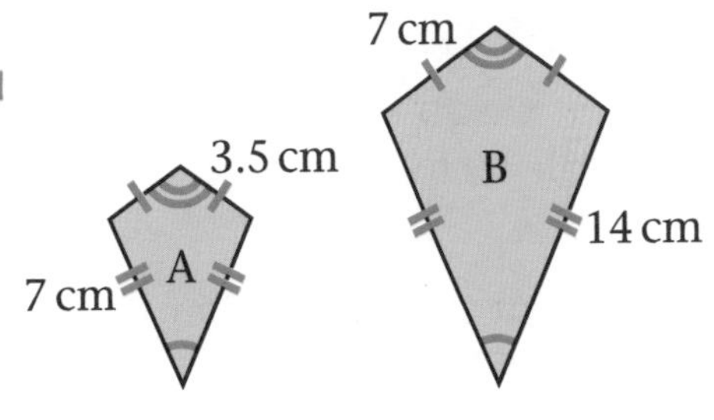

e

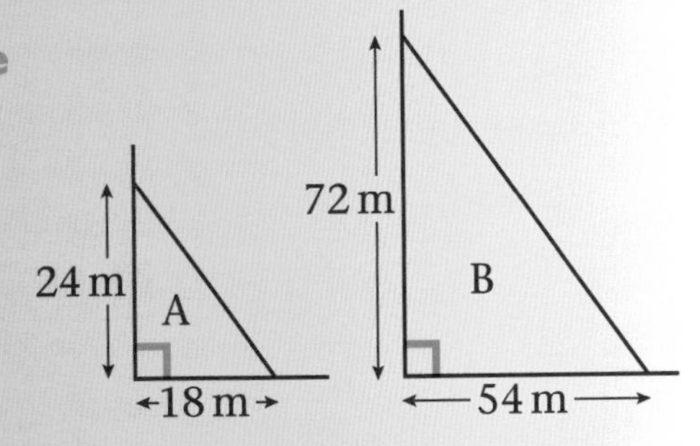

f

1.5 m
2 m
0.7 m
A

4.5 m
6 m
2.1 m
B

g

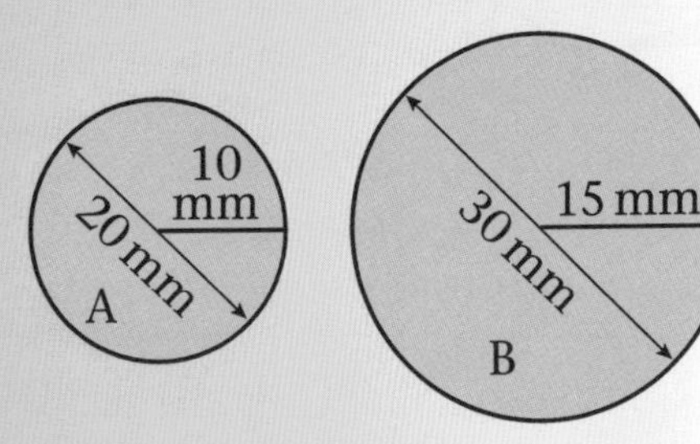

4 Copy the following shapes and enlarge them by the given scale factor to produce a similar figure.

a  
scale factor: 2

b 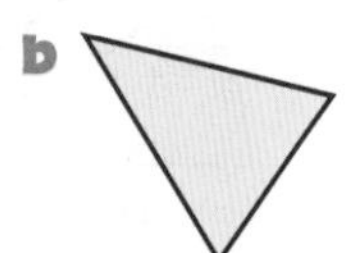
scale factor: 2

c 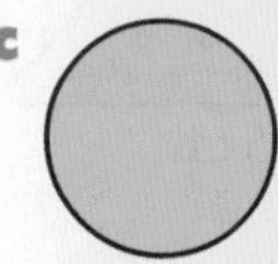
scale factor: 3

d 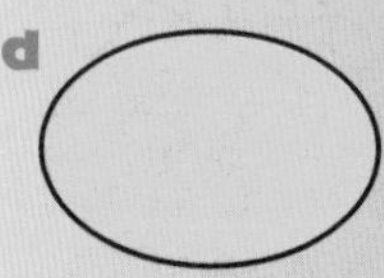
scale factor: 1.5

e  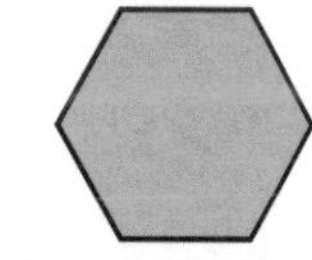
scale factor: 3

f 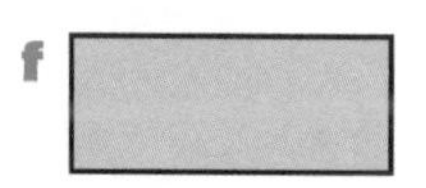
scale factor: 2.5

g 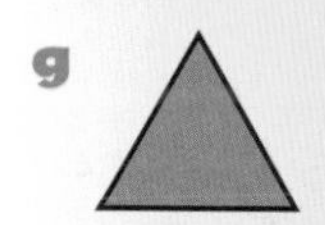
scale factor: 4

h 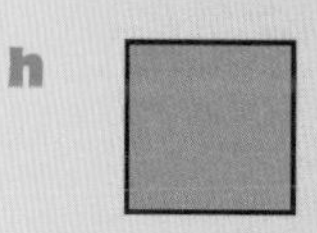
scale factor: 3.5

5 Pick out the non-similar figure from the following.

a i  ii  iii 

b i 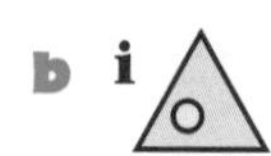 ii  iii 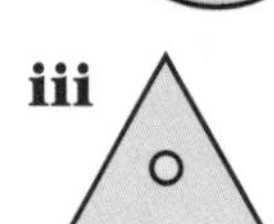

c i   ii   iii  

d i 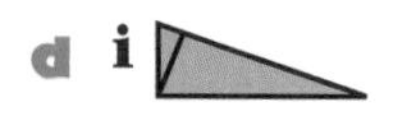 ii 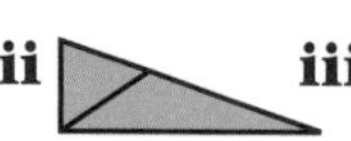 iii 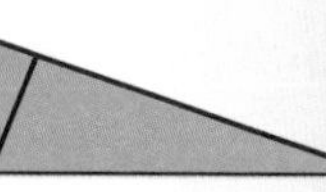

e i  ii  iii  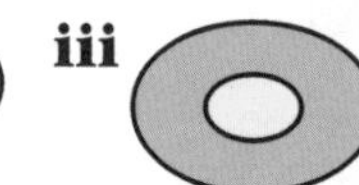

f i  ii  iii  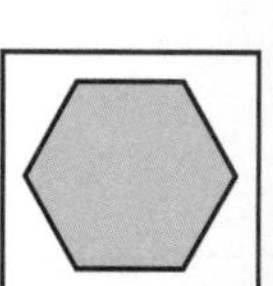

Challenging Exercises

6 Here is a pair of similar triangles.

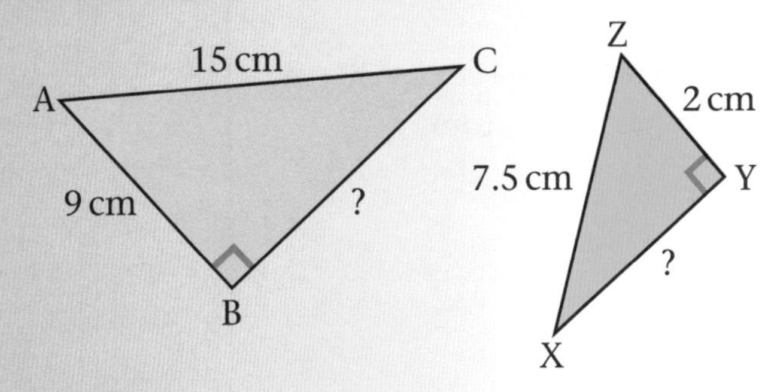

- **a** Find the lengths of BC and XY.
- **b** What is the perimeter of each triangle?
- **c** What is the area of each triangle?
- **d** What is the ratio of the perimeters?
- **e** What is the ratio of the areas?
- **f** Do you notice any connection between your answers?

7

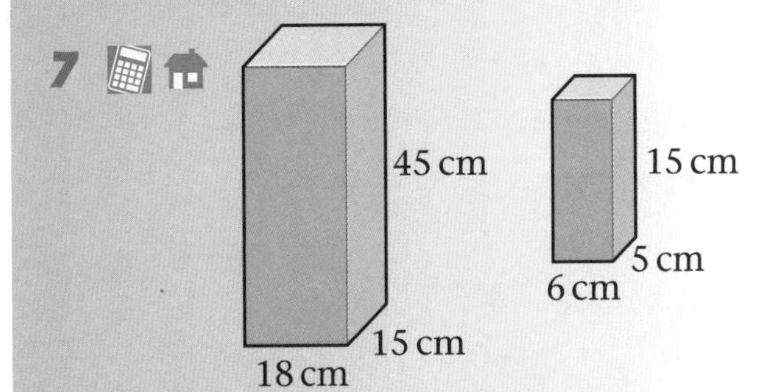

- **a** Give reasons why these two cuboids are similar.
- **b** What is the surface area of each cuboid?
- **c** What is the volume of each cuboid?
- **d** What is the ratio of their surface areas?
- **e** What is the ratio of their volumes?
- **f** Do you notice any connection between your answers?

8 The ratio of the dimensions of the doors of a cupboard is 2 : 3.
The top cupboard door measures 60 cm by 30 cm.
What are the dimensions of the bottom cupboard door?

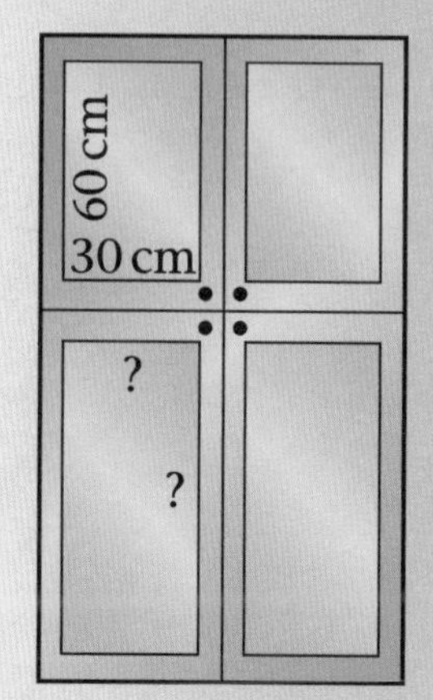

9 A picture frame is 20 cm by 12 cm.
The masking frame leaves a picture space 15 cm by 10 cm.
If the picture frame stays the same, how can you change the dimensions of the masking frame so that the shapes remain similar?

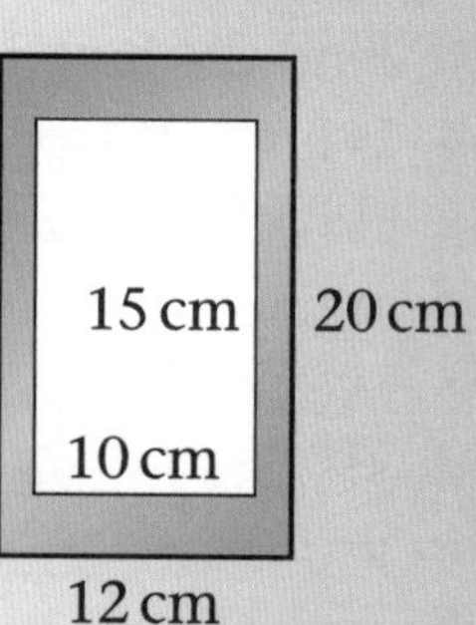

10 The diagram shows 3 boxes, R, S and T.

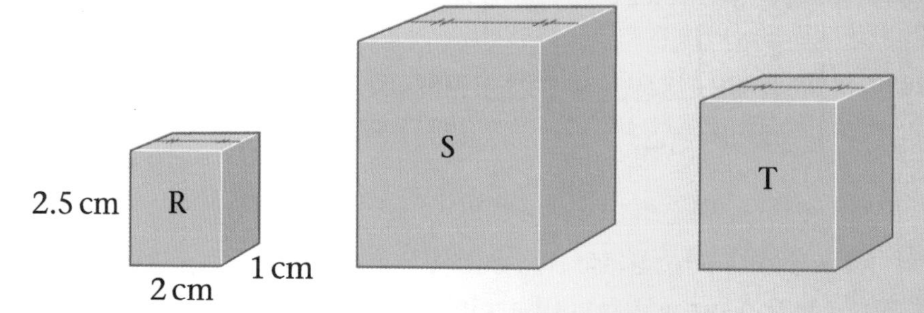

a What is the volume of R?

b What is the surface area of R?

c The dimensions of S are double those of R. What are they? Calculate the volume and surface area of S.

d The ratio of the surface area of R to T is 9 to 16. What are the dimensions of box T? Calculate the volume and surface area of T.

Circles 9

Essential Exercises

1

A circle diagram with centre O; labelled points A, B, C, D, E, G on the circle and a line H–G–F touching it at G.

Write down the words missing from the statements below.

a The perimeter of the circle is also called the __________.

b O is the __________ of the circle.

c ✓ OA, OB, OC are __________ of the circle.

d AB is the __________.

e AB divides the circle into two __________.

f The area between OB and OC and BC is a __________.

g ✓ BC is an __________.

h DE is a __________.

i The area between DE and the perimeter is a __________.

j The straight line FGH, which touches the circle at point G, is a __________.

2 Draw any triangle and carry out the following instructions.

a Join each vertex to the mid-point of the opposite side. Write O where these lines meet.

b Using compasses draw a circumscribed circle, centre O, to pass through each vertex.

c Now use your compasses to draw an inscribed circle O. This should touch the mid-point of each side, inside the triangle.

Consolidation Exercises

3 **a** Draw a circle with radius 4 cm.
b Draw a chord.
c Join the ends of the chord to the centre of the circle.
d What type of triangle have you formed? Explain.
e Repeat **b** and **c**. What can you say about these triangles? Explain.

4 **a** Draw a circle with radius 4 cm. Mark the centre O.
b Draw a diameter AOB.
c Draw a tangent PQ to the circle at A.
d Measure the angle PAO and write down your answer.
e What can you deduce from what you have found?

Challenging Exercises

5 **a** Draw a circle radius 5 cm.
b Keep the radius the same and place the point of your compasses on the circumference.
c Draw an arc, across the circle, to cut the circumference at A and B.
d Do the same from A and from B.
e Now repeat using the new points of intersection.
f What pattern have you made?
g Draw more circles and see if you can make any more patterns.

6 **a** Draw a circle of radius 5 cm.
b Keep the radius the same and place the point of your compasses on the circumference.
c Draw an arc to cut the circumference at A.
d Now place the point of your compasses on A and draw an arc to cut the circumference at B.
e Continue around the circumference. If you have been accurate, you should have marked the circumference six times.
f Use your ruler to join these marks. What do we call each of these lines?
g Measure each of these lines. What do you notice?
h What shape have you drawn?

PLANS AND ELEVATIONS

Essential Exercises

1 Identify these solids from the descriptions given.

- **a** The front and side elevations are both triangles and the plan is a square.
- **b** The front and side elevations are both rectangles and the plan is a circle.
- **c** The front and side elevations are both circles and the plan is a circle.
- **d** The front and side elevations are squares and the plan is a square.
- **e** The front and side elevations are rectangles and the plan is a rectangle.

2 Identify these solids from these elevations and plans.

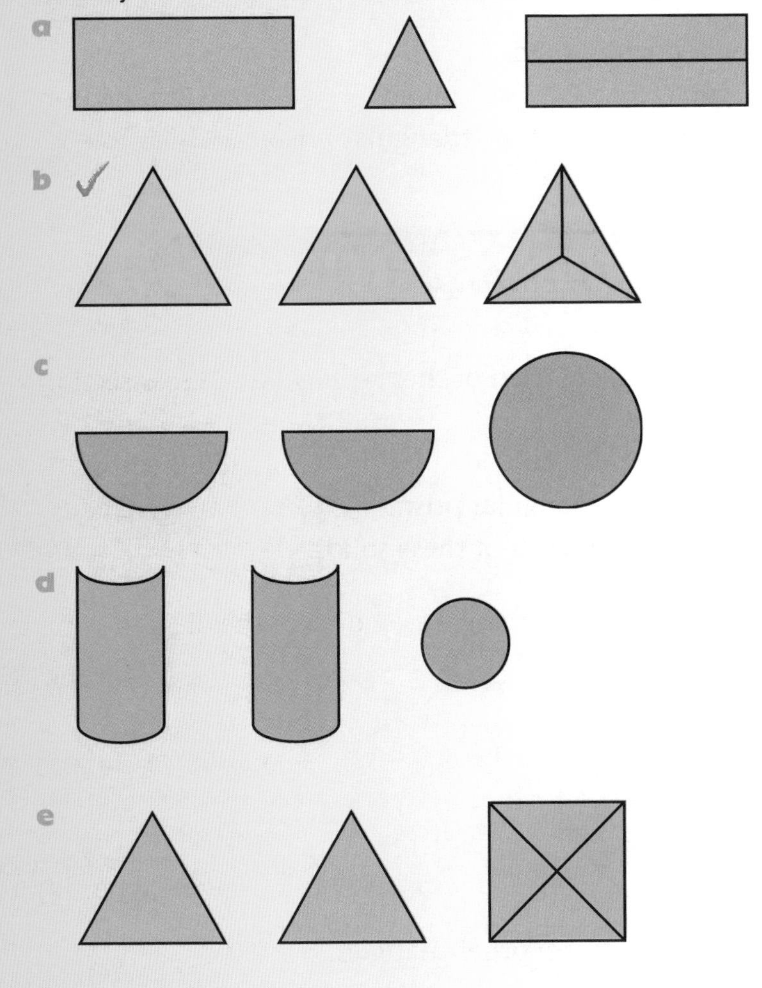

Consolidation Exercises

3 **a** How many different solids could have an isosceles triangle as a front elevation? Write down their names and sketch them.

b How many different solids could have an equilateral triangle as a front elevation? Write down their names and sketch them.

c How many different solids could have a rectangle as a front elevation? Write down their names and sketch them.

d How many different solids could have a square as a front elevation? Write down their names and sketch them.

4 **Me and my shadow**

Draw the shadow of the following solids.

a sphere **b** cube **c** cuboid **d** tetrahedron
e cylinder **f** hemisphere **g** triangular prism

Challenging Exercises

5 If you cut through the middle of each of these solids, what cross-section is formed?

a cube **b** ✓ cuboid **c** tetrahedron
d square-based pyramid **e** triangular prism

Now find another cross-section for each of these solids.

6 Join 3 vertices of a cube to form a triangle as shown in the diagram.

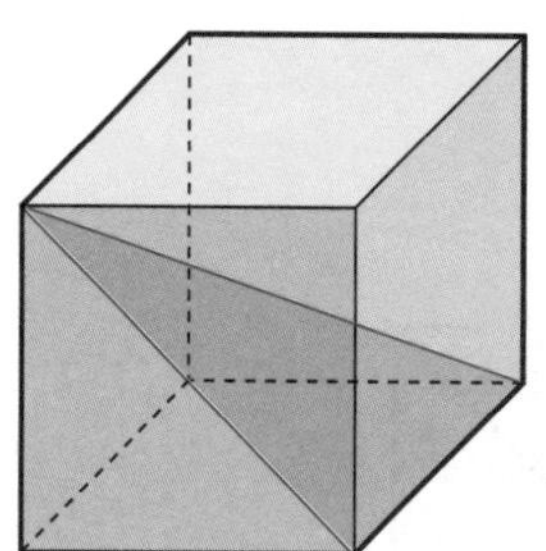

Join more groups of 3 vertices to form other triangles.
How many can you form?
Draw each of them.

TRANSFORMATIONS AND CONGRUENCY

Essential Exercises

1 Which transformation is described in each of the following statements?

a The shape stays the same size. The image is the object reversed. The object and image are congruent.

b The shape stays the same size. The image is the object moved. The object and image are congruent.

c The shape stays the same size. The image is the object turned. The object and image are congruent.

d The shape changes size and position. The object and image are similar.

2 Mark the axes of symmetry on these solids.

a cube **b** cuboid **c** triangular prism

d square-based pyramid **e** tetrahedron **f** octahedron

3 Give 5 examples of symmetry you see in everyday life, e.g. a butterfly.

Consolidation Exercises

4 Transform the object in the diagram below as follows:

a reflect T in the line $y = x$ and label the new object T′

b rotate T′ through 180° about (0, −2) and label the new object T′′.

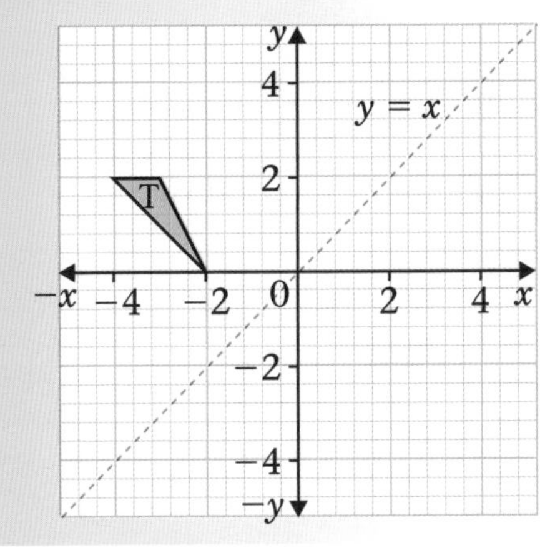

5 **a** Plot the coordinates of these 4 points: P(0, 0), Q(2, 1), R(3, 3), S(1, 2). Join PQ, QR, RS, SP. What shape have you drawn?

b Reflect the shape in the x-axis.

c Reflect the shape in the y-axis.

d Describe what you find.

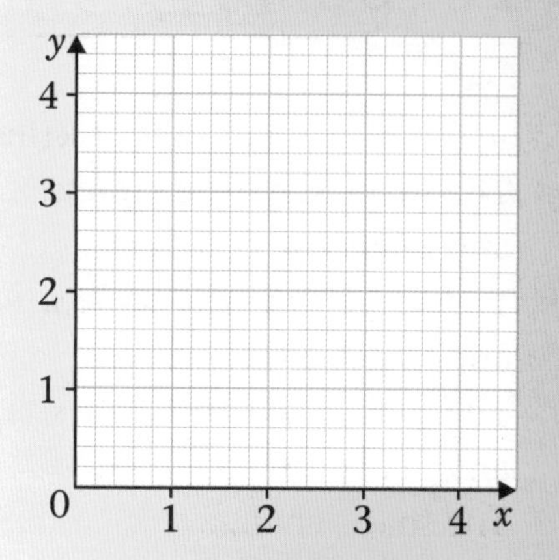

6

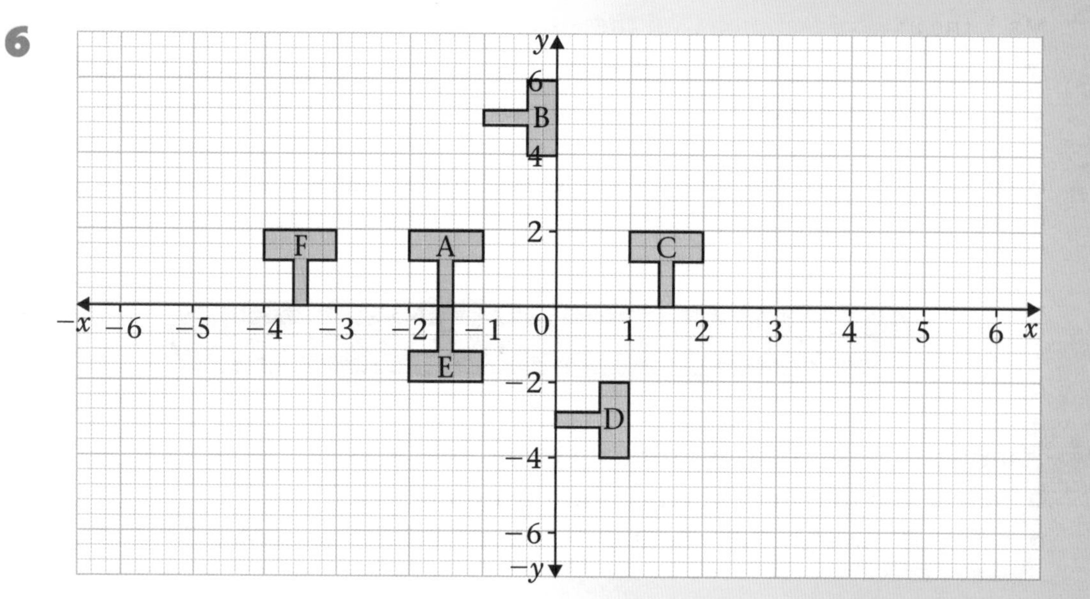

All these T shapes are congruent.
Describe the transformations from shape A to each of the other shapes.

7 Identify planes of symmetry for each of these solid shapes.

a cube

b cuboid

c triangular prism

d square-based pyramid

e tetrahedron

f octahedron

Challenging Exercises

8 This diagram shows an octahedron.

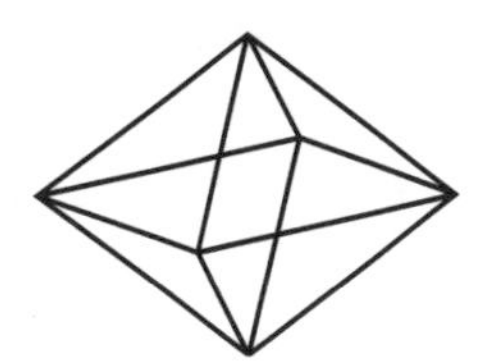

a How many planes of symmetry are there?

b Mark any axes of rotational symmetry.

c What is the order of rotational symmetry?

9 This shape is reflected in the y-axis and rotated 90° clockwise about the origin.

Does the order of transformation matter? Explain.

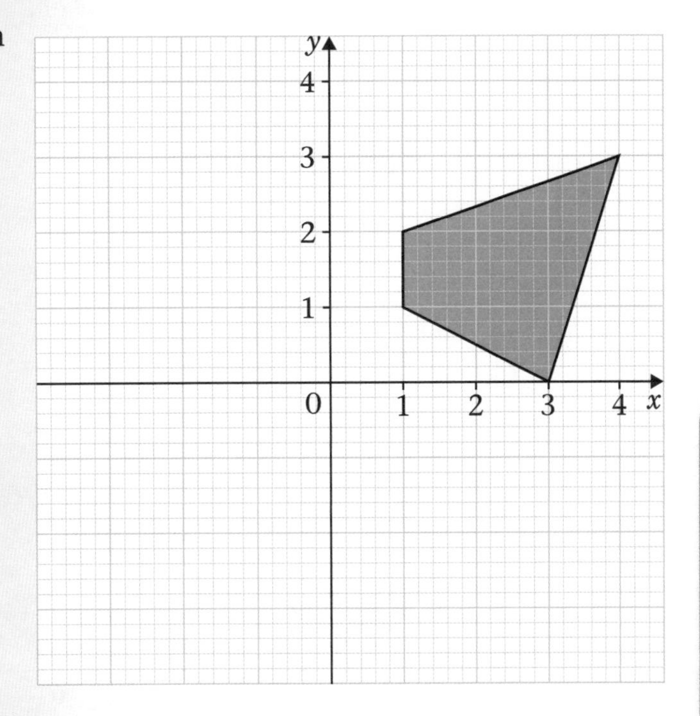

10 You have 6 unit cubes. How many different shapes can you make with the cubes?

Draw each shape.

For each shape, show any planes of symmetry.

Are there any congruent shapes?

11 What shapes are formed by the combined object and image when you do the following:

a reflect a right-angled triangle along its hypotenuse

b rotate a square a quarter turn about a corner

c rotate a scalene triangle 180° about the mid-point of one side?

Enlargements

Essential Exercises

1 Calculate the scale factor for the following enlargements.

a

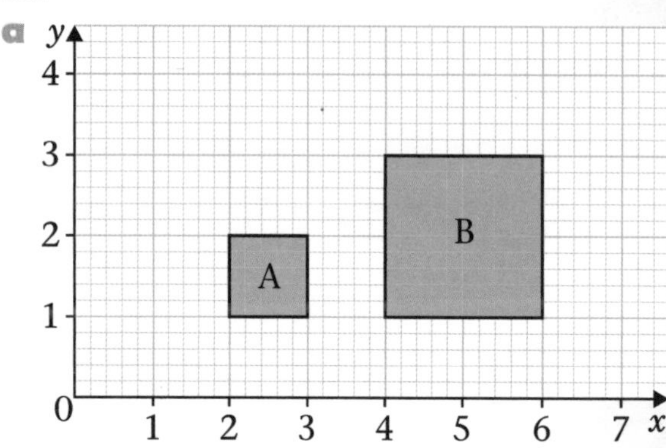

b

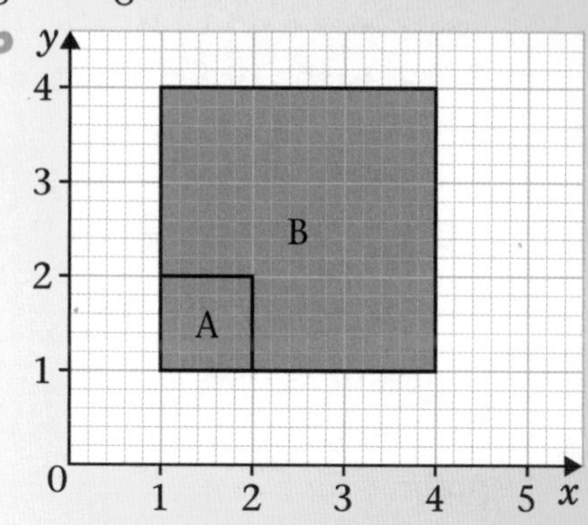

c

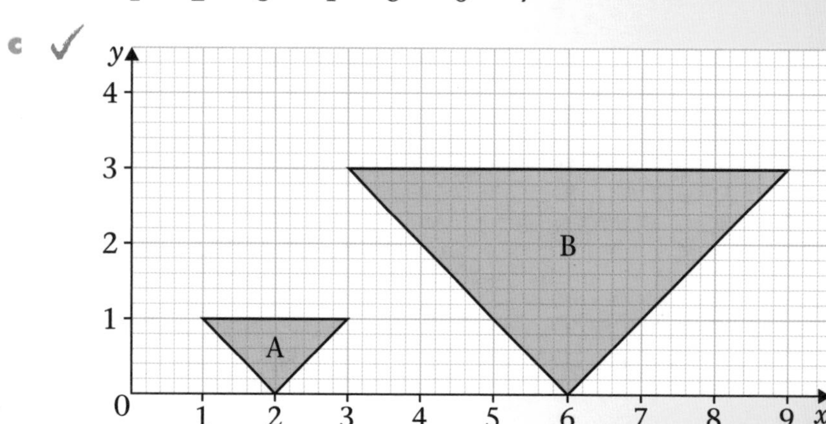

d

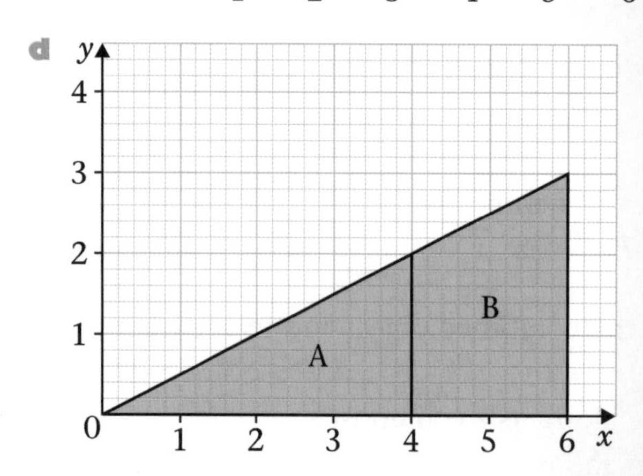

Now copy each diagram onto squared paper and find the centre of enlargement for each. Mark it X.

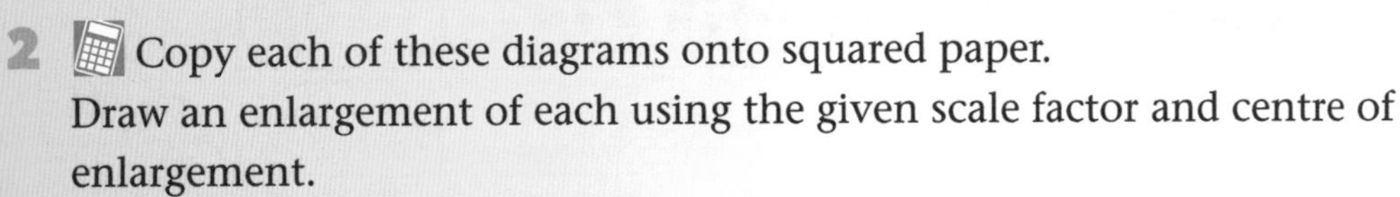

2 Copy each of these diagrams onto squared paper.
Draw an enlargement of each using the given scale factor and centre of enlargement.

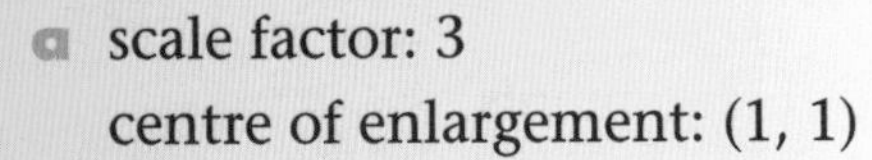

a scale factor: 3
centre of enlargement: (1, 1)

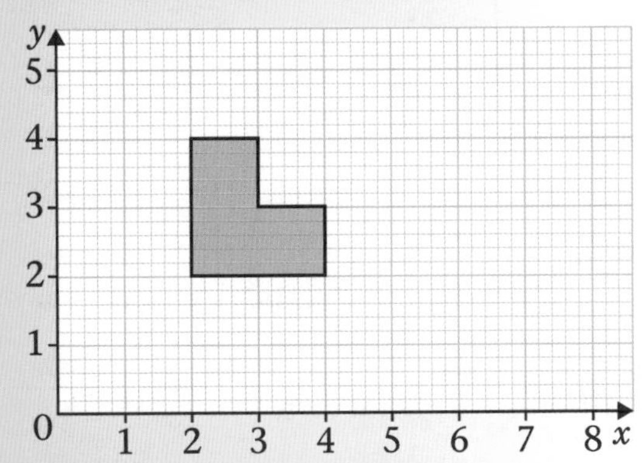

b scale factor: 2
centre of enlargement: (4, 1)

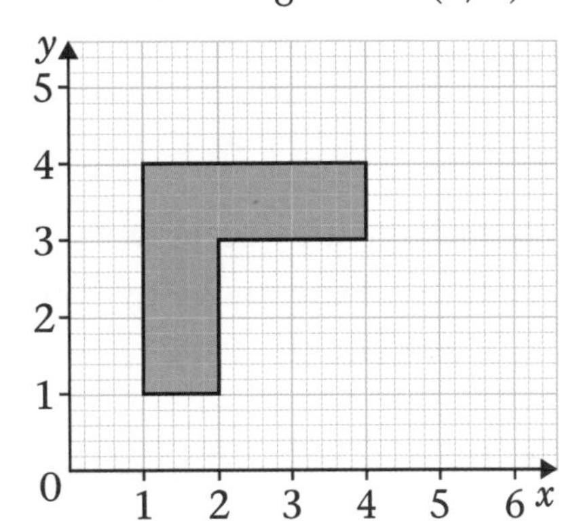

c scale factor: 1.5
centre of enlargement: (0, 0)

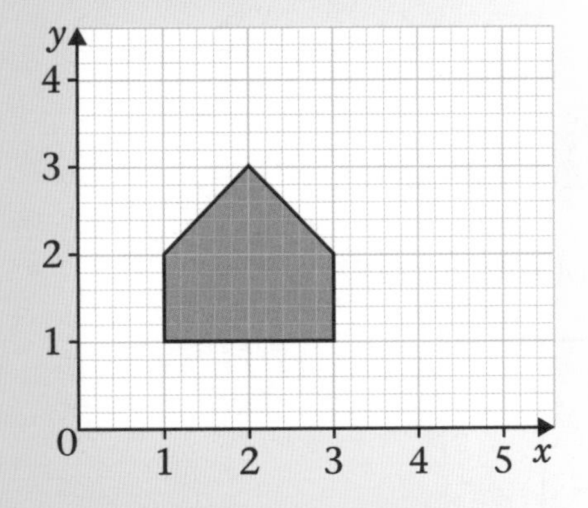

d scale factor: 2.5
centre of enlargement: (0, 2)

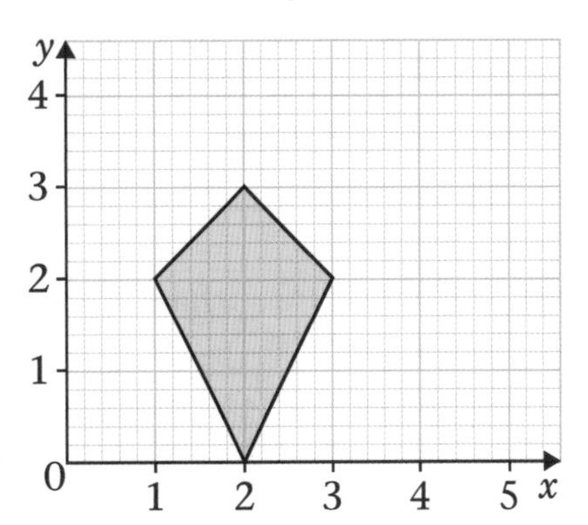

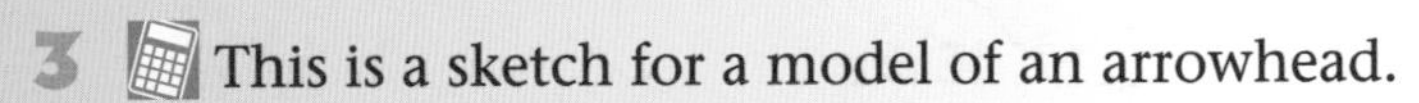

3 This is a sketch for a model of an arrowhead.

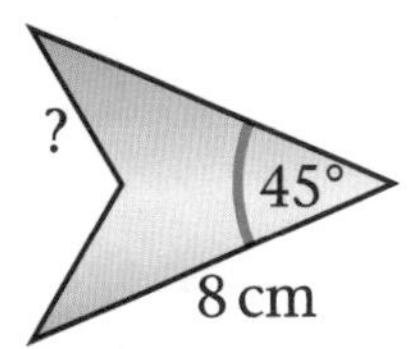

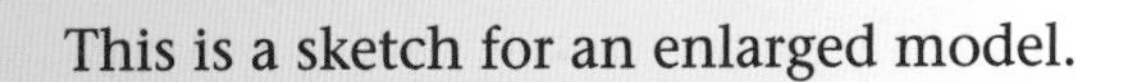

This is a sketch for an enlarged model.

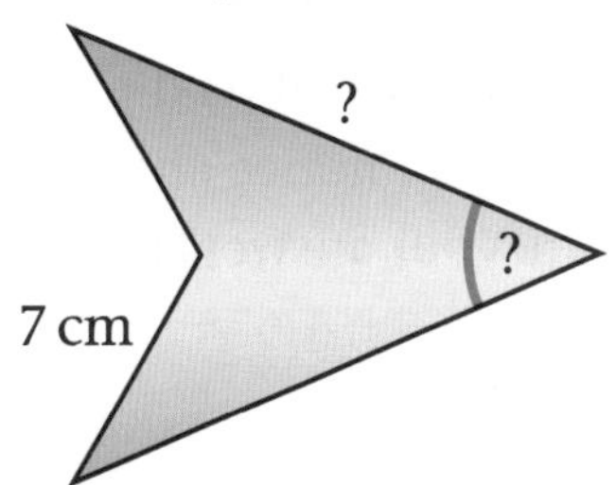

The scale factor for the enlargement is 2.

a Find the missing values.

b If the scale factor was 2.5, what would the missing values be?

Consolidation Exercises

4 Copy this shape onto squared paper.

a Enlarge it by scale factor 2.
b Enlarge the image by scale factor 3.
c Calculate the scale factor for mapping the original object onto the final image.
d Find a relationship between the different scale factors.

5 Copy this shape onto squared paper.
a Enlarge it by scale factor $\frac{1}{2}$.
b Enlarge the image by scale factor $\frac{1}{2}$.
c Calculate the scale factor for mapping the original object onto the final image.
d Find a relationship between the different scale factors.

6 a Find the surface area and volume of this cuboid.

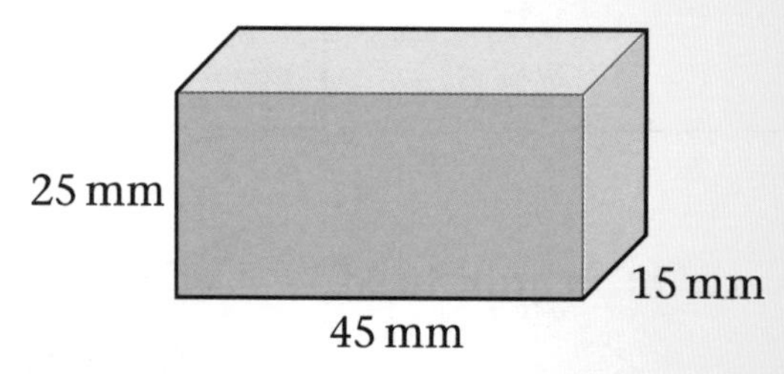

b Now find them again if:
  i you double all its dimensions
  ii you enlarge all its dimensions by a scale factor of 3.
c What do you notice about your answers?
d How are your answers connected?

7 In questions **a–f** shape B is an enlargement of shape A. Calculate the scale factors and then find the area of each shape. How are the scale factors and areas connected?

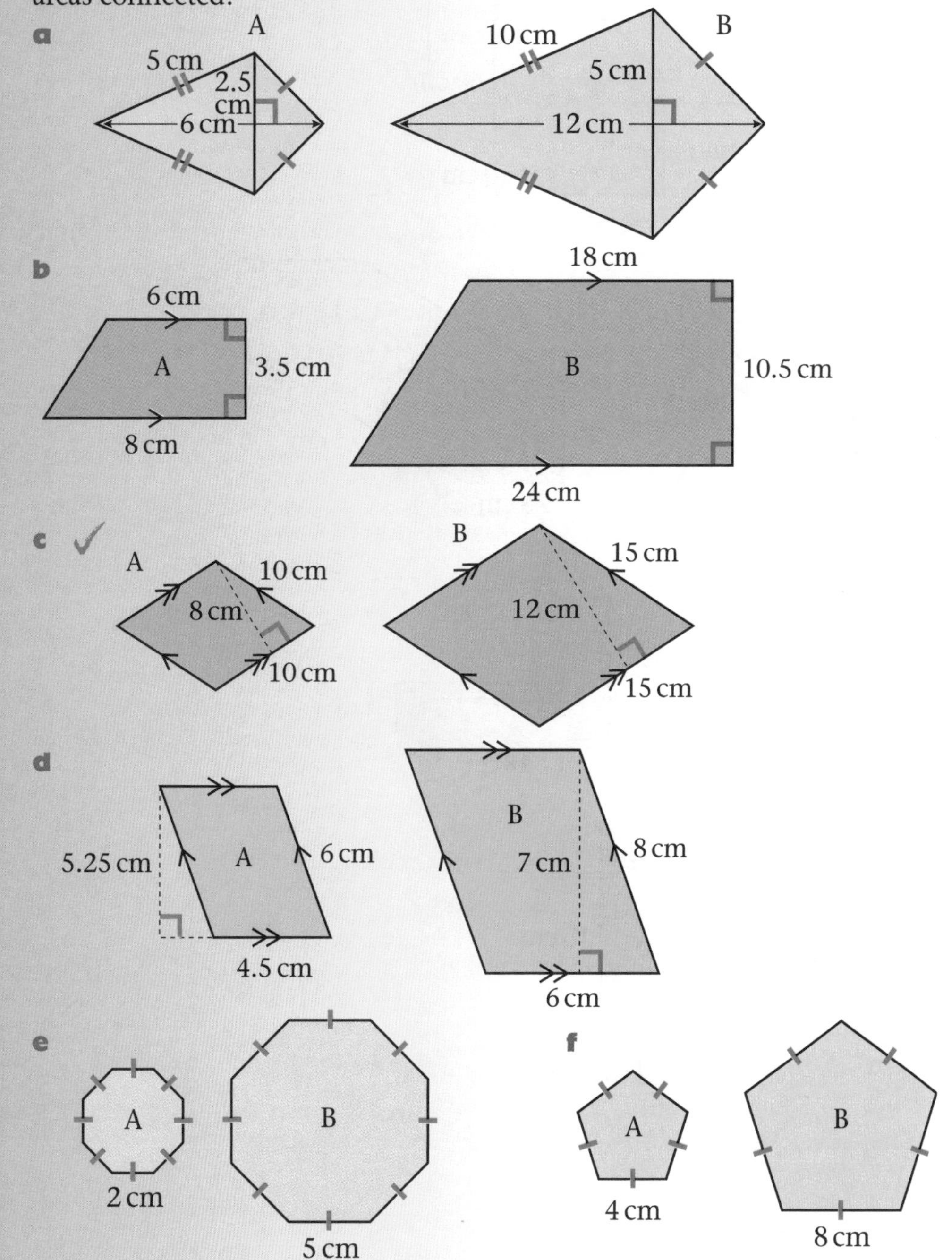

8 In questions **a–f** shape B is an enlargement of shape A. Calculate the scale factors and then find the volume of each shape. How are the scale factors and volumes connected?

a

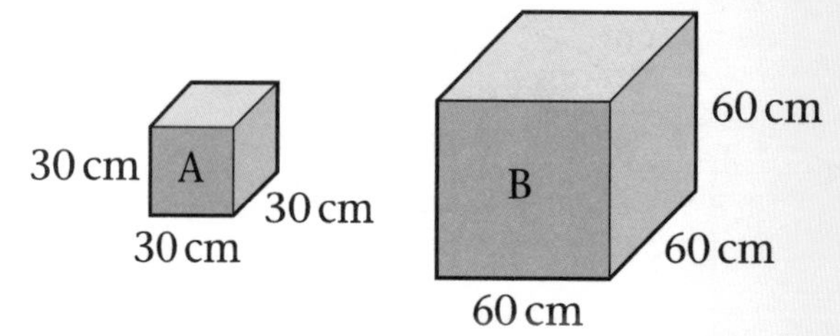

b

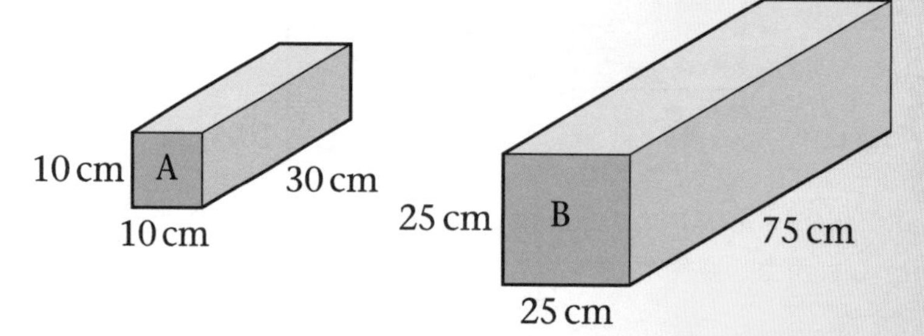

c

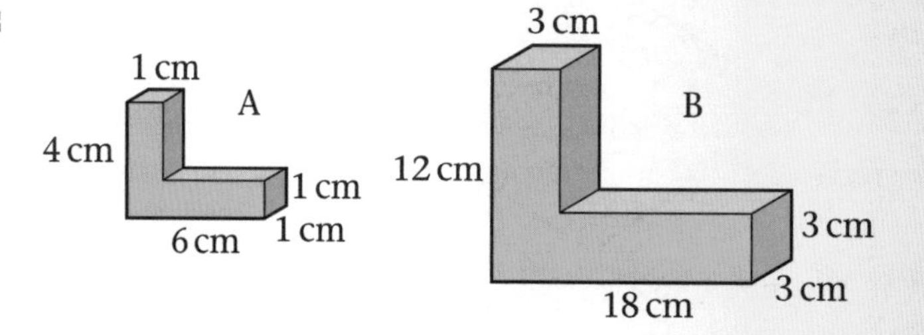

d

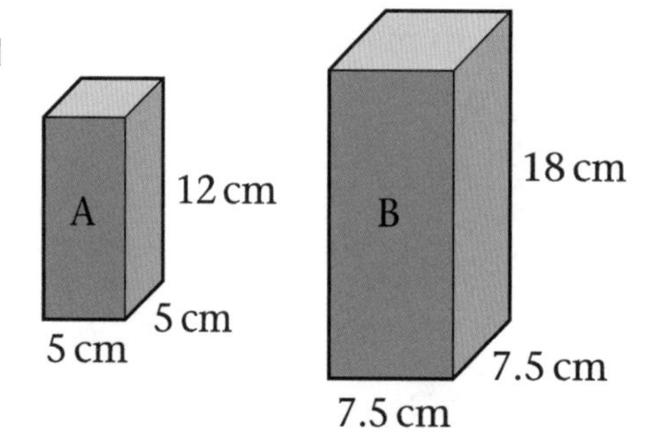

e ✓

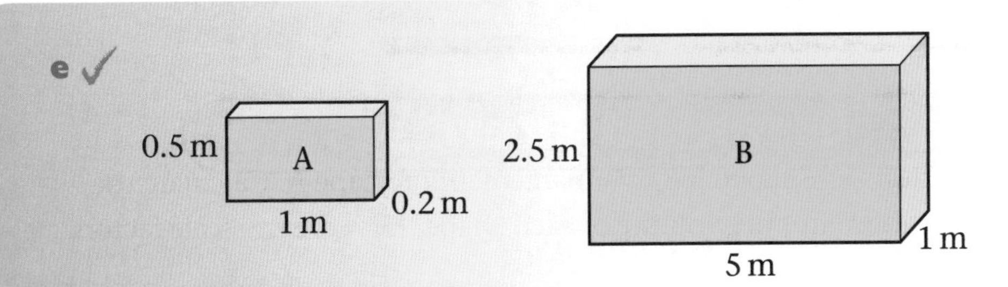

f

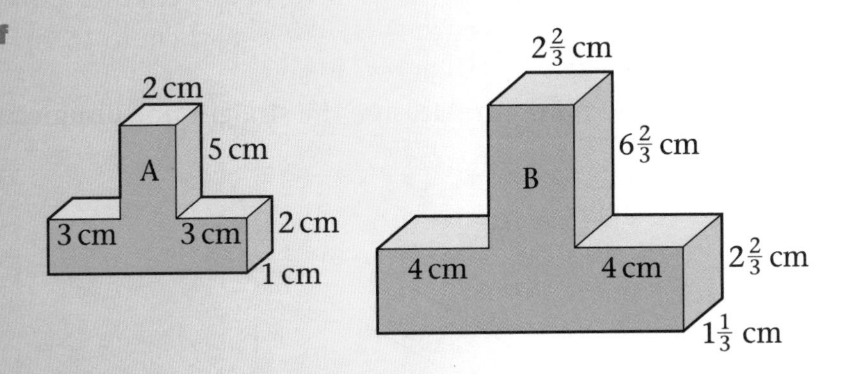

9 **a** Take a piece of A3 paper, measure its dimensions and fold it in half.

b This is now the size of a piece of A4 paper. Measure its dimensions and fold it in half.

c This is now the size of a piece of A5 paper. Measure its dimensions and fold it in half.

d This is now the size of a piece of A6 paper. Measure its dimensions.

e Calculate the scale factor of enlargement from A3 to A5, A4 to A6 and A3 to A6.

f Draw a diagram of the different sizes of paper with a common corner. Comment on the centre of enlargement.

10 A photograph is taken with a digital camera. Its size on the computer screen is 21 cm by 15 cm. Calculate the scale factor of enlargement if photographs of the following sizes are required for printing.

a 10.5 cm by 7.5 cm **b** 15.75 cm by 11.25 cm

c 26.25 cm by 18.75 cm **d** 31.5 cm by 22.5 cm

e 42 cm by 30 cm

What do you notice about your answers? What does this tell you about the prints?

Scale drawing

Essential Exercises

1 Convert these scales to the form 1 : *n*.

a 1 cm to 1 m **b** 2 cm to 1 km **c** 1 cm to 2 km

d 1 cm to 5 m **e** 1 cm to 25 m **f** 1 cm to 15 km

2 a Here is a map of northern Britain. Measure the straight line distances from Galashiels to:

i Jedburgh
ii Hawick
iii Dumfries
iv Carlisle

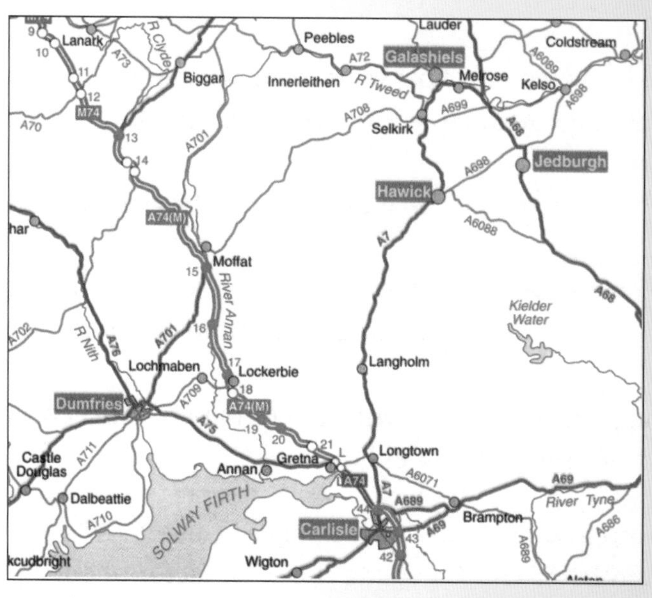

b If the scale of the map is 1 : 1 315 000, calculate the actual distances for **i**, **ii**, **iii** and **iv**.

Consolidation Exercises

3 The following diagrams are drawn to a scale of 1 : 20. What are the actual measurements?

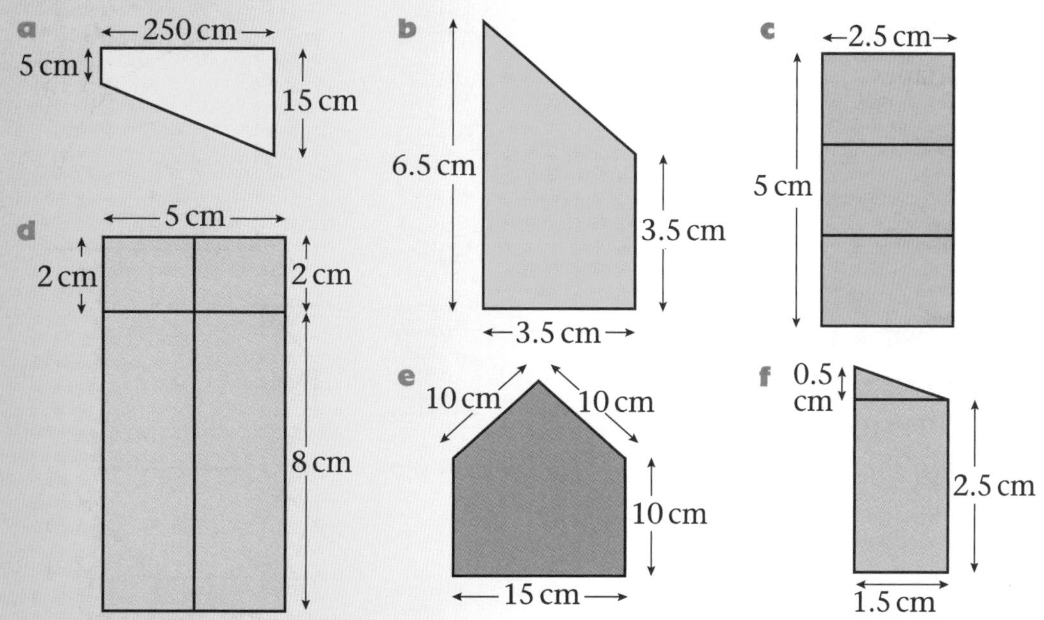

4 This is the scale drawing of the ground floor of a house.

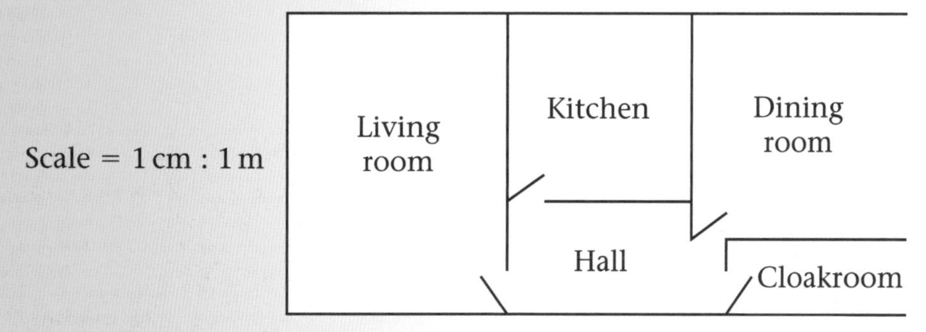

a What are the actual dimensions of these rooms according to the given scale?

i hall

ii dining room

iii living room

iv kitchen

b The owner wishes to build a conservatory, with dimensions 2 m by 3.5 m, onto the back of the house. Calculate the scale measurements.

c Copy the plan and add on the conservatory.

Challenging Exercises

5 Show that these two shapes are similar.
Find the ratio of the areas of the two shapes.

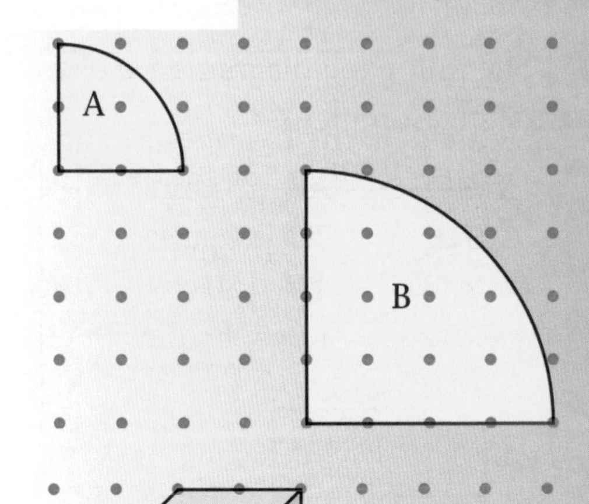

6 Show that these two solid shapes are similar.
Find the ratio of the volumes of the two shapes.

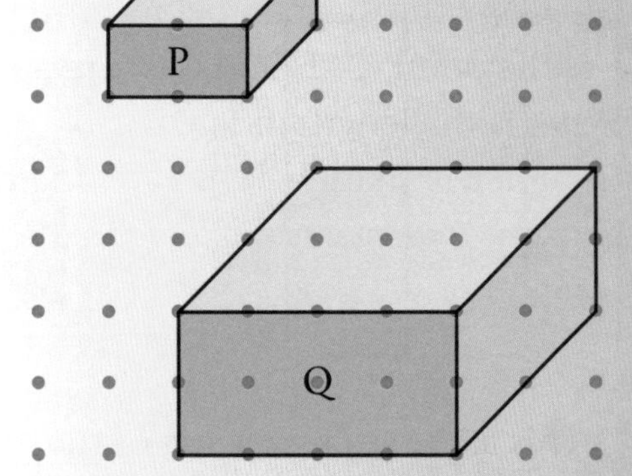

7 A plane flies from Birmingham to Edinburgh and then to Aberdeen.
Draw a scale drawing of its journey.
What is the distance of the direct return journey from Aberdeen to Birmingham and its bearing?

Scale = 1 : 6 000 000

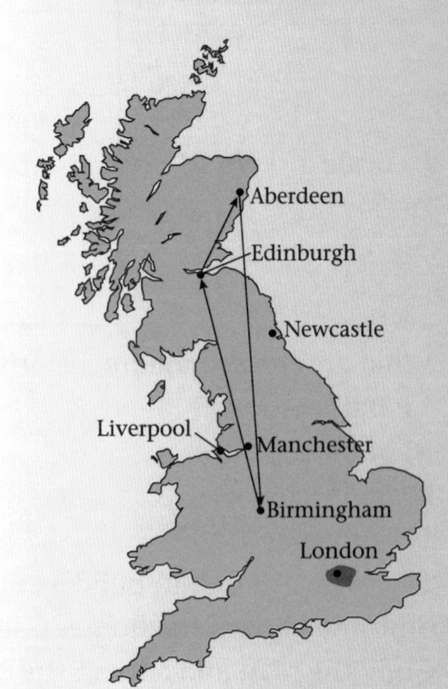

Lines and Ratio

Essential Exercises

1 Calculate the hypotenuse for each of these right-angled triangles.

a △ABC: AB = 5 cm; BC = 7.5 cm
b △CDE: CD = 7 cm; DE = 13 cm
c ✓ △EFG: EF = 20 cm; FG = 21 cm
d △KLM: KL = 36 mm; LM = 23 mm
e △LMN: LM = 12.6 cm; MN = 16.4 cm
f △PQR: PQ = 2.4 m; QR = 3.5 m

2 Copy the diagram below onto squared paper.
P is the point (2, 1) and Q is the point (6, 5).
What is the length of PQ?
Complete a triangle PQR with angle R = 90° and PQ as the hypotenuse.
Now use Pythagoras' theorem to calculate PQ.

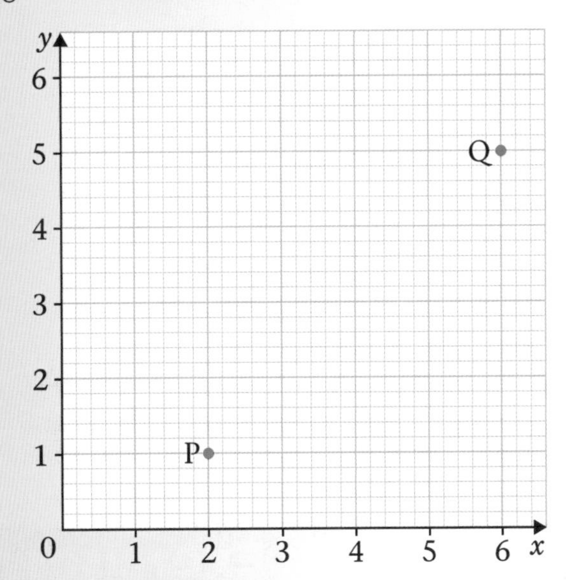

3 The coordinates of point P are (1, 5).
The *x*-coordinate of point Q is 11.
Line PQ is 12 units long.
What is the *y*-coordinate of Q?
What are the coordinates of the mid-point of PQ?

Consolidation Exercises

4 Find the length of these lines then check your answers using Pythagoras' theorem.

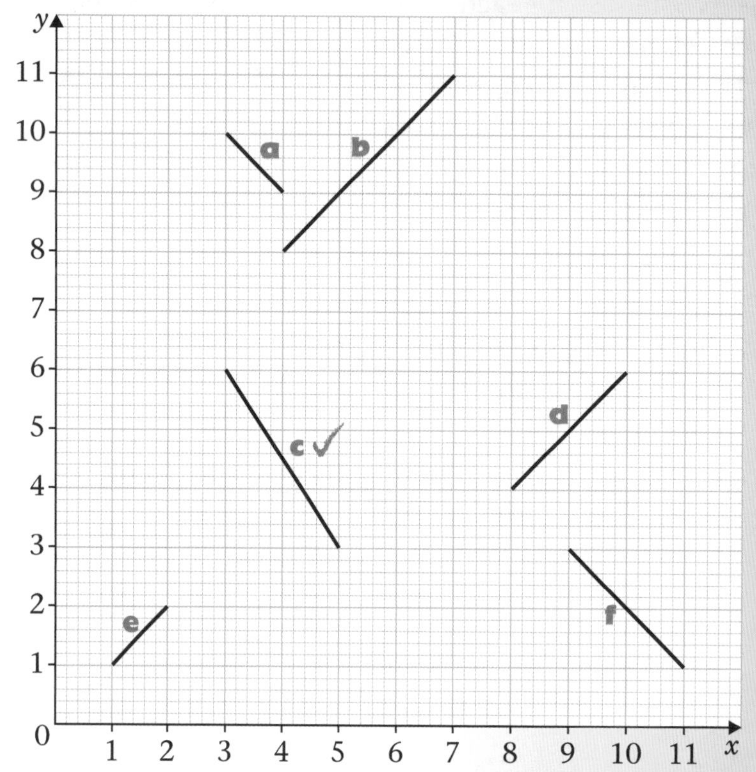

5 If the sides of a triangle are in the ratio of 3 : 4 : 5, the triangle has a right angle. Are these triangles right-angled?

a 1.5 cm, 2 cm, 2.5 cm **b** 4 cm, 8 cm, 7.5 cm **c** 6 cm, 6 cm, 6 cm

d 9 cm, 12 cm, 15 cm **e** 12 cm, 16 cm, 20 cm **f** 60 mm, 80 mm, 100 mm

Challenging Exercises

6 Draw the line of the equation $y = x + 5$.

Mark two points A and B, with their coordinates, on your line.

Calculate the gradient of this line segment.

What are the coordinates of the mid-point of AB?

CONSTRUCTIONS

Essential Exercises

1 Using ruler and compasses construct the following shapes.

- **a** Triangle ABC: AB = 7 cm; BC = 8 cm; CA = 9 cm. Measure the size of $\hat{A}$.
- **b** Triangle PQR: PQ = 7.6 cm; QR = 3.9 cm; RP = 5.2 cm. Measure the size of $\hat{P}$.
- **c** Quadrilateral ABCD: AB = 8 cm; BC = 3.3 cm; DA = 7.5 cm; $\hat{A} = 65°$. Measure the size of $\hat{D}$.
- **d** Quadrilateral PQRS: PQ = 3 cm; QR = 2.8 cm; SP = 2.8 cm; $\hat{P} = 135°$. Measure the size of $\hat{R}$.
- **e** Regular pentagon ABCDE: side = 3 cm. Measure the size of any interior angle.
- **f** ✓ Regular hexagon ABCDEF: side = 3 cm. Measure the size of any interior angle.

2 Is it possible to construct the following triangles?

- **a** $\hat{A} = 70°$, $\hat{B} = 70°$, $\hat{C} = 40°$
- **b** $\hat{P} = 120°$, $\hat{Q} = 35°$, $\hat{R} = 30°$
- **c** AB = 24 cm, BC = 13 cm, BA = 13 cm
- **d** CD = 4.5 m, DE = 6 m, EC = 5.5 m
- **e** PQ = 40 mm, QR = 60 mm, $\hat{R} = 40°$
- **f** AB = 3 cm, $\hat{A} = 37°$, $\hat{B} = 100°$

Consolidation Exercises

3 Draw any triangle.

- **a** Using compasses, construct the three angle bisectors.
  What do we call the points where these bisectors cross the triangle sides?
  Mark them P, Q, R.
- **b** Using the point of intersection of the angle bisectors as the centre, draw an inscribed circle touching the sides of the triangle at P, Q and R.
- **c** Measure the radius of the circle.

4 Draw any triangle.

a Using compasses, construct the three perpendicular bisectors of the sides.

b Using the point of intersection of the bisectors as the centre, draw a circumscribed circle touching the vertices of the triangle.

c Measure the radius of the circle.

Challenging Exercises

5 **a** Using a ruler and compasses draw two intersecting circles. Mark the centres, O^1 and O^2 and join them with a straight line.

b Draw a straight line through the two points of intersection P^1 and P^2. What do we call this line?

c Measure the angle between the two straight lines.

d What is the shape $O^1P^1O^2P^2$?

6 A triangle LMN has $\hat{M} = 40°$ and side LM = 6.7 cm.
The length of LN is either **a** 4.3 cm or **b** 4.8 cm.
Construct both triangles using only compasses to measure the length of side LN.
What differences do you notice between the triangles?

7 **Use ruler and compasses for these questions.**

a Construct a regular hexagon with sides 4 cm.
Construct the perpendicular bisectors of each side.
Draw the circumcircle (a circle touching all vertices) of the hexagon.

b Construct a regular hexagon with sides 5 cm.
Construct the angle bisectors of each interior angle.
Draw the inscribed circle of the hexagon.

Essential Exercises

1 Construct the following loci:

- **a** the path traced by the handle of a door, width 75 cm
- **b** the path traced by a conker on a string, length 46 cm
- **c** the front point of the saddle of a bicycle being ridden 2 m from a straight hedge
- **d** the corner of a square being rolled along a straight line
- **e** the path traced by the tip of my finger when I raise a straight arm, length 60 cm, above my head
- **f** the mid-point of a chord of a circle, radius 4 cm, moving so that it is parallel to the diameter.

2 Draw a circle, radius 5 cm, centre O and a chord PQ.
Describe the locus traced by M when:

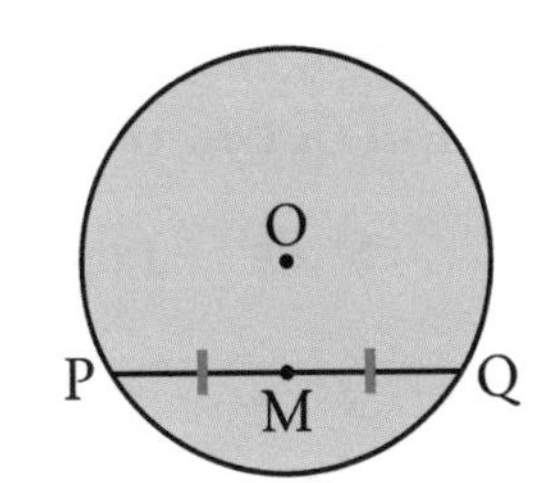

- **a** PQ is moved so that its new position is always parallel to the original
- **b** PQ is moved so that P is fixed
- **c** P and Q move round the circumference.

Consolidation Exercises

3 Two dogs are tethered in this garden.
Buster's and Fido's chains are both 4.5 m long.
Buster's chain is attached to a pole (P) in the corner.
Fido's chain can slide along a rail (R).

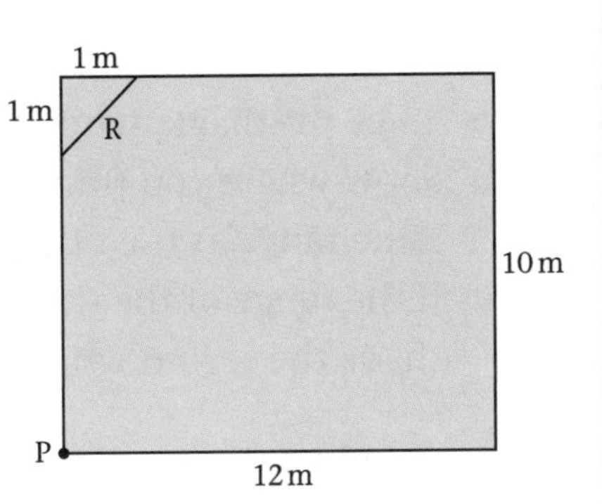

- **a** Construct a scale drawing of the garden. Draw on your diagram the loci traced by the dogs.
- **b** Is there any part of the garden where both dogs can go? If so, mark it.
- **c** The owner wishes to build a circular pond in her garden. Suggest a size and place for the pond, away from the dogs' area.

4 A boy goes for a walk. He leaves his home and walks a distance of 0.5 m parallel to the kerb until he reaches the corner of the road. He crosses the road to the park gates on the diagonally opposite corner, a distance of 9 m. He enters the park and walks so that he is never more than 20 m from the gate.
Draw a diagram of his walk, shading the area he walks in the park.

Challenging Exercises

5 Three mobile phone transmitters are needed to service a country area shown below. Each transmitter has a range of 30 km. The diagram shows the position of two of the transmitters.

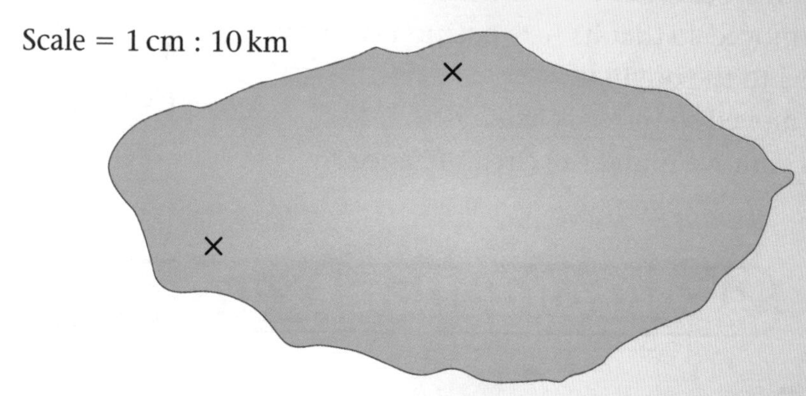

a Trace the diagram and show the area covered by the two transmitters.
b Show where you think the third transmitter could be placed if it has the same range as the other two.
c If the range of the third transmitter actually lies between 25 km and 30 km, shade the region where the third transmitter could be placed.

6 An ant sits on the centre of the top of a cylindrical tin, radius 3 cm and height 16.5 cm.
a It walks a straight path to the edge of the tin. Sketch the loci.
b It then walks around the tin moving lower and lower until it reaches the bottom. Sketch the loci.

USING UNITS

Essential Exercises

1 Convert the following units into the units shown in brackets.

a ✓ 25 500 cm^2 (m^2) **b** 20 000 m^2 (ha) **c** 550 mm^3 (cm^3)
d 2500 cm^3 (*l*) **e** 4.5 m^2 (cm^2) **f** 3.75 cm^3 (mm^3)

2 If £1 = 1.54 euros, convert the following amounts to euros. Give your answer to 2 d.p.

a 85p **b** £15 **c** £1.75
d 25p **e** £120 **f** £25

3 Convert the following times into the unit of time shown in brackets.

a 2 h 30 min (min) **b** first quarter of the year (days)
c 1 week (h) **d** 1 day (min)
e 12 h (s) **f** 1 leap year (weeks)

Consolidation Exercises

4 £1 = $1.52 and £1 = 182.70 Yen (¥). Using the exchange rates convert the amounts to the currencies shown in brackets.

a £50 ($) **b** $350 (£) **c** £125 (¥)
d ✓ 18 270¥ (£) **e** $152 (¥) **f** 9135¥ ($)

5 A cuboid has the dimensions shown in the diagram.

a Give the lengths in: **i** mm, **ii** m.

b Calculate the surface area in:
i mm^2
ii cm^2
iii m^2.

c Calculate the volume in:
i mm^3
ii cm^3
iii m^3.

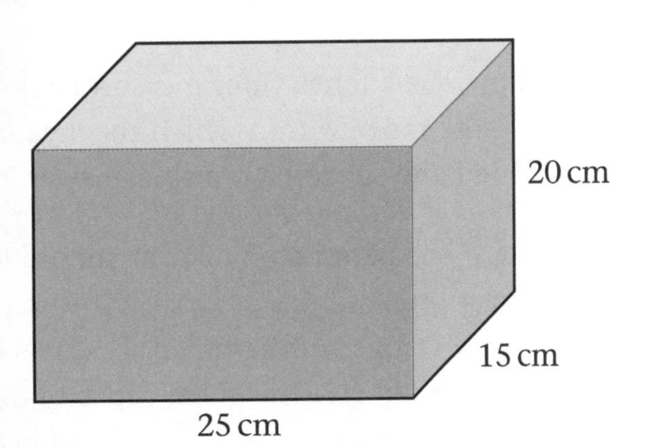

6 Below is a recipe for biscuits, with quantities given in imperial measures. Rewrite the recipe in metric units.

3 oz margarine
2 tbs syrup
$\frac{1}{2}$ tsp bicarbonate of soda
a pinch of salt
3 oz caster sugar
8 oz self-raising flour
2 tsp ginger

Do all the measures need to be changed?

Challenging Exercises

7 The following measurements are not exact. Complete the possible range of values for each.

a 23.5 mm ≤ 24 mm < ___
b 39.5 cm ≤ _____ < 40.5 cm
c ____ ≤ 43 kg < 43.5 kg
d 685 cm³ ≤ ____ < 695 cm³
e 57.5 mm² ≤ 58 mm² < ___

8 A group of friends are going on holiday to Spain for a fortnight. They decide to take £30 per day to cover food and incidentals.

a How much money should they take with them for the whole holiday?
b If the exchange rate is £1 = 1.54 euros, how many euros should they take?
c They ask the *bureau de change* to round the number of euros up to the nearest thousand. How many £s would they then need to exchange?

9 The kitchen floor measures 7 m by 6 m to the nearest metre. Give the range within which the area lies. Consider the degree of accuracy needed and suggest a sensible answer for the area.

10 The petrol tank of a car should have a capacity of 60 litres to the nearest litre.
Give the range within which the capacity lies. Consider different dimensions which would give the given capacity to the nearest litre.
Suggest the most sensible set of dimensions allowing for the appropriate degree of accuracy.

RATES OF CHANGE

Essential Exercises

1 Copy and complete these ratios:

a speed = __________ **b** density = ________ **c** pressure = _________.

2 Convert these rates to the units shown in brackets.

a 30 miles per hour (metres per second)
b 45 kilometres per hour (miles per hour)
c 35 miles per gallon (miles per litre)
d 3.5 kilograms per centimetre squared (pounds per square inch)
e 250 kilograms per centimetre cubed (pounds per cubic inch)

Consolidation Exercises

Copy and complete these tables using the ratios for speed and density.

3

	Distance	Speed	Time
a	200 miles	70 mph	
b		4 km/h	2 h 30 min
c	4.5 km		45 min

4

	Density	Mass	Volume
a ✓	19.5 g/km^3	600 g	
b		980 g	1 litre
c	4 g/cm^3	3 kg	

5 A car manual suggests tyre pressures of:
31.5 lb/sq. in. (front)
27 lb/sq. in. (back).
Convert these pressures to kg/cm^2.

Challenging Exercises

6 Suggest units to measure the average speed of:

a a marathon runner

b a cat chasing a mouse

c an express train travelling from London to Manchester

d an aeroplane flying from New York to Los Angeles

e a ship sailing from Hong Kong to New Zealand.

7 The distance from Manchester to London is 200 miles. The Intercity train journey usually takes about $2\frac{1}{2}$ hours.

a What is the average speed for the journey to London in mph?

b What is the average speed for this journey in km/h?

c The train is delayed by 30 min, on the journey back to Manchester, due to signal failure. What is the average speed for the whole return journey in mph?

8 This graph illustrates Jack's journey to school by bicycle.

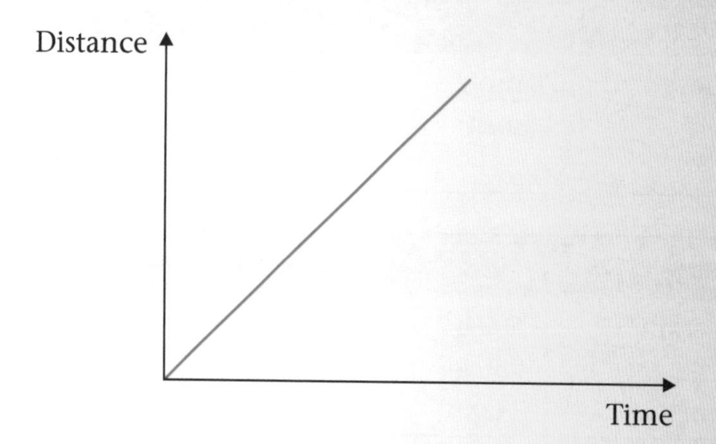

Write down the correct statement describing his journey from the list below.

Jack cycles faster and faster

Jack cycles slower and slower

Jack cycles north east

Jack cycles at a steady speed

Jack cycles uphill

CIRCLE FORMULAE

Essential Exercises

1 Calculate the circumference of these circles using the π button on your calculator. Write your answer to 3 s.f.

a

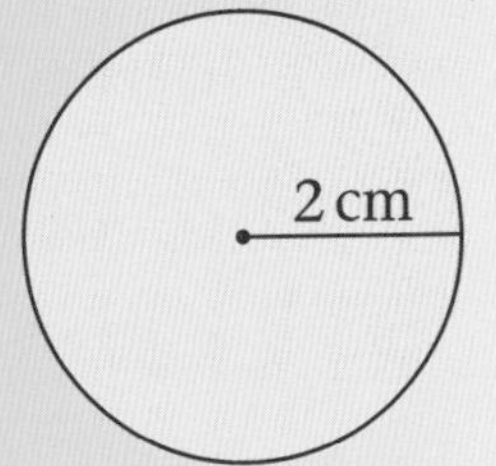

b ✓

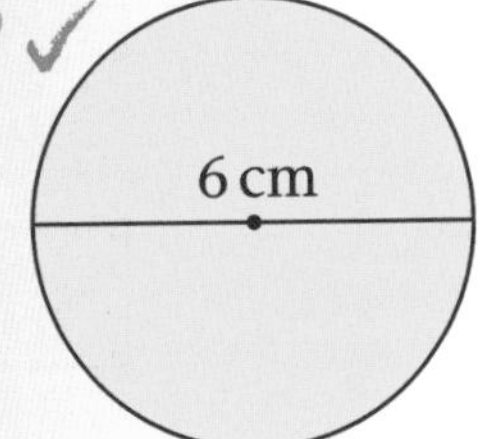

c

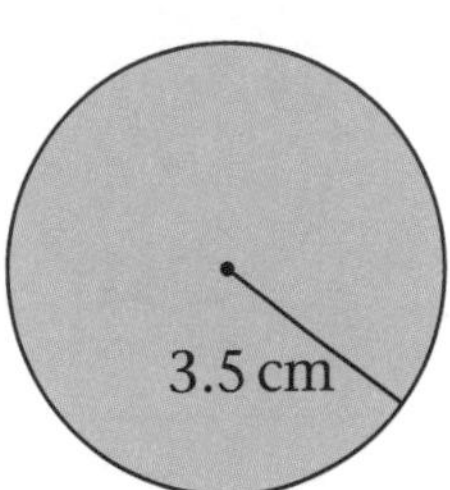

d

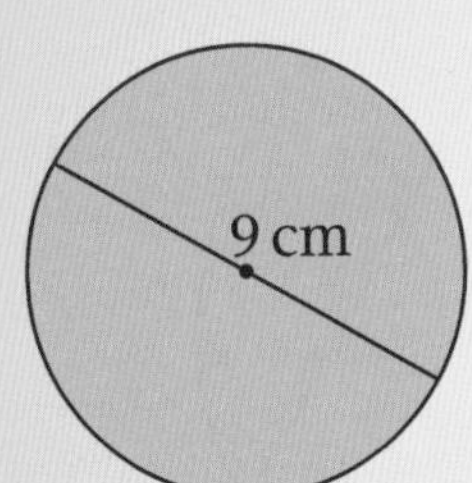

e

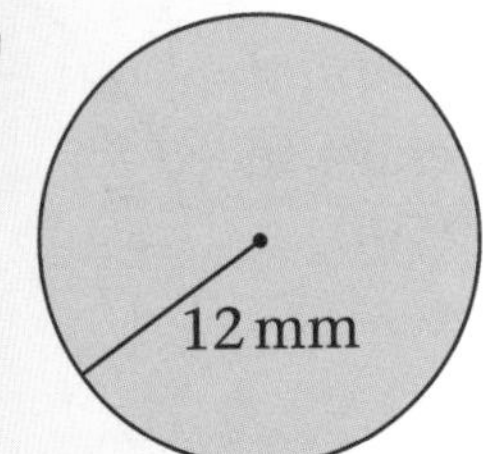

f

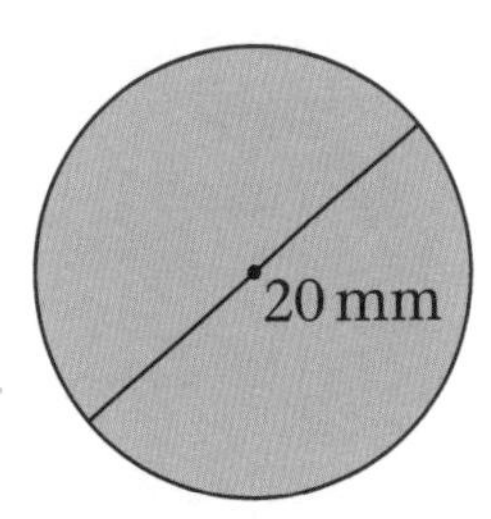

2 Calculate the area of these circles using $\pi = 3.14$. Write your answer to 3 s.f.

a

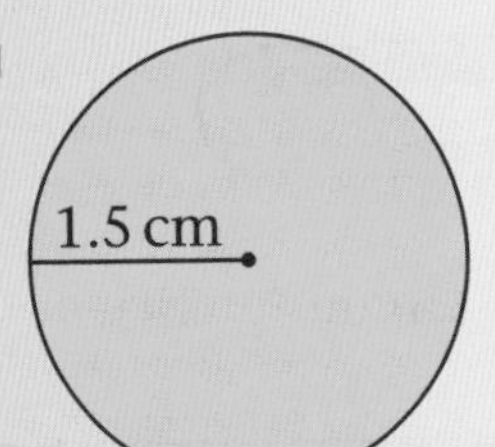

b

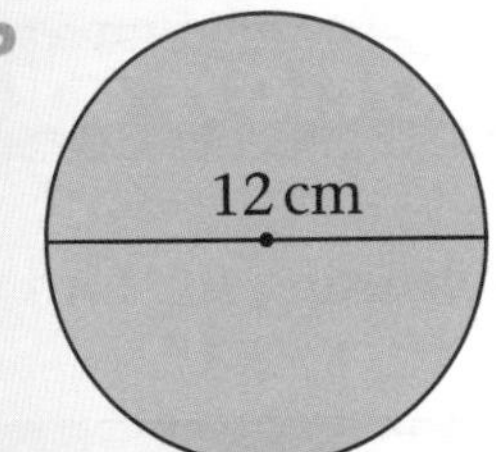

c ✓

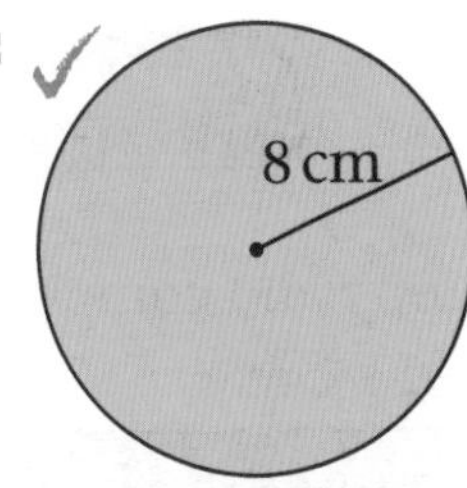

d

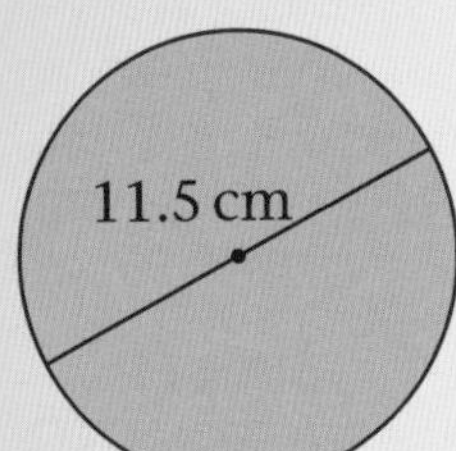

e

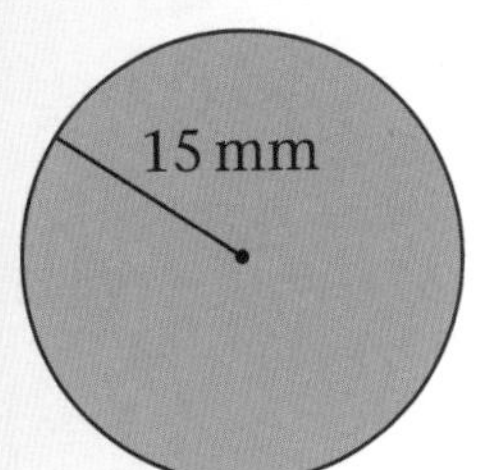

f

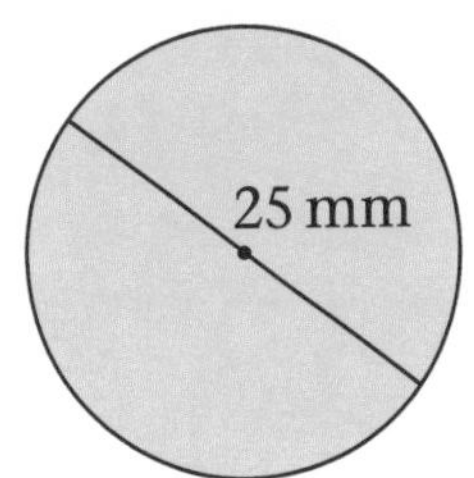

3 Find the shaded area in the following.

a

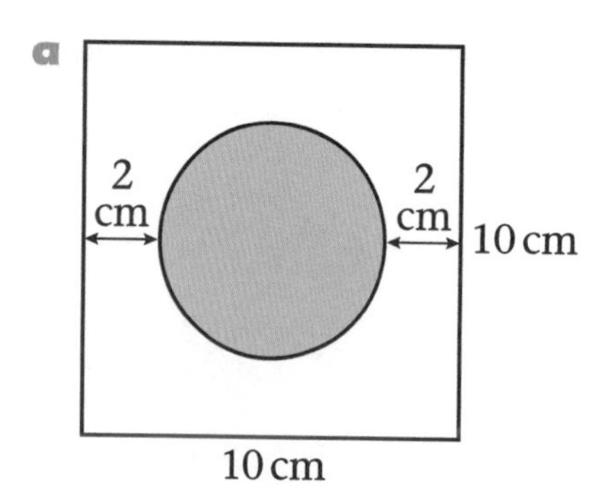

b

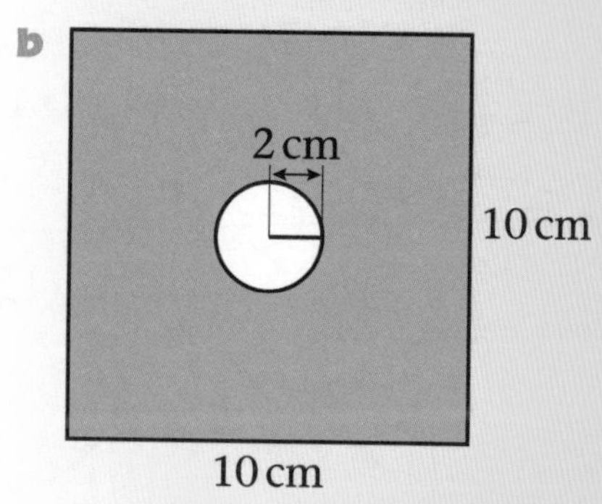

c

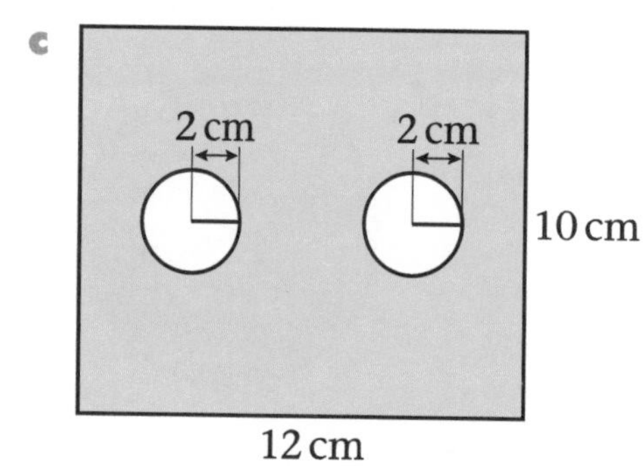

d

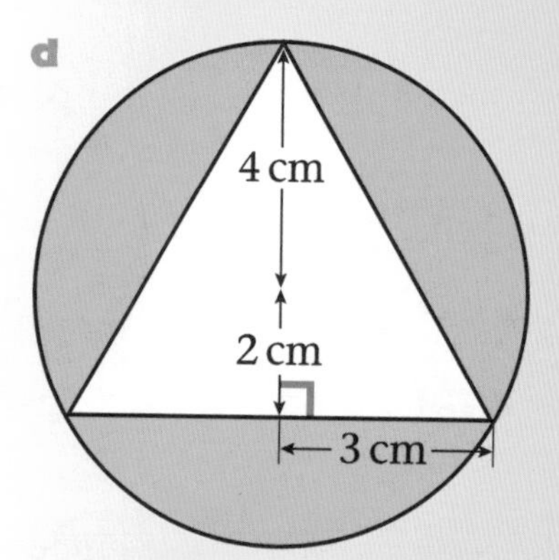

Consolidation Exercises

4 Copy and complete this table using the formulae for circumference and area of a circle.

	Radius	Diameter	Circumference	Area
a	3 cm			
b		64 mm		
c			31.4 cm	
d			44 cm	
e				380 cm^2
f				95 m^2
g		24 m		
h	15 cm			

5 Calculate the area of these sectors.

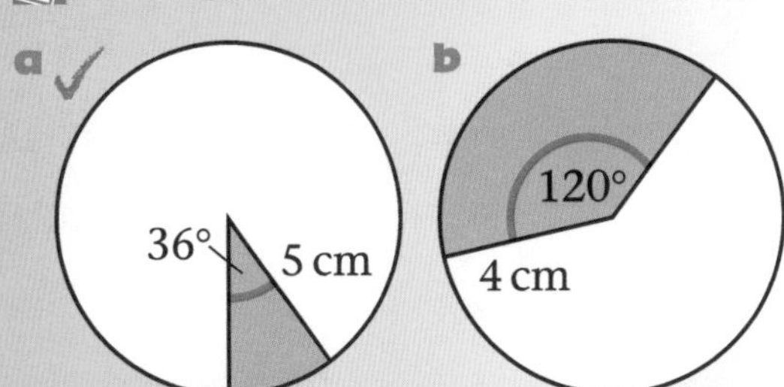

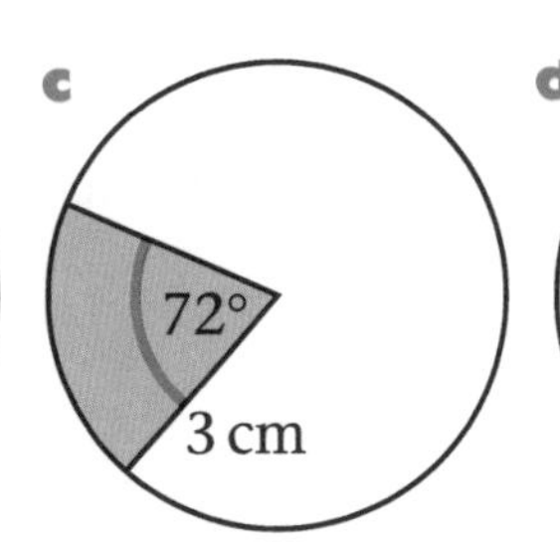

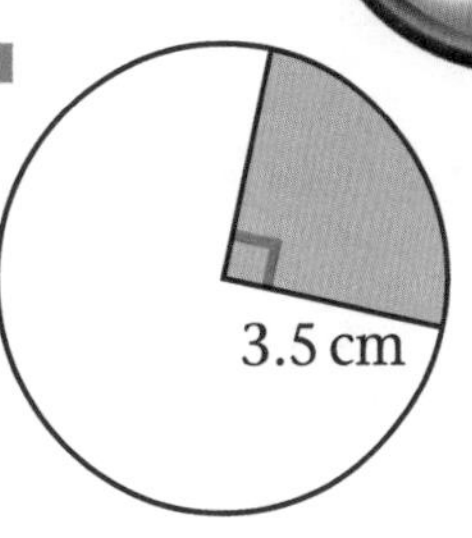

Challenging Exercises

6 A circular rose bed of radius 2.5 m has a path round it of width 50 cm.

Find:

a the area of the rose bed

b the area of the path in m^2

c the area of the path in cm^2.

7 Jack runs on a circular running track, diameter 30 metres.

How far does he run if he covers:

a 1 lap

b 5 laps

c 10 laps?

8 A party pizza has a diameter of 40 cm. Each guest will be given a 60° slice.

a ✓ What is the surface area of the pizza?

b What is the surface area of each slice?

c How many slices can be cut from the pizza?

d How many pizzas are needed for 30 guests?

e Will anyone be able to have second helpings?

9 An arc 6 cm long subtends an angle of 40° at the centre of the circle. Find the:

a circumference **b** radius **c** area of the circle.

10 Each of the lines on this diagram of a window is a strip of lead.

a Find how much lead will be needed for the whole window.

b Draw an accurate diagram of the window choosing an appropriate scale.

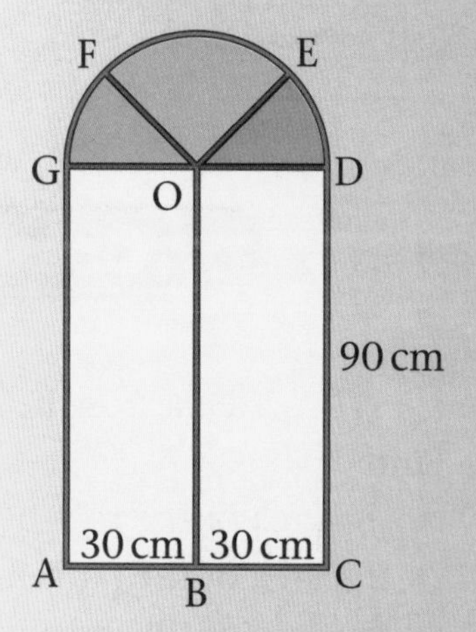

11 A circular table has a radius of 65 cm. A tablecloth over-hangs the edge by 20 cm. What is the area of the tablecloth?

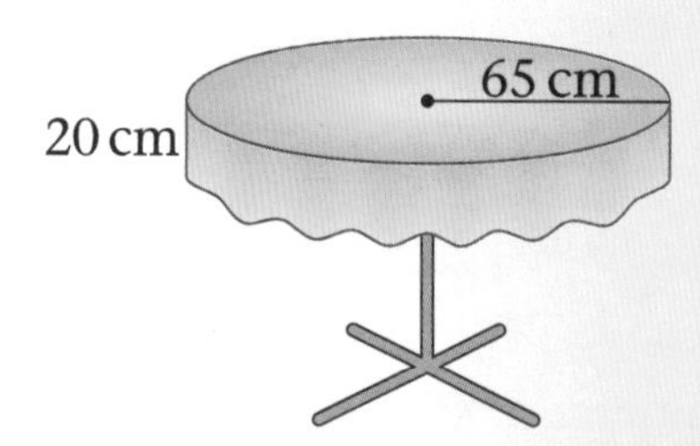

If four people sit at the table, how much space does each person have? Could any more people be seated at the table?

12 Calculate the amount of plastic wasted when a circular disc is cut from a 10 cm square piece of plastic. What percentage is wasted?
Now draw the same square with a circumscribed circle.
Calculate the amount of plastic wasted when the square is cut from the circle.
Which method wastes more plastic?

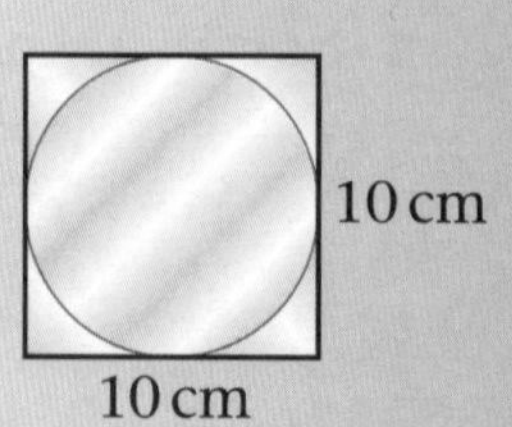

PRISMS

Essential Exercises

1 Calculate the surface area of these prisms.

a

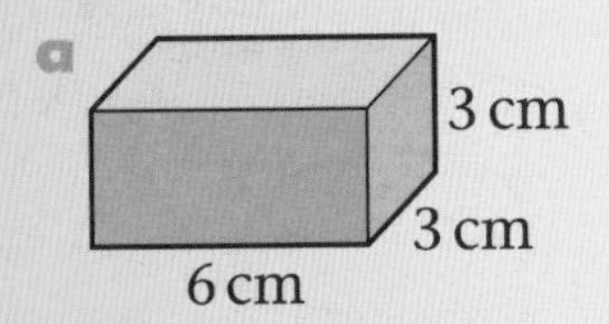

b

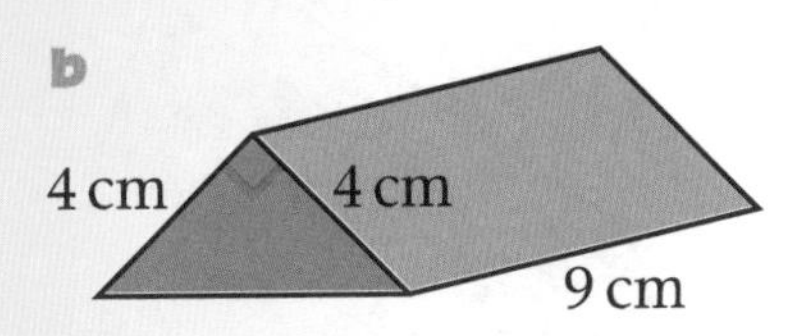

c

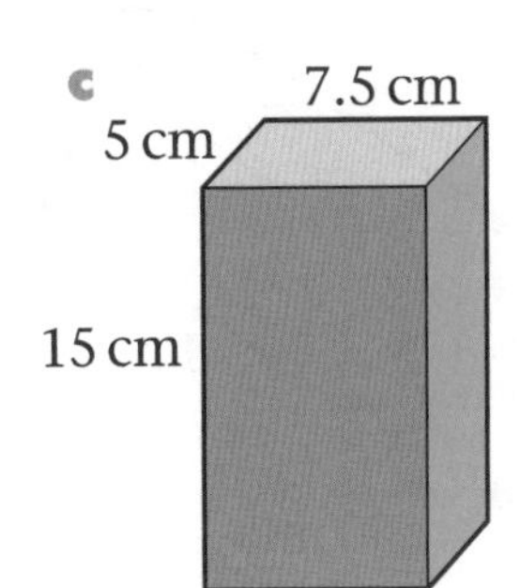

d

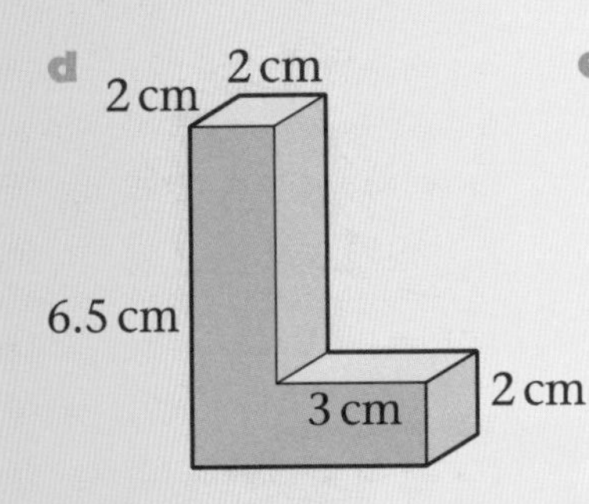

e

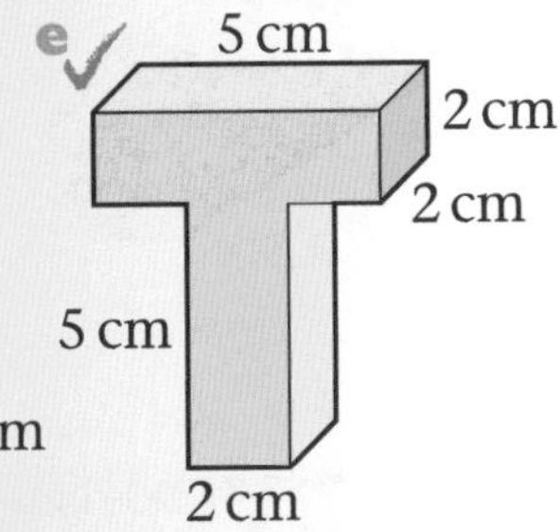

f

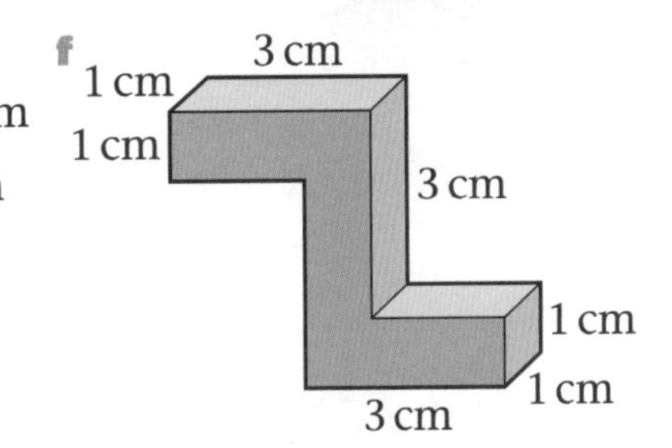

2 Calculate the volume of these prisms.

a

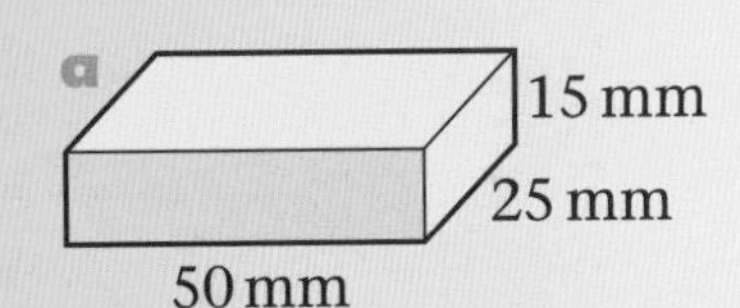

b

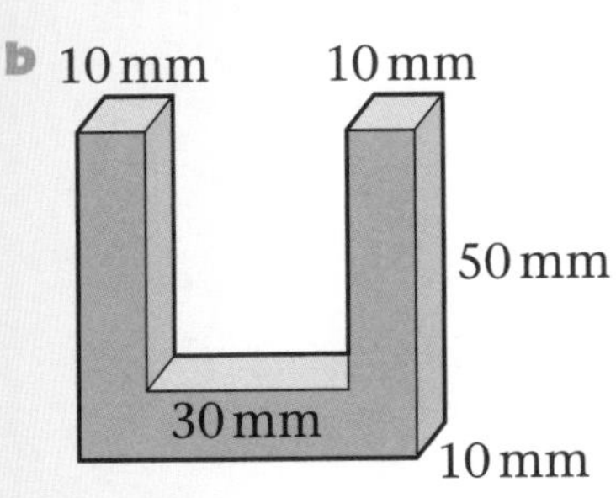

c

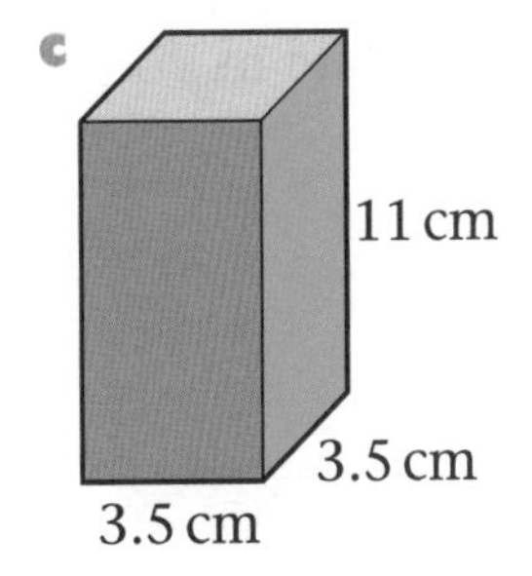

d

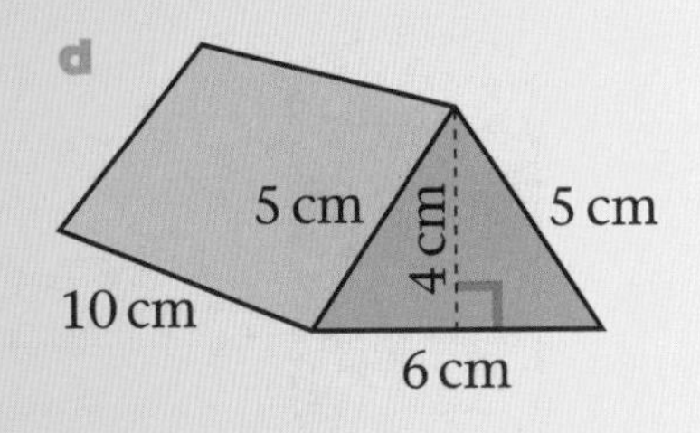

e

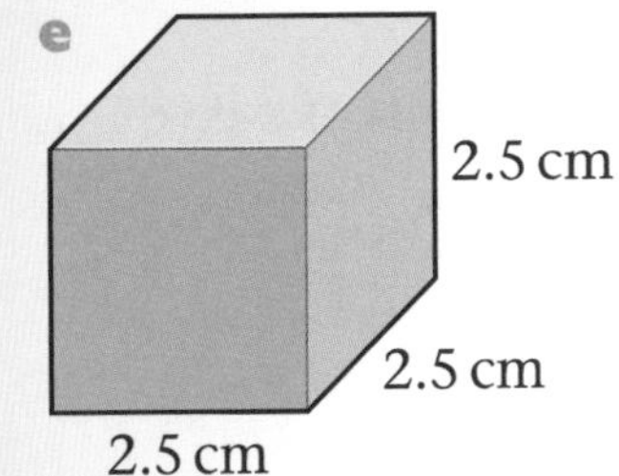

f

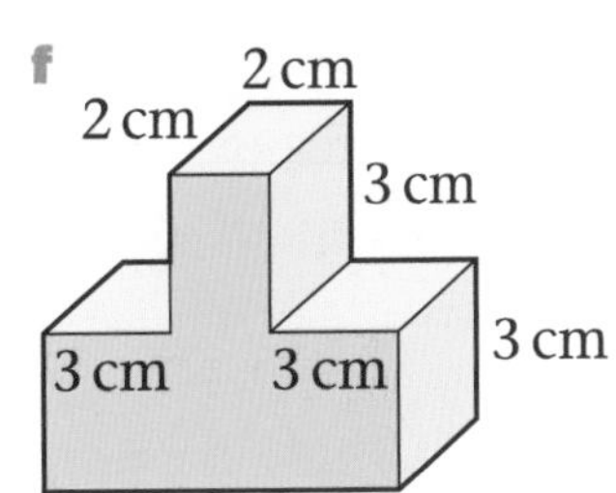

Consolidation Exercises

3 The volume and length of each prism is given. Find the area of each cross-section.

a

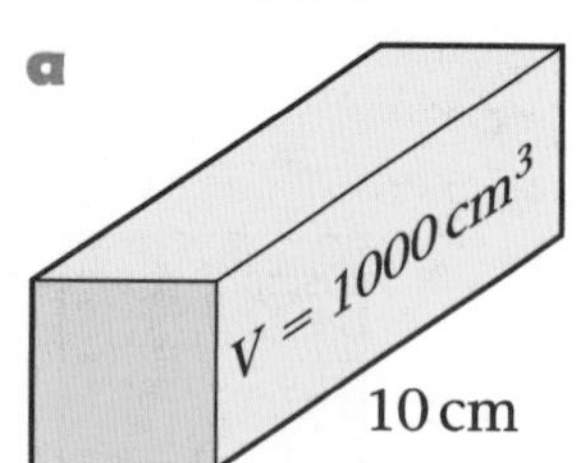

b

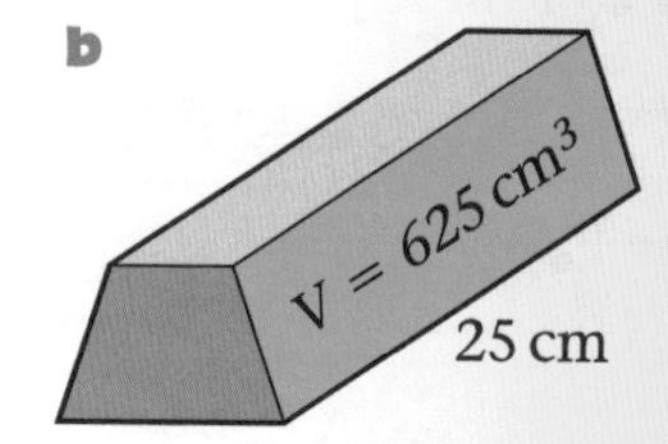

c

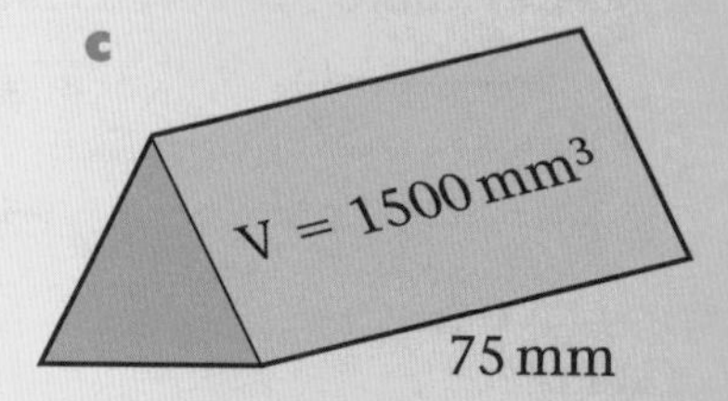

d

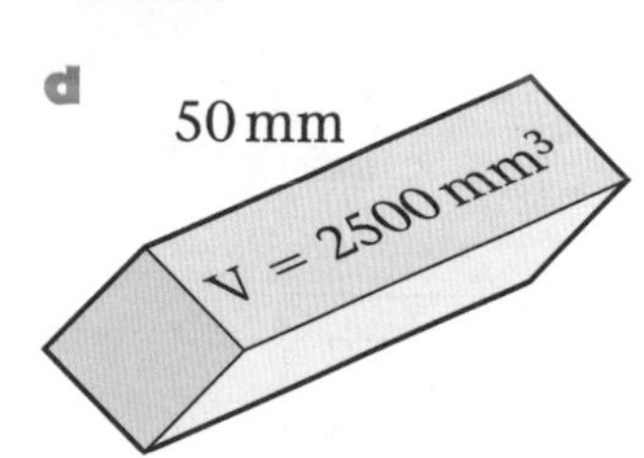

e

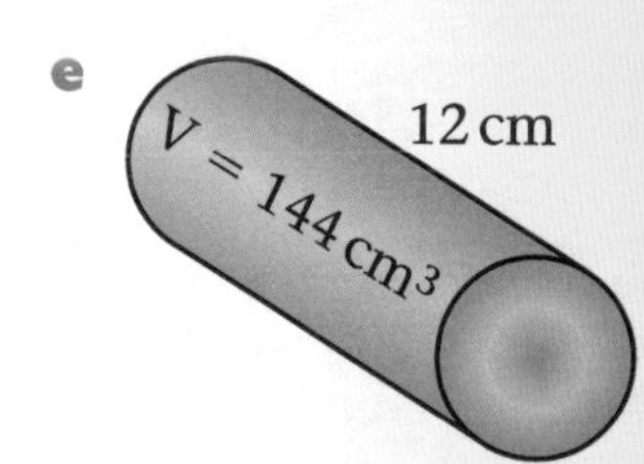

f

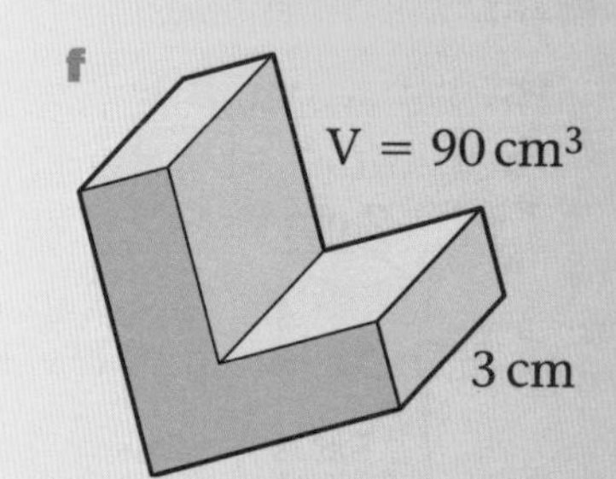

Challenging Exercises

4 This prism is made up of cuboids.
Calculate its volume.

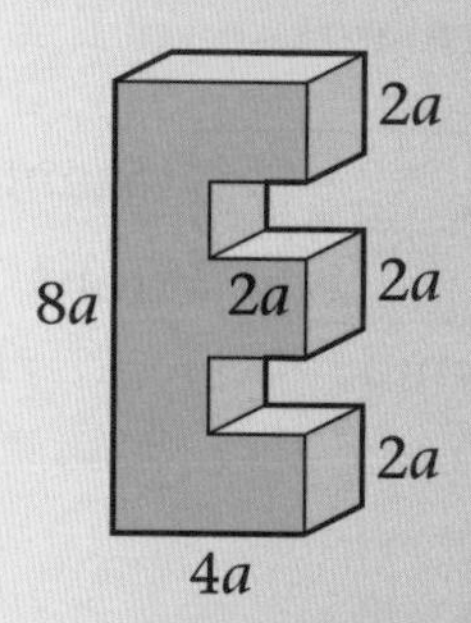

5 Find:

a the area of the label on this tin of baked beans

b the capacity of the tin.

6 This box of chocolates is in the shape of a regular hexagonal prism.

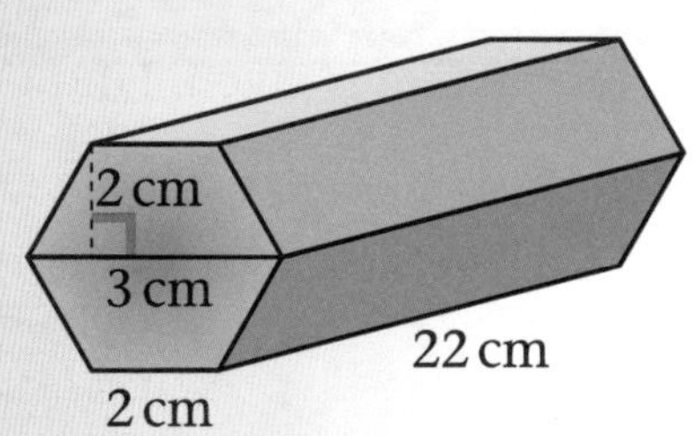

Calculate:

a the area of the cross-section

b the capacity of the box

c the number of chocolates which can fit into the box; each chocolate is a 1 cm cube.

7 These two packets of cereal have the same volume.

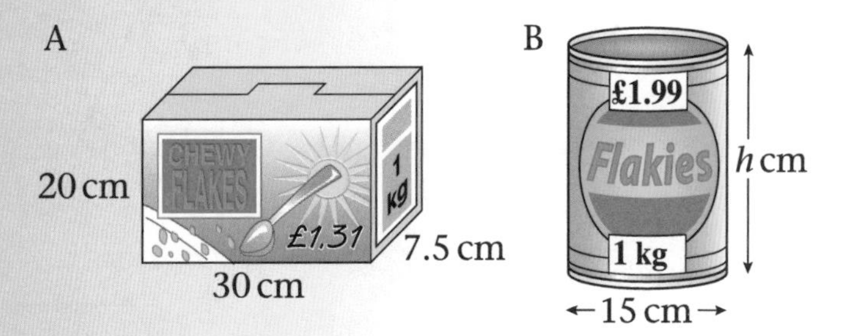

Calculate:

a the volume of cereal A packet

b the height of cereal B packet

c the cost of 1 g of cereal A and the cost of 1 g of cereal B.

Trigonometry

Essential Exercises

1 Find the missing lengths in these triangles.

a
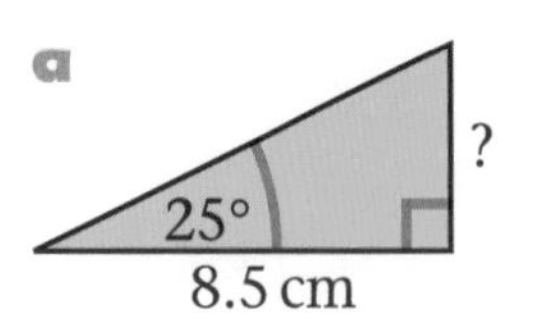

b
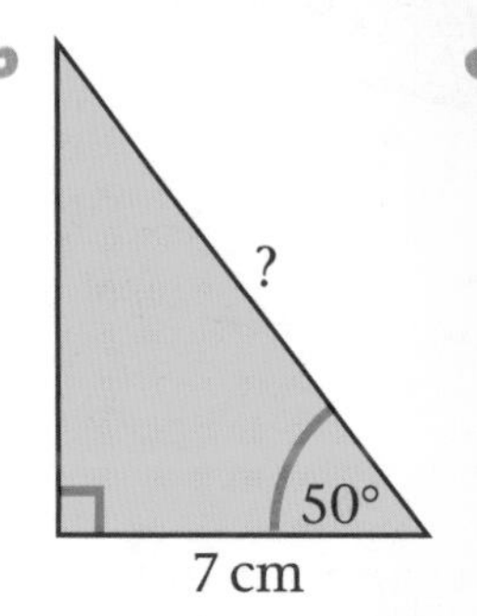

c
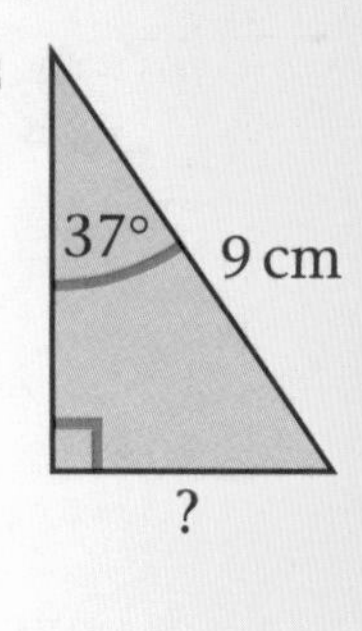

d
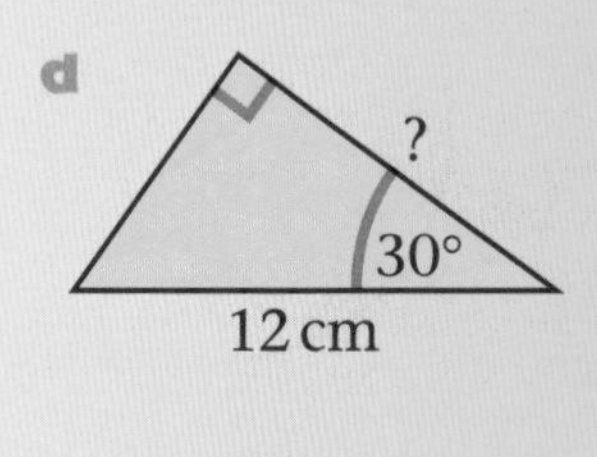

e
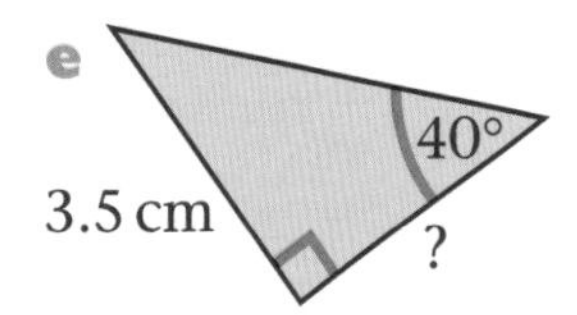

f
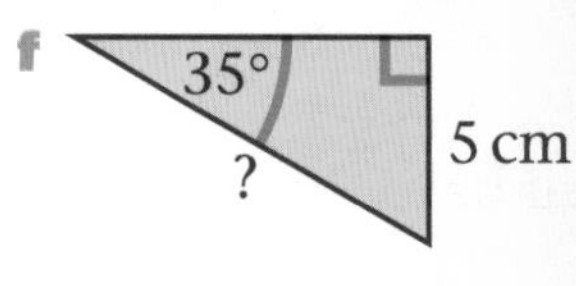

g
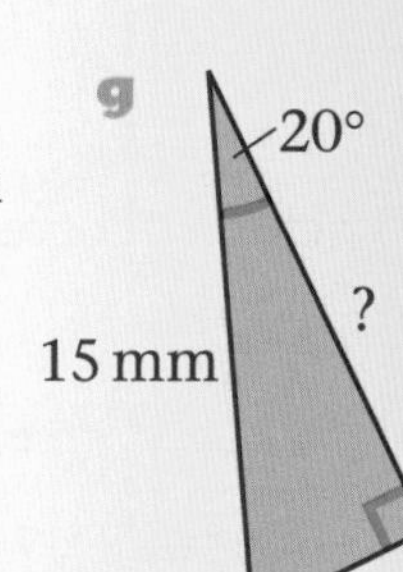

h
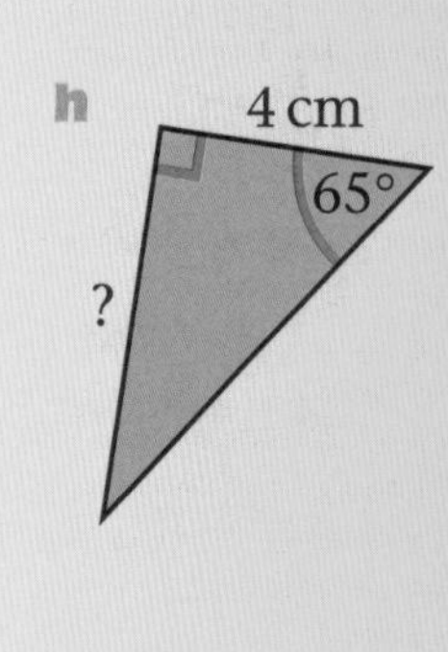

2 Find the marked angle in each triangle.

a
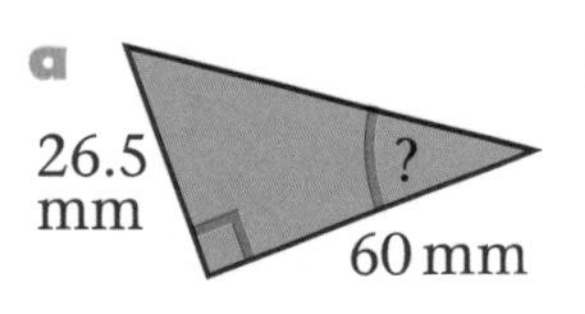

b
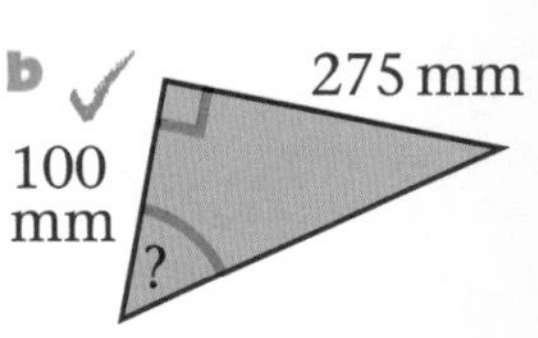

c
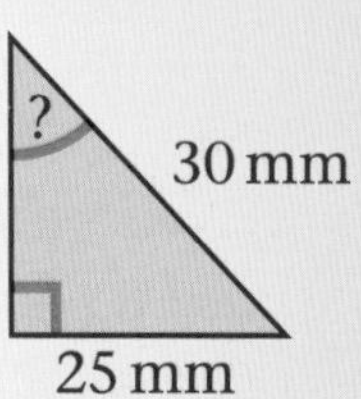

d
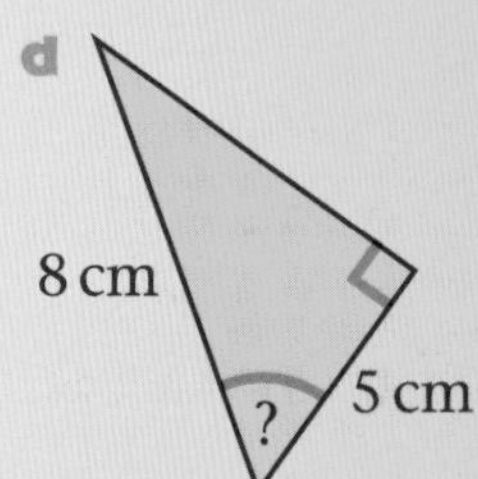

e
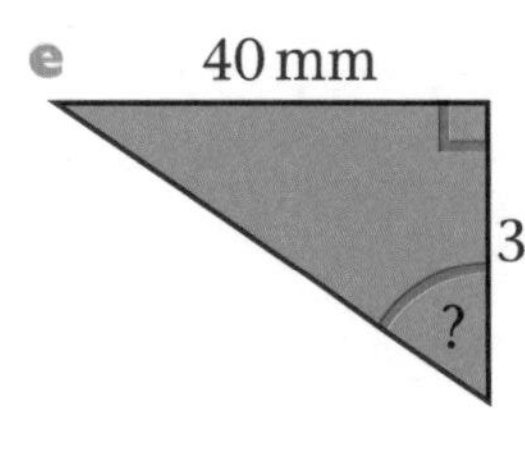

f
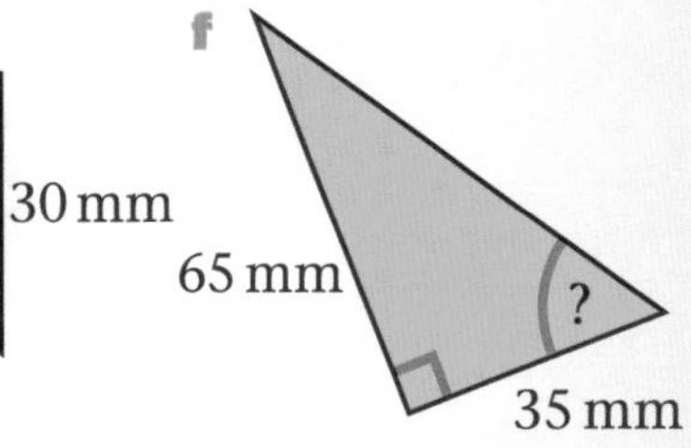

g
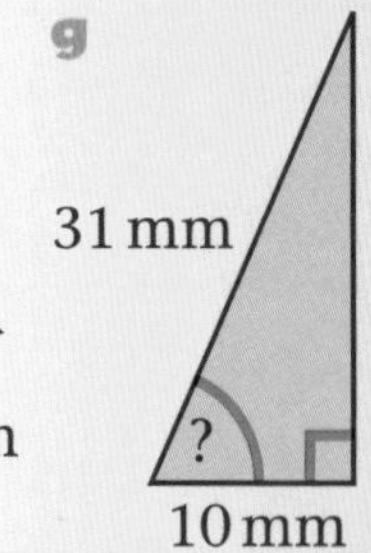

h
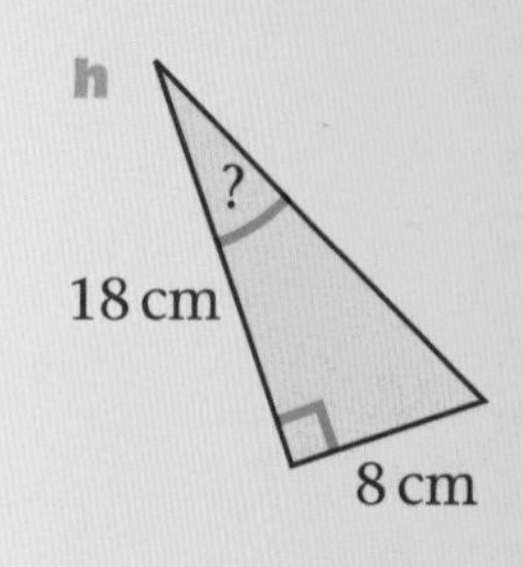

Consolidation Exercises

3 Calculate the lengths of the missing sides in these inscribed triangles.

a

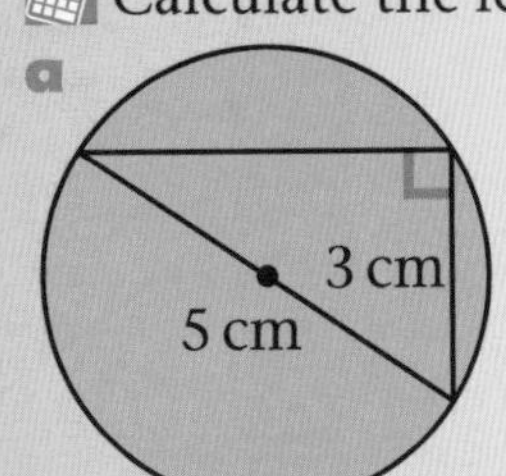

b

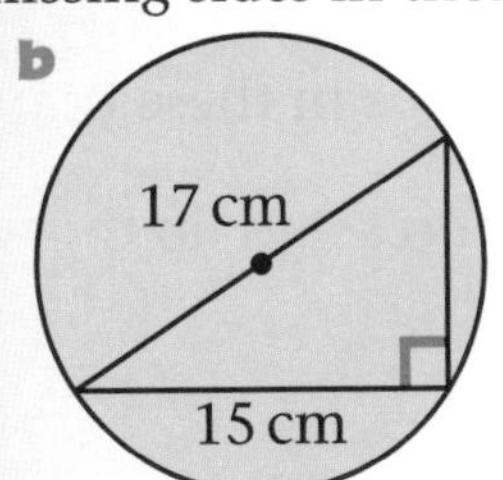

c

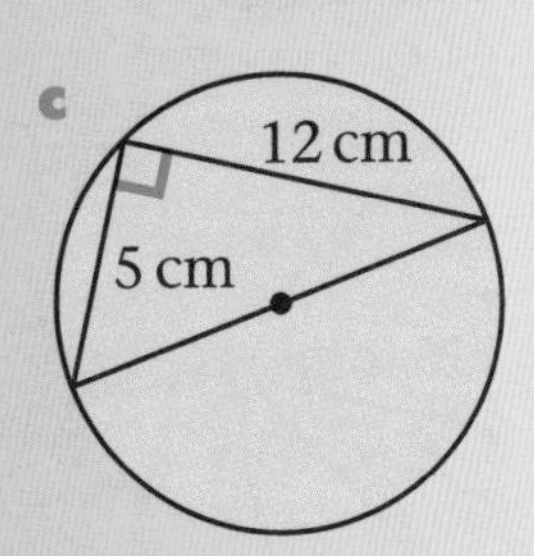

d

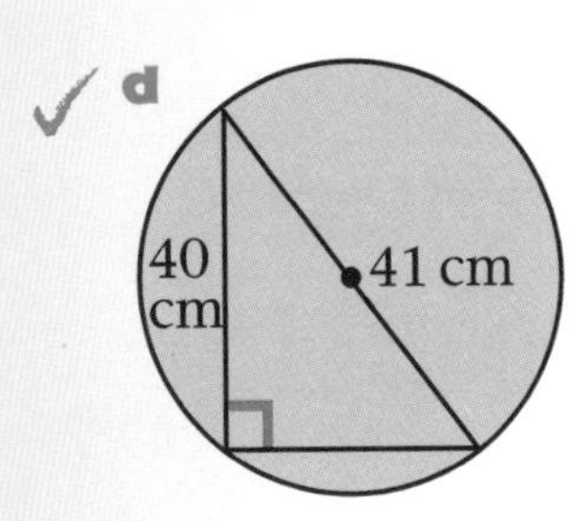

4 Find the length of RS and the size of angle Q in each of the following triangles.

a

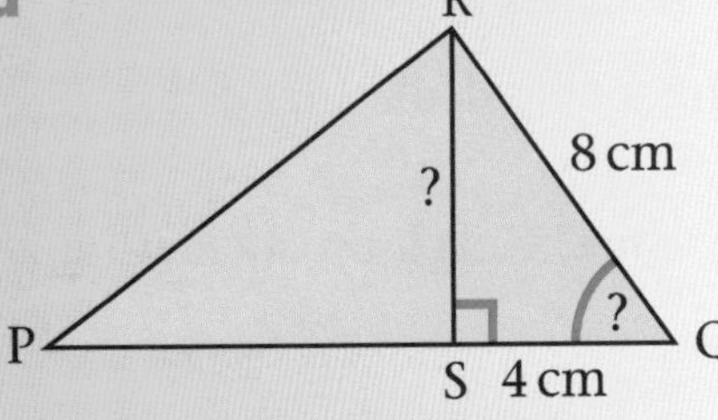

b

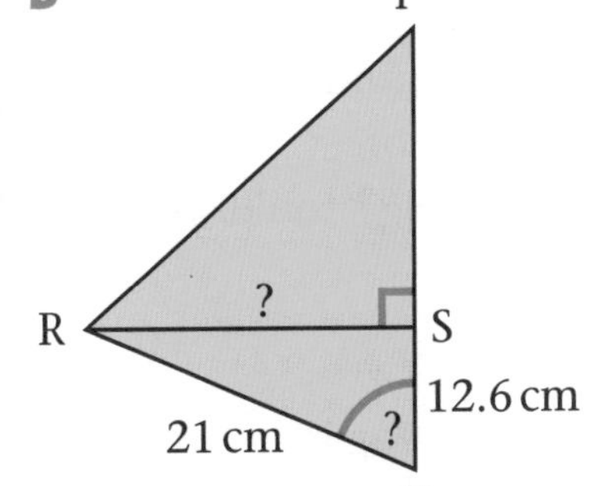

c

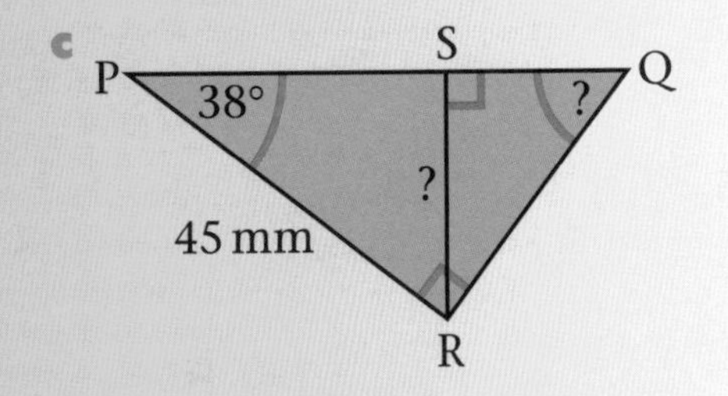

d

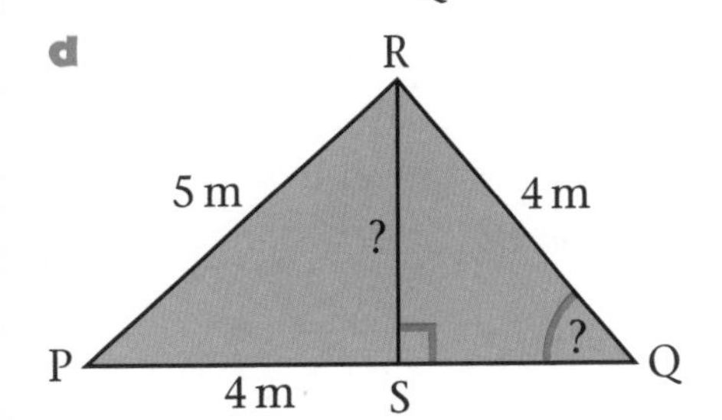

Challenging Exercises

5 A ladder is leaning against a wall.
Find:

a the length of the ladder

b the distance the ladder reaches up the wall.

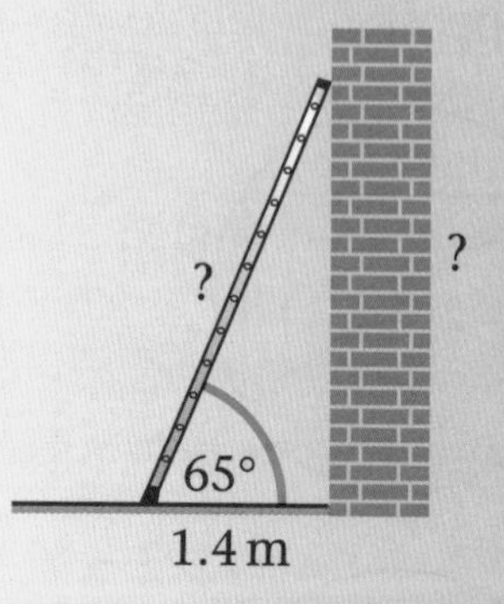

6 Calculate the length of chord PQ shown in the diagram.

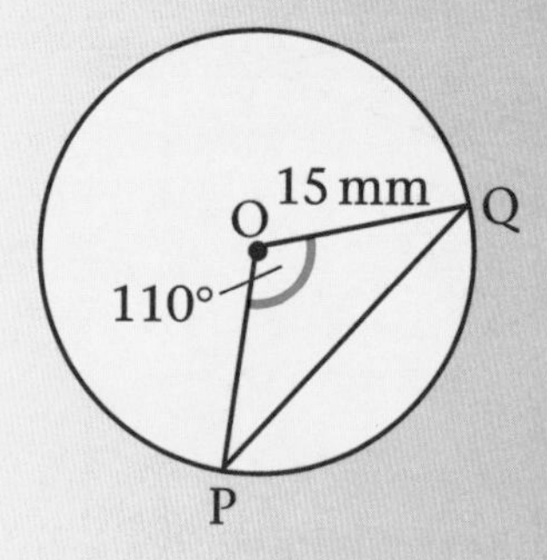

7 A girl cycles 12 km due north and then 5 km due east.

a Draw a diagram to illustrate her route.

b How far is she from her starting point? Check by calculating, using Pythagoras' theorem.

c On what bearing should she cycle directly back? Check by calculating, using trigonometry.

8 The kite string is 32 m long.
The angle it makes with the ground is 40°.
How high is the kite above the boy's hand?

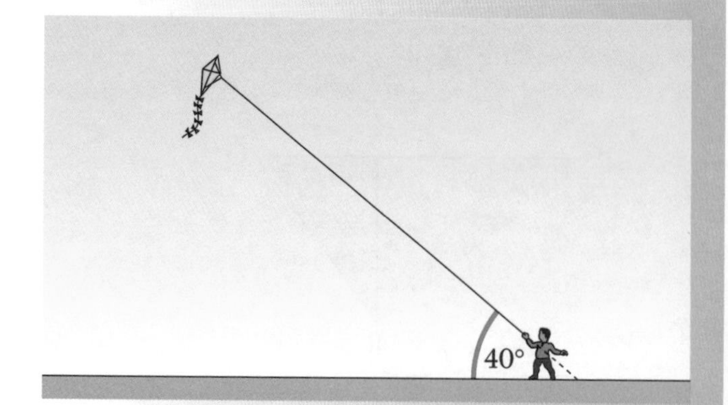

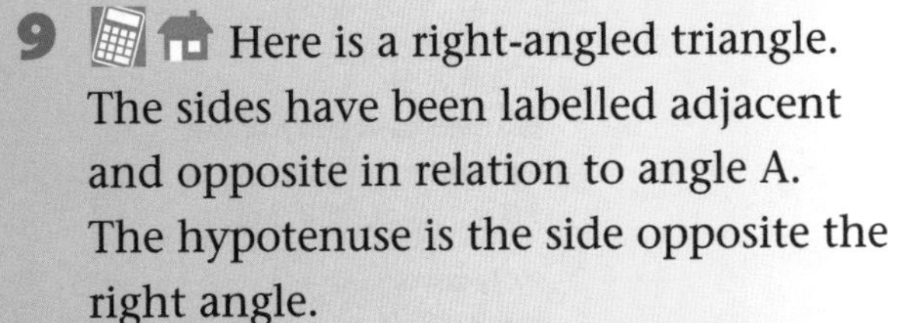

9 Here is a right-angled triangle. The sides have been labelled adjacent and opposite in relation to angle A. The hypotenuse is the side opposite the right angle.

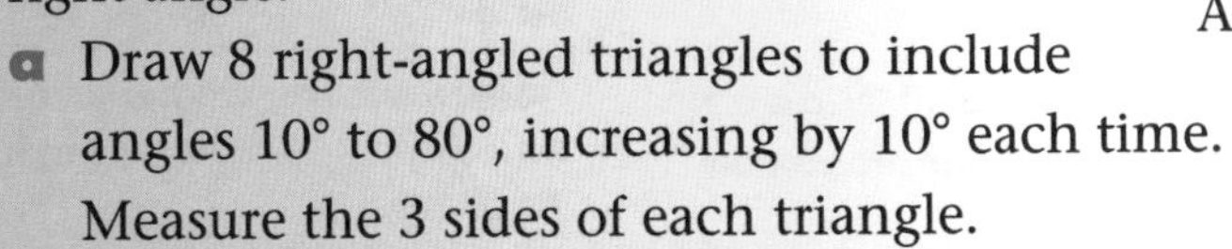

a Draw 8 right-angled triangles to include angles 10° to 80°, increasing by 10° each time. Measure the 3 sides of each triangle.

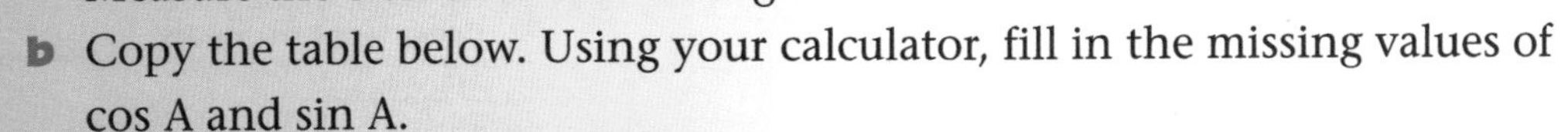

b Copy the table below. Using your calculator, fill in the missing values of cos A and sin A.

A	cos A	sin A
0°		
10°		
20°		
30°		
40°		
50°		
60°		
70°		
80°		
90°		

What do you notice about the values in your table?

c Plot your values on a graph. Comment on your graph. Now check your results in **a** with your table in **b**.

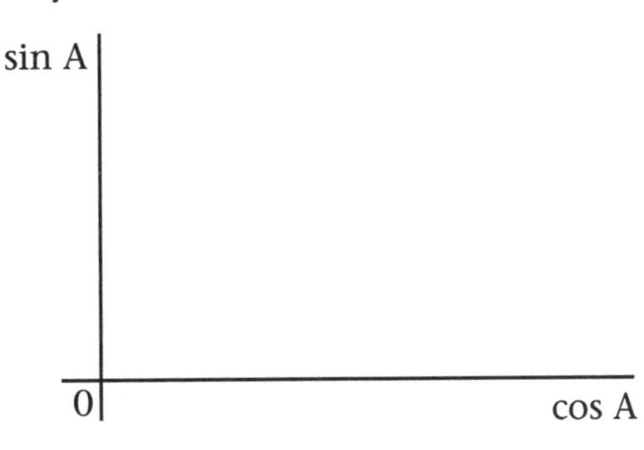

ANSWERS TO SELF-CHECK QUESTIONS

YEAR 7

Angles and shapes

2i d **3a** perpendicular
5b 4, 4

Angles and lines

2a 30° **3a** 125° **6d** 150°

Triangles and quadrilaterals

2a scalene **6a** 5

Solid shapes

3b 6, 8, 12

Transformations

1a

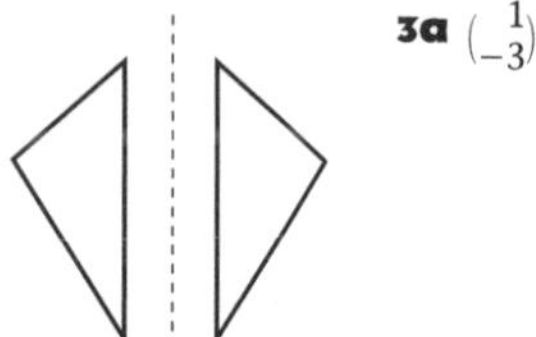

3a $\binom{1}{-3}$

Coordinates

2 A(−5, 1)
4

Measurement

3e 36° **5b** 1 cm, 120°

Nets

4a triangular prism
6 6 faces, 9 edges, 5 vertices

Units

4c −32 °C **7a** 8500 g

Using units

1c 30 ml, 30 g
3a 3 litres, 49 litres, 49/52

Types of angles

1a 90° **2c** obtuse
3a iv **b** iii **c** i **d** ii

Area and perimeter

3c 12 cm, 44 cm
9a 38 m^2 **10a** 11 m^2

Surface area

1a 1350 mm^2
3b 148 cm^2 **4a** 154 m^2

YEAR 8

Finding angles

1a

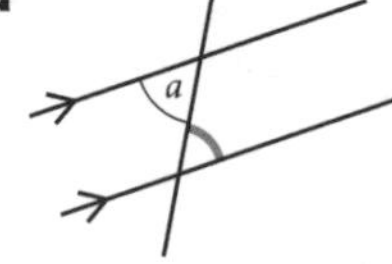

3c i 65° **4a** 125° **9** 28°

Triangles and quadrilaterals

1f equilateral
4e kite **7a** 163°

Solid shapes

1a 16
3b A cuboid has 6 rectangular faces, 12 edges and 8 vertices
6a sphere/hemisphere/cylinder

Transformations

1

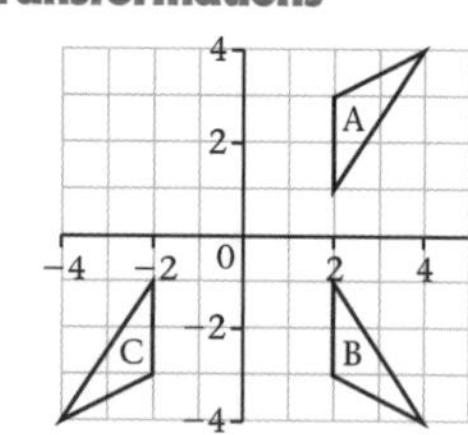

Rotation 180° about (0, 0)
9 rhombus because isosceles triangle has 2 equal sides

Enlargements

1e $\frac{1}{3}$ ($0.\dot{3}$)
6 similar (equal angles proportional sides); enlargement (SF = 4, centre A)

Drawing to scale

1e 135 cm

Coordinates

3c (5, 4.5) **5b** sum = 5

Constructions

2c 20 cm

Simple loci

2e

Using units

1f 4.5 *l* **4e** 13 h 45 min
5d 8.75 cm^2 **6a iii** 314 km

Bearings

3f 180° **5c** 145°

Areas

1d 54 cm^2 **2c** 525 mm^2 **4g** 9.6 cm

Volume and surface area

1e 20 unit cubes
2d V = 18 000 mm^3, SA = 5300 mm^2
5e V = 26 cm^3, SA = 82 cm^2

YEAR 9

Names and properties

3e kite
5d bisect at right angles

Polygons

1g 36° **5b** 36°

Angles, lines and Pythagoras

2a 5.7 cm **7a** 28.3 mm
14 5 m, 6.4 m

Congruent triangles

2a yes, SAS
3c AC = 50 mm, $A\hat{C}B$ = 57°, EF = 30 mm, $E\hat{F}D$ = 33°, $E\hat{D}F$ = 57°

Similar shapes

1b BC = 5 cm **3c** 3

Circles

1c radii **g** arc

Plans and elevations

2b tetrahedron **5b** rectangle

Enlargements

1c 3, (0, 0)
7c scale factor = 1.5
area A = 80 cm^2
area B = 180 cm^2
area A = area B × (scale factor)^2
8e scale factor = 5
volume A = 0.1 m^3,
volume B = 12.5 m^3
volume A = volume B × (scale factor)^3

Lines and ratio

1c 29 cm **4c** 3.6 cm

Constructions

1f 120°

Using units

1a 2.55 m^2 **4d** £100

Rates of change

4a 30.8 km^3

Circle formulae

1b 18.8 cm **2c** 201 cm^2
5a 7.85 cm^2 **8a** 1257 cm^2

Prisms

1e 88 cm^2
6a 10 cm^2 **b** 220 cm^3 **c** 176

Trigonometry

2b 70° **3d** 9 cm